FREAKS

ABOUT THE AUTHOR

Jan Bondeson is a senior lecturer and consultant rheumatologist at Cardiff University. His many critically acclaimed books include *The London Monster* (also published by Tempus), *The Cabinet of Medical Curiosities*, *The Great Pretenders* and the best-selling *Buried Alive: The Terrifying History of Our Most Primal Fear*.

FREAKS

The Pig-Faced
Lady of Manchester
Square & Other
Medical Marvels

JAN BONDESON

TEMPUS

First published 2000 as *The Two-Headed Boy and Other Medical Marvels* by
Cornell University Press

This edition first published 2006 by arrangement with
Cornell University Press

Tempus Publishing Limited
The Mill, Brimscombe Port,
Stroud, Gloucestershire, GL5 2QG
www.tempus-publishing.com

British Library Cataloguing in Publication Data.
A catalogue record for this book is available from the British Library.

ISBN 0 7524 3662 7

Typesetting and origination by Tempus Publishing Limited
Printed and bound in Great Britain

CONTENTS

I

THE TWO
Inseparable Brothers
AND A
PREFACE

I many Prodigies haue seene,
Creatures that haue preposterous beene,
to nature in their birth,
But such a thing as this my theame,
Makes all the rest seeme but a dreame,
the like was nere on earth.

Thus begins the ballad 'The Two Inseparable Brothers', written by Martin Parker, one of London's most prolific authors of valedictory poems, songs and ballads of the 1630s and 1640s. On 23 November 1637, a certain Robert Milbourne registered this ballad as 'a Picture of the Italian yong man with his brother growing out of his side with some verses thereunto'. The admittedly coarse illustration shows exactly that: a man with a much smaller conjoined twin brother growing out of his body. This was the famous Lazarus Colloredo, who had already toured Italy, Germany, Spain and France, and who was

now ready to make his bow before King Charles I and his liege
subjects in London. On 4 November 1637, Sir Henry Herbert,
Master of the Rolls, had granted 'Lazaras, an Italian' permission
to 'shew his brother Baptista, that grows out of his navell, and
carryes him at his syde'.

> A Gentleman well qualifide,
> Doth beare his brother at his side,
> inseparably knit,
> As in this figure you may see,
> And both together liuing be,
> the world admires at it.

Throughout his career, Lazarus Colloredo was described as
a 'gentleman', and it is likely that he was of above-average
breeding. A later handbill about him actually states that he was
an Italian count, but this is unlikely to have been the truth. A
letter from Dr Augustin Pincet, of Genoa, to the celebrated
Fortunio Liceti, tells that the two inseparable brothers were born
on 20 March 1617; their parents were Baptista and Pellegrina
Colloredo, living in the parish of Saint Bartholomeus de Costa in
Genoa. Both twins were baptised at the font: the larger one was
named Lazarus; his tiny brother, Joannes Baptista. Their parents
were healthy, and had previously had several healthy children.
Dr Pincet examined the twins and found that while Lazarus was
healthy and complete in every respect, Joannes Baptista had a
stunted and malformed body, lacked one leg, and did not open
his eyes. He was amazed that Lazarus was the only one to suckle
his mother and to emit excrements and urine. When his tiny
brother got some droplets of milk on his lips, his lips moved as
if he tried to swallow them. Dr Pincet was astonished that this
monstrum novissimum – this novel species of monster – actually
seemed fully capable of life. So too was Dr Paulus Zacchias, who
described the inseparable brothers in his *Questionum Medico-
Legalium*. He had seen them in Rome in 1617 and later in 1623.
Their mother had died in 1620. Lazarus had a handsome face

and curly golden hair. From his belly, near the cartilage of his rib cage, grew another child. Joannes Baptista was devoid of any sense, wrote Zacchias, except that of sensation. He moved his arms, and frothy saliva dribbled from his mouth.

> But that to ratifie this truth,
> Now in the Strand this wondrous youth
> is present to be seene,
> And he with his strange burden, hath
> Bin shewne (with maruaile) as he saith
> to our good King and Queene.

Lazarus Colloredo's stay in London appears to have been quite successful. He was received in an audience by King Charles I and Queen Henrietta, and there exists a curious old engraving of him, with the somewhat confusing caption 'Israel and his twin brother exhibited to King Charles II', which I have seen. I am convinced that it actually portrays Lazarus Colloredo, however, since the position of the twin is almost exactly the same as in other engravings of him. Another confusing circumstance is that the individual in this engraving is rather youthful-looking, and that the engraving is marked '*aet.* 17'; it is reasonable to propose that this was an older engraving of him, perhaps made at the onset of his career, which Lazarus himself or some other person had brought to London.

> This yong-man doth completely walke,
> He can both read, write, sing, or talke,
> without paine or detraction,
> And when he speaks the other head,
> Doth moue the lips both ruby red,
> not speaking but in action.

In 1638, Lazarus Colloredo toured France. In Paris he was seen by M. Henri Sauval, who spoke to him at length and recorded some extraordinary facts in his *Histoire et Antiquités de la Ville de*

Paris. Both Lazarus and his brother had blonde hair, and they did not look like Italians. Lazarus told him that when they had been young, Joannes Baptista's head had been much smaller; now, it was twice as big as his own. The imperfect twin's open mouth, dribbling with saliva, showed some large teeth, and he had appalling halitosis. Lazarus also said that they had three times been ill, and that the doctors had bled him twenty times for various ailments; the learned medics had never hazarded purgation, however, since they feared that this might have been too much for a digestive system shared by two human beings. M. Sauval was greatly impressed when Lazarus accepted his challenge to play handball at the Paris ball-house; the Italian played with skill and vigour, with his brother tightly tied to his own body. After the game, Lazarus told M. Sauval that he had once been in big trouble: a man had teased him at a public house, and Lazarus had struck him a mighty blow on the head and killed him. He had been sentenced to death, but was reprieved after he had shown, to the court's satisfaction, that if he were killed, his brother, who was innocent of the deadly assault, would be unjustly murdered!

> One arme's about his brother cast,
> That doth embrace his body fast,
> the other hangeth by,
> These armes haue hands with fingers all,
> Yet as a childs they are but small,
> pinch any part hee'l cry.

Lazarus later made another tour of the British Isles, and went to Norwich, as shown by a record in the Mayor's Court Book for 21 December 1639: 'This daie Larzeus Colloretto have leave to shewe a monster until the day after twelve, he shewing to the Court a lysence signed with his Maties owne hand.' In 1640, he was in Gdansk in Poland, where he told an English traveller that he was going to Turkey next. In 1642, Lazarus returned to the British Isles. A day or two before Easter he visited Aberdeen, as evidenced by John Spalding's curious *Memorialls of the Trubles in Scotland and in England*. He had two servants with him, who, like himself, were well dressed. He had also brought with him a large portrait of himself, which he hung out at his lodgings, to advertise himself. When the show was to begin, one of the servants blew a trumpet and called out that Colloredo was now receiving visitors; the other servant stood by the door and collected money from the curious Scots who flocked to see this marvel: according to Spalding, 'this gryte wark of God was admired of be many in Abirdene and throw the countries as he trauellit.' Spalding was himself among the visitors, and could confirm the earlier observations of their anatomy: Lazarus was perfectly formed, but the twin's malformed head was drooping backward and downward, and the eyes were closed. The twin had three fingers on each hand, six toes on the sole foot, and 'the prik of ane man, bot no balcod'. He also confirmed that the twin 'had a kind of lyf, and feilling', but that he ate nothing, and was fed from the nourishment taken by Lazarus. When Colloredo was travelling, he carried his brother within a fold of his great cloak and cape, and no person could guess his unique deformity.

> Th'imperfect once the small poxe had,
> Which made the perfect brother sad,
> but he had neuer any,
> And if you nip it by the arme,
> Or doe it any little harme,
> (this hath been tried by many,)
> It like an infant (with voyce weake)
> Will cry out though it cannot speake,
> as sensible of paine...

There are fewer observations of Lazarus Colloredo and his brother after they left Scotland in 1642. The best description of Lazarus is that by the celebrated Danish anatomist Thomas Bartholin, who saw him being exhibited in 1645. It is worth quoting verbatim:

Twice I saw with astonishment Lazarus Colloredo, a Genoese, aged about twenty-eight; first in Copenhagen and later in Basle in Switzerland. This Lazarus had a little brother born with him, growing out of his breast and adhering to him at the level of the xiphoid cartilage of the breastbone. The little brother had a left leg and foot; he had two arms, but just three fingers on each hand. If pressure was made against his chest, he moved his hands, ears and lips. He received no food or nourishment but through the body of his greater brother Lazarus. Their vital and animal parts appeared to be distinct, as the little brother might sleep when Lazarus was awake, stir whilst Lazarus was sleeping, and sweat when Lazarus was without perspiration. They had both been baptised, the greater one named Lazarus at the font, the smaller John Baptist. The head of the little brother was well formed and covered with hair. His respiration was weak, since I could hold a feather to his mouth and nostrils, and it moved but slightly. His mouth was always open and gaping, and had no lack of teeth. No part of him seemed to increase in size except the head, which was larger than that of Lazarus, deformed and with long dangling hair. They both had beards, but whilst that of Lazarus was well combed and kept clean, that of the other was neglected.

Yet nothing doth the lesser eate,
He's onely nourish'd with the meate
wherewith the other feeds,
By which it seemes though outward parts
They haue for two, yet not two hearts,
this admiration breeds.

In a handbill issued in Strasbourg, where Lazarus Colloredo exhibited himself in August 1645, the usual facts about him are repeated. Interestingly, it also states that although Joannes Baptista was without understanding, voice and speech, the two brothers could actually *communicate* with each other. There is no record of Lazarus Colloredo and his strange twin brother after they toured Italy in 1646 and were seen by Dr Johannes Hellweg in Nuremberg in 1649; it is likely that Colloredo either died or retired from show business shortly after this year. The fame of these inseparable brothers survived them, however. In 1777, the *Gentleman's Magazine* reproduced an engraving of Colloredo, copied from Bartholin's work, with an explanatory text by Dr J. Greene giving a true account of 'a Man with a Child growing out of his Body'. The same engraving was reissued as a plate in 1815, and later reproduced in several nineteenth-century works of popular *biographia curiosa* with more or less confused commentary. Both Gould and Pyle's *Anomalies and Curiosities of Medicine* and C.J.S. Thompson's *The Mystery and Lore of Monsters* quote Bartholin's description of Colloredo. Some later commentators have doubted, from the extraordinary nature of his deformity and the fact that no similar case of parasitic conjoined twinning has been observed in the nineteenth or twentieth century, that Colloredo ever existed. Others have suspected that Bartholin was exaggerating. The discovery of several independent descriptions of Colloredo and his brother, like those by Paulus Zacchias, Henri Sauval and John Spalding, as well as the handbills issued in Strasbourg in 1645 and Verona in 1646, proves without doubt not only that they definitely existed, but also that Bartholin's description contained no exaggeration.

> Through Germany, through Spain & France,
> (Deuoyd of danger or mischance)
> and other Christian Lands
> They travell'd haue, nay rather one
> For both, so many miles hath gone,
> to shew th' work of Gods hands.

It would have been fashionable just to dismiss the inseparable brothers as a unique freak of nature, and just another 'curiosity' that impedes the serious study of the history of medicine. A more constructive approach is to examine more closely the many aspects of their influence on contemporary culture, as well as to study, in an interdisciplinary manner, how they have influenced the history of teratology, and also made appearances in literature and popular culture.

᠅

Having surveyed Lazarus Colloredo and his strange brother, how can we explain this strange deformity? Conjoined, or Siamese, twins can be divided into several subgroups. Among these are craniopagus twins, who are joined by the skulls; thoracopagus twins joined by the ribcage; omphalopagus twins joined by the belly; pygopagus twins joined by the hips; and ischiopagus twins joined by the sacrum. Another, parallel classification differentiates between symmetrical conjoined twins, with two complete individuals, and asymmetrical ones, where one of the twins is an incompletely developed parasite. The German teratologists Friedrich Ahlfeld, Ernst Schwalbe and Hans Hübner all considered the case of the Colloredo brothers and diagnosed them as thoracopagus parasiti-cus conjoined twins. The modern definition of thoracopagi entails that the twins should have joined thoraxes, however, and this was not the case with the Colloredo twins; in modern terminology they should be classified as omphalopagus parasiticus conjoined twins, since they were joined near the umbilicus.

It is also possible to establish the exact mechanism behind this form of parasitic conjoined twinning. Conjoined twins are the result of imperfect splitting of a fertilised ovum, and the site of conjunction depends on where the splitting has not occurred. Lazarus and Joannes Baptista Colloredo began their intra-uterine life as two equally sized omphalopagus conjoined twins, but Joannes Baptista's body lost at least part of its contact with the umbilical vesicle. The parts of his body that were not in contact with this vesicle, and not supplied with blood from the body of Lazarus, began to atrophy. The inner organs did not develop normally either, and it is unlikely that the parasitic twin had a functional heart and lungs, nor any functional gut or urinary system. There must have been a gradual development of a collateral circulation, enabling Joannes Baptista to survive on the oxygen-rich blood and the nutrients digested by his brother. The contemporary accounts agree that Joannes Baptista was capable of movement and reflex actions, and that his lungs and larynx were sufficiently well developed for him to cry out. The fact that his head increased in size can only have been due to the development of hydrocephalus caused by insufficient drainage of cerebrospinal fluid.

Lazarus and Joannes Baptista Colloredo represent one of the very few convincing cases of viable omphalopagus parasiticus twins. The German teratologist Hans Hübner described two stillborn instances, both from the nineteenth century, and the old monster medicine records describe several more or less fabulous instances. The famous Ambroise Paré described, in his *Des Monstres et Prodiges*, a man with a second, parasitic head proceeding from the epigastric region. This man lived to an adult age and took nourishment using both heads; this latter, rather unlikely, circumstance has led to the case being (probably erroneously) considered doubtful. While visiting Genoa (!) in 1699, a certain Dr Walther saw a fourteen-year-old boy who was carrying from the abdomen a parasitic twin with a head, neck, shoulders and chest. The celebrated anatomist Jacques-Bénigne Winslow made a similar observation at about the same time. This may well be a reference to the celebrated James Poro, born in Genoa in 1686, who later exhibited himself in London. He was described by James Paris du Plessis in his manuscript *History of Prodigies*, and none less than Sir Hans Sloane, Secretary to the Royal Society of London, commissioned his portrait to be painted. James Poro had a second head growing from just below the chest. The parasitic head was well shaped, du Plessis wrote, although an engraving of Poro does not support this; it had some kind of independent life, although it could not speak or open its eyes. James Paris du Plessis had also seen a twenty-year-old German, born near Ratisbon in 1678, who had a parasitic twin growing from his waist on the right side. This twin had a chest, an arm and a well-developed head and face, with a downy beard and two long locks of hair on the head. He took nourishment with a good appetite, and *could speak as distinctly as his brother*. All these individuals would also be classified as omphalopagus parasiticus conjoined twins, with a variable degree of resorption of the lower body.

There is no hint in the contemporary sources of any discussion to separate Lazarus Colloredo from his brother by means of a surgical operation. The extent of the junction between their bodies is not immediately apparent from the illustrations, but, from the descriptions of Pincet and Zacchias, it appears to have been of considerable thickness. It may well be that they had a common liver, and it is certain that the conjoined area contained several large arteries. An attempt to separate Lazarus from his brother with seventeenth-century techniques would have ended fatally. With modern surgical techniques, such an operation would have been a relatively simple matter: Lazarus and his brother would have been separated at an early age, and this would probably have restored Lazarus to a normal life. Joannes Baptista would of course have lost his lingering half-life once he was removed from his brother and host. If Lazarus Colloredo had been born today, would his parasitic twin have been cut away like a wart or mole, or would ethical arguments have been raised about deliberately killing a creature that was definitely a human being, and who definitely showed signs of independent life? The latter is unlikely, however, since it will be later demonstrated in this book that 'sacrifice' surgery of extensively conjoined twins, in which one twin is deliberately killed to serve as an organ donor to the one best fit for survival, has been practised several times in the 1980s and 1990s.

Even disregarding Martin Parker's long ballad about them, Lazarus Colloredo and his brother made an impact on seventeenth-century poetry. They were mentioned in several contemporary poems and pamphlets; these allusions have proved obscure to present-day literary historians and even prompted speculation that the authors had had a very weird view of the relation between the biblical Lazarus and John the Baptist. The poet Alexander Brome wrote, in a poem about a close friend of his, that:

My self am from myself, but here and there I
Suppose my self grown an Ubiquitary;
We are a miracle, and tis with us
As with John Baptist and his Lazarus.

The cavalier poet John Cleveland also knew about Lazarus
Colloredo and his brother, although he made the same mistake
as Alexander Brome and mixed them up. His satirical poem
Smectymnuus was inspired by a clerical club of that name, consisting of five divines who had written a tract about the merits
of bishops and presbyters, which was published in 1641. John
Cleveland, who was always ready to attack the roundhead clergy
with cutting satire, took affront at the contents of this pamphlet, and the outrageous pen-name of the five authors, which
had been formed by adding their initials together. In the poem
Smectymnuus, or the Club Divine, he blasted all five faces of this
'Monstrous Brotherhood of Five' with the words:

So the vaine satyrists stand all a row
As hallow teeth upon a Lute-string show.
Th' Italian Monster pregnant with his Brother,
Natures Dyræresis, halfe one another,
He, with his little Sides-man Lazarus,
Must both give way unto Smectymnuus.

Next *Strubridge Faire* is *Smec*'s; for loe his side
Into a five fold *Lazar's* multipli'd,
Under each arme there's tuckt a double Gyssard,
Five faces lurke under one single vizzard.

The literary influence of Lazarus Colloredo and his brother
appears to have survived them, as evidenced by *Unheavenly Twin*,
one of the short stories by Robert Bloch, the author of *Psycho*
and one of the heirs of H.P. Lovecraft in the American tradition
of macabre fiction. This story takes place in Malone's Boarding
House, which is the winter home, in between tours, for a party

of sideshow 'freaks'. The narrator is an 'armless wonder' and there is also a giant, a dwarf, a human skeleton, a fat lady and Ordo the Dog-faced Man, among others. The weirdest of all is Count Vomar, who never joined in the poker and bridge games of the others and always ate alone. The reason for this is that he is unique even among his peers. Out of his waist grows a mal-formed twin, and although Vomar hides it in a wide dressing gown, just as Colloredo had used a cloak for the same purpose, the others are disconcerted to see the twin's beady eyes glare at them from underneath his dress. During the shows, Vomar is disgusted by the people exclaiming with horror at the 'thing' squirming on his stomach, and these experiences have embittered him and made him a loner. The twin has an independent life and intelligence; it lives off the bloodstream of its host, and while Vomar himself grows leaner, the twin increases in size. Vomar confides to the narrator that his situation is a desperate one: the twin has a superior intelligence and wishes to dominate, or even destroy, its host. The ending of the story is that the hideous, bloated body of the evil twin is discovered feeding on the body of the lifeless Vomar. Robert Bloch wrote several stories and film scripts using sideshow interiors, and it is likely that he found an illustration and a brief description of Lazarus Colloredo in one of his source books; his imagination did the rest.

The most obvious point of approach to Lazarus Colloredo and his brother is that of simple human interest, however. As in many of the chapters of this book, one is drawn into admiration for a man born with a most fearful physical deformity, but who nevertheless not only survived in a time not noted for kindness or compassion for the disabled and deformed, but actually man-aged to create a tolerable existence for himself by turning his unique deformity into profit. He spoke with kings, queens and nobles; saw the larger part of Europe; earned much money; and could live in relative comfort. One unverified account told that Lazarus Colloredo actually married, and that he was the father of several children. It is telling that Lazarus Colloredo is often described as a gentleman, with the polite, affable manners of a

courtier. Spalding's Scottish history of 1642 specifically stated that
he was the master of two servants, and that he had no showman
or impresario to direct him. Many of the people we encounter
in this book were not so lucky, but were the victims of human
vampires in the shape of showmen, who exploited and humiliated
them in a most dismal and degrading way. In a way, Colloredo
combined the roles of freak and showman: he applied for a licence
to show his monster, advertised it well, and spoke courteously to
the freak show visitors. In turn, the audience treated him well
and made him a wealthy man, but they pinched and slapped his
semi-conscious brother to make him give his shrill cry.

My structuring of the tale of the two inseparable brothers serves
as a blueprint for the remainder of this book, which deals almost
entirely with various aspects of the history of teratology, the science of monstrous births. Its scope and general layout somewhat
resembles that of Dr Charles J.S. Thompson's book *The Mystery
and Lore of Monsters*, a collection of essays on 'some giants, dwarfs,
and prodigies' that was first published in 1930. C.J.S. Thompson
was honorary curator of the historical collection of the Royal
College of Surgeons of London, and a gentleman of great eru-
dition. One does not have to be a politically correct zealot to
object to the title of Thompson's book: to refer to a pair of
conjoined twins or an individual with pituitary gigantism as a
'monster' was a thing of the past among most educated people
in the 1930s. Today, such individuals are alternately referred to as
'freaks' or 'very special people', among other more or less inspired
neologisms. The term 'freak' is actually of some interest, as it
originates in the expression 'freak of nature', implying that the
malformed child was a unique, unclassifiable phenomenon, the
result of some strange 'maternal impression', a witch's curse, or
divine displeasure. From the early seventeenth century onwards,
medical science struggled to understand and classify these 'freaks
of nature', and to incorporate all kinds of human congenital

malformations in a system of teratology. By the late nineteenth century, it had succeeded: impressive standard works, such as those by the Frenchman Geoffroy Saint-Hilaire, the Germans Förster, Ahlfeld and Schwalbe, and the American George Jackson Fisher, left no variety of human congenital malformation undescribed. The late nineteenth and early twentieth centuries also saw great advances in the study of inherited diseases. The early popular books on human malformations, like those by Gould and Pyle and Thompson already mentioned, took these advances in teratology and clinical genetics into account, and in spite of their age, they are often quite sophisticated, medically speaking, compared with more recent works in the same genre. The vast majority of these modern books have been written by social scientists, and while they are strong on sociological speculation and cautiously 'politically correct' banter adhering to whatever school of historiography is currently in favour, they are weak on historical scholarship and even weaker with regard to medical insights. This of course impedes any attempt at an interdisciplinary approach.

The modern sociological treatises are also responsible for the re-emergence of the notion of a multitude of 'freaks of nature' with no rational explanation even within the realm of modern medicine, and certainly do nothing to diminish public ignorance and bigotry about these matters. Indeed, correct medical information on 'freaks' and human deformities is difficult to come by, except in the form of highly advanced textbooks aimed at professionals within this area, and this gap has been filled by other, more sinister forces. Religious movements claiming that a deformed child is the punishment of God, or the result of sins in a previous life, have no lack of adherents in the United States as well as in Europe. The notion of inexplicable 'freaks of nature' that are outside the boundary of medicine has even led to a resurfacing of the old doctrine of 'maternal impressions' – that the mother's experiences during pregnancy determine the shape of her child. This age-old doctrine, which I described at length in my previous book *A Cabinet of Medical Curiosities*, still has supporters on the Internet, and also, it appears, with certain

Christian fundamentalists. Indeed, the cyberspace domain is a mine of misinformation and bigoted nonsense on these matters. Various oddballs and political extremists do their best to supply explanations – from their own warped minds – for 'freaks of nature'. A recent search on the Internet about Julia Pastrana, a Mexican woman unfortunate enough to be born with a rare genetic syndrome of excessive hairiness, illustrates this in a vivid manner. One 'hit' was a racist magazine claiming that she was a baboon-human hybrid; another was a Bigfoot homepage that speculated that she might well be a distant relation of this elusive creature; a third claimed, in no uncertain terms, that she was Darwin's missing link.

The main theme of this book is the human interest, however. Rather than to dismiss people like Daniel Cajanus, the Swedish Giant, Nicolas Ferry, the King of Poland's court dwarf, and the dicephalus Tocci brothers as 'freaks', I have regarded them as human beings, born with sometimes appalling congenital deformities, and tried to chronicle their lives and vicissitudes as closely as possible. A remarkable feature of many modern books on 'freaks' is their tendency to concentrate on only one (read American) cultural context. Instead, the centre of this book is firmly based in London, although various French, German, Dutch and Scandinavian sources have also been used. Another aim was not to limit the discussion only to the medical point of view, but to bring in aspects of ethnology, literature and cultural history as well. I have had access to the matchless collections of the British Library, containing printed books as well as manuscripts, prints and drawings. Many other London repositories, like those of the Colindale Newspaper Library, the Royal College of Surgeons of England, the Royal Society of Medicine, the Wellcome History of Medicine Library, and the Guildhall Library, have also been consulted. To bring the research fully up to date, various computerised databases and citation indexes have been extensively used, through the Internet or the British Library computer network. I am very pleased that, like its American counterpart, this book has now gone into paperback.

2

The Hairy Maid
AT THE
HARPSICHORD

H er name was Barbara Urslerin and she really did play the harpsichord. John Evelyn saw her being exhibited in London in 1657. He was amazed by her strange appearance, and described her thoroughly in his diary:

> The Hairy Maid, or Woman whom twenty years before I had also seene as a child: her very Eyebrowes were combed upwards & all her forehead as thick & even as growes on any woman's head, neatly dress'd: There comes also two locks very long out of Each Eare: she had also a most prolix beard & moustachios, with long locks of haire growing on the very middle of her nose, exactly like an Iceland Dog: the rest of her body not so hairy, yet exceedingly long in comparison, armes, neck, breast and back; the colour of light browne, & fine as well dressed flax.

Barbara Urslerin was born near the village of Kempten, not far from Augsburg in Germany, in February 1629 (some sources say 1633). As she told John Evelyn and other visitors, none of her family, neither parents nor relations, had been hairy. She was now married, she said, and had one normal child, of which she was very proud. John Evelyn approvingly stated that the Hairy Maid was 'for the rest very well shaped, plaied well on the Harpsichord &c.' It is likely that he had really seen Barbara twenty years earlier, since all records agree that she had been exhibited since a very early age. John Evelyn had been among her admirers in London as early as 1637, when she was just eight years old. In 1639, she was seen in Copenhagen, and later in Belgium, by the celebrated anatomist Thomas Bartholin. Her parents were taking her all around Europe, he wrote, to show her for money. Bartholin examined the lively little girl, and found that her entire body was covered with soft, blonde hair. She had a luxuriant beard, and even from the ears themselves grew long, beautiful curls of hair, all handsomely dressed.

In 1646, the Frenchman Elie Brackenhoffer visited a fair in Paris. In his diary, he described its various attractions: a lioness, a five-footed cow, a monstrous dolphin, an Italian water-spouter, a man without hands, a rope dancer and a dromedary. He had come across similar animal and human curiosities quite a few times before and gave them scant attention, but he had never seen anything like the Hairy Maid, and described her in detail. She was eighteen years old, she said, and of German ancestry. Her hair was luxuriant and soft as silk, with the long curls beautifully dressed. M. Brackenhoffer, who was apparently either a lecher or a determined lover of curiosities, then proceeded to undress her, after the payment of an additional fee. Her back was covered with thick, soft hair like a coat of fur. Her breasts, he noted approvingly, were round and white, and less hairy than the rest of the skin. M. Brackenhoffer ended his account by stating that he had ascertained that she was a true woman, and not a hermaphrodite.

Barbara Urslerin lived during the heyday of the old monster medicine, when scholars and medical men were always on the hunt for marvels and curiosities; she had the honour of being mentioned in almost every chronicle of medical rarities of the time. The learned Hieronymus Welsch saw her in Rome in 1647 and later in Mailand in 1648, and described her in his *Observationes medicarum episagma*. In November 1653, she passed through her home town of Augsburg. An artist drew a beautiful portrait of her, which was later purchased by a physician in Basel; in the late nineteenth century it was still kept in a collection in that city, and reproduced in an obscure German article. Barbara Urslerin visited Frankfurt in 1655, and later the same year she was seen in Copenhagen by the physician Georg Seger. Her entire body, including the face, was covered with soft, blonde, curly hair. Her luxuriant beard reached down to her waist. She told Seger that she had married a year before, but that she did not have any children. On the exhibition handbill, which Seger gave as a figure to his paper, she was depicted seated at the harpsichord; this was an engraving from a portrait by Isaac Brünn, which has remained the best-known illustration of her. The text related that her father and mother were Balthasar and Anna Ursler from Augsburg, and that she was 'hairy all over with beautiful yellow curls growing from the face, and large curls growing from each ear'.

In 1655, Barbara Urslerin came to London for the first time. According to a note quoted by James Caulfield in his *Portraits, Memoirs and Characters of Remarkable Persons*, she was twenty-two years old at the time. A German man named Johann Michael Vanbeck (or van Beck) had married 'this frightful creature' only to make money by putting her on show. They had toured many parts of Europe. In 1656, a fine portrait of her was engraved by Gaywood. In 1660, Barbara was touring France. When they came to Beauvais, her husband, van Beck, applied to the local bailiff for permission to exhibit a strange prodigy of nature, a woman with a hairy, bearded face and moustaches. He did not mention that this monstrous woman was actually his wife, but instead pointed out that she had already received much attention from the curious in Paris and other French cities. An engraving of Gaywood's portrait was now used as the exhibition handbill, and a copy was enclosed with van Beck's letter. The local police were pleased to allow van Beck to show his hairy wife for money, and to advertise her by striking a tambourine in the marketplace, if he promised that the exhibition was a decent one and that it was closed down in good time in the afternoon. The last thing we know about Barbara Urslerin is that in 1668 she was seen in London by the Dane Holger Jacobsen. He boldly suggested that the Hairy Maid must be the loathsome result of a copulation between a woman and a humanoid ape, a hypothesis which was outdated already in his time. Jacobsen had seen a large ape called Mammonett, which was kept as a pet in the King of Denmark's gardens, and could well remember that this creature often 'tried to take lascivious liberties with women' who visited the royal gardens. He ended his brief description of this 'monstrous hairy girl' by emphasising that the length and softness of her hair was excessive all over the body, and that he had thoroughly examined her genitals, to see if they had any similarity with those of a monkey.

Anatole Le Double and François Houssay, two French anthropologists who wrote the book *Les Velus*, a valuable early treatise on excessive hairiness, are not the only people who asked themselves what finally happened to Barbara Urslerin. It is possible to follow her travels all around Europe from 1637 to 1668 in some detail, but after the latter year she completely disappears. It may be that she retired from the monster shows, but this does not seem very likely: her husband had been relentless in exploiting her, and showed no sign of letting his most valuable possession go to waste. If the husband had died, there were many other showmen ready to take over the management of this hairy celebrity. The most likely explanation is that Barbara herself died in or about 1668. The many either coy or lewd allusions to visitors to the exhibition undressing and fondling the Hairy Maid prompted Le Double and Houssay to query whether prostitution had played any part in the exploitation of her. This is possible, but by no means necessary. At this time, it was the custom that any person paying to see a human or animal curiosity also had the right to thoroughly examine the creature on show, to make sure there was no imposition. A six-legged calf had its extra legs pulled, a giant's trousers were pulled up so that it could be ascertained that he did not wear stilts, and Lazarus Colloredo's parasitic twin was pinched until he uttered a cry. None of Barbara Urslerin's visitors had seen anything like her before, and those who wanted to make sure she really was a true woman, from motives of lechery, curiosity, or scientific inquiry, were free to do so, after paying an additional fee.

The Isaac Brünn engraving of Barbara Urslerin has appeared in many European works on monstrosities and *biographiae curiosae*. It was later reproduced in a queer French magazine, appropriately named *Bizarre*. Today it is posted on an Internet site aimed to titillate those belonging to weird 'sexual minorities'. The French author Jean Boullet instead reproduced the remarkable Gaywood engraving, which is a far better likeness of her, as well as artistically superior, with the telling caption 'Belle et Bête'; in one body, the personified characteristics of both.

THE WILD MAN FROM THE CANARIES

It is almost a relief to turn the attention from the Hairy Maid at the Harpsichord to another, slightly more edifying story of an individual affected with inherited excessive hairiness. Petrus Gonzales, the hero of this strange tale, was born in the Canary Isles in the year 1556. At this time, there was widespread belief in a particular race of hairy savages or 'wild men'. The belief that monstrous races of cynocephali, sciapods and troglodytes inhabited parts of Asia and Africa was a time-honoured part of medieval mythology, which had been originated by the writings of Pliny. The wild men, fierce, hairy, carrying a club, and always ready to carry off women into the deep woods, were another medieval stereotype, implying a violent nature, lack of civilisation, and want of a moral sense. According to legend, wild men existed not only in the African and Asian backwoods, but small remnants of these savages were still hiding in the deep forests of Germany, France, and Scandinavia. Some of the early observations of Asian or African wild men were definitely misinterpretations of encounters between early explorers and anthropoid apes. In the fifteenth and sixteenth centuries, the wild man was much used in heraldry: the symbolism of the urge to civilise and dominate what appeared rude and wild was the use of a wild man, club in hand, as upholder of the arms of some noble family.

The discovery of an infant in the Canary Isles whose face and body was just as hairy as that of a wild man or a great ape was quite a sensation. Little Petrus Gonzales, of whose parents we know nothing, was in fact lucky to escape being killed as a monster or demon by the superstitious country people; instead, he was taken to Paris by the express order of King Henri II of France, who wanted to study this prodigy more closely. Petrus Gonzales' entire body, particularly his head and face, was covered with long, soft, wavy hair, and even at an early age his face already resembled that of a terrier dog. In 1557, the savant Julius Caesar Scaliger wrote that Paris had just obtained a novel curiosity: a young boy from Spain, taken from the Indian Isles, who was entirely covered with hair. The Frenchmen called this boy Barbet, the same name used to signify a race of shaggy Belgian dogs, which the people of Flanders called *Watterhund*. Another observer, a certain Dr Boschius, told Count Ulysses Aldrovandi that King Henri had recently received a young boy, hairy all over like a dog. Probably astounded that this extraordinary 'wild boy' seemed intelligent and alert, Henri II ordered that he should be taught Latin and given a good education, since the king wanted to find out whether such a wild boy was at all educable. Little Petrus should be kept at the royal court as a curiosity, and his progress carefully monitored. Henri II's successors honoured this agreement scrupulously, and Petrus Gonzales spent his entire youth at the French court. Many visiting princes and noblemen were introduced to this prodigy, whose hairy face, resembling that of a shaggy dog, looked simply amazing when he was dressed in his richly embroidered court costume. Even more astonishingly to the visitor who had read about the savagery of the race of wild men, the king's hairy 'savage' was intelligent, well informed and spoke excellent Latin. In 1573, the seventeen-year-old Petrus Gonzales was given permission to marry a young French lady.

Whether this match was made according to his own choice or arranged as some court festivity is not known, but Gonzales and his wife remained united by wedlock for several decades and had at least four children. Allegedly to prevent the 'wild' Petrus Gonzales from feeling homesick, he was given a cave to dwell in with his entire family, like some bizarre ornamental hermit, in one of the royal parks. Most of the time he resided at the court in Fontainebleau, however, where the king showed him to visiting dignitaries like some trained dog or monkey.

By 1581, Petrus Gonzales was the father of two children. Although his wife was perfectly normal, both children were as hairy as their father. This marvellous hairy family was Europe's greatest curiosity of their time. Many princes and noblemen wanted to see them, and later in 1581 the entire family was sent for an extended tour all over Europe. Firstly, they visited Duchess Margaret of Parma's court in Flanders. In early 1582, they went to Munich, where their life-sized portraits were painted at the order of Duke Albrecht IV of Bavaria, who was known as a lover of curiosities. These portraits were later given to Archduke Ferdinand of Tyrol, who installed them in his famous Kunst-Kammer at Schloss Ambras outside Innsbruck. The children – a daughter of five or six years and a son of three or four – are dressed in rich, costly garments, which increase the startling contrast to their hairy faces. They look like little animal dolls dressed up in human clothes by their childish owner. The wife is pretty and demure, and her clothes are Dutch-looking in style. Petrus Gonzales himself is dressed in a rich, ankle-length garment like a cassock. His face is as hairy as ever, and at the age of twenty-six he has a venerable-looking beard, but the expressive look in his brown eyes seems to say, 'I am not what you think I am'.

Two other paintings of the Gonzales family were also made during their stay in Bavaria, by Albrecht IV's court artist Joris Hoefnagel. One of these depicts Petrus Gonzales and his wife, the other the two children. Hoefnagel included these two portraits in a volume of his *The Four Elements*, entitled *Animalia Rationalia et Insecta*; they are the only humans to be portrayed. Petrus Gonzales was found at Tenerife in the Canaries, Hoefnagel writes, and later received a superior education at the French court. He was a scholar and a man of letters, and a sonorous speaker of Latin. Not long after their visit to Munich, the Gonzales family went to Vienna, at the order of Emperor Rudolf II. Here, a group portrait of them was painted in oil on parchment by court artist Dirck van Ravesteyn; it was later kept in one of the emperor's large folders of zoological drawings. In this portrait, Petrus Gonzales is standing up and his wife is seated; their two children are standing in front of them, the little boy leaning on his mother's lap. The girl is holding a tame owl, or rather owlet, which is facing the artist just like the four people.

In 1583, Petrus Gonzales and his family came to Basle, where they were seen by the celebrated anatomist Felix Plater. In a valuable note, published posthumously in his *Observationum*, Plater affirmed that the adult Petrus Gonzales seen by him was certainly the same person as the young 'wild boy' who was taken from the Canaries to the court of Henri II many years earlier. The king and his successors had valued Gonzales greatly and had taken good care of him. He was now on his way to Italy, where several princes had desired to make his acquaintance. Petrus Gonzales' abundant facial hair was excessively soft, and the eyebrows were so long and bushy that he had to trim them to be able to see. According to Felix Plater, he had two children, a boy aged nine and a girl aged seven. Both had hairy faces, the boy more than the girl; the skin along the spine of the backs of both children was also covered with long, soft hair.

The next account of the Gonzales family is that in the *Monstrorum Historia* of Count Ulysses Aldrovandi. He was one of the leading naturalists of the sixteenth century, and his vast collections of anatomical, zoological and botanical specimens were justly famous. In the mid-1590s, Count Aldrovandi had met and examined, by permission of the Marchioness of Sorania, the eight-year-old daughter of Petrus Gonzales. This little girl, whose face was covered with thick, soft hair just like her father's, was introduced to Count Aldrovandi by the marchioness herself, when on a trip to Bologna. Count Aldrovandi then ordered an artist to draw the entire Gonzales family: the forty-year-old father, the twenty-year-old son, and the two daughters, one twelve, the other eight years old. It is very likely that the son was the same little boy depicted in the Ambras and Hoefnagel pictures. What had happened to his elder sister is left unsaid; nor is it known whether the wife of Petrus Gonzales was still alive. The two young girls in Aldrovandi's drawings indicate that during his stay in Italy Gonzales had fathered two more children, both of them girls and both sharing his excessive hairiness.

Another remarkable memorial of the Gonzales family is an engraving of the Medusa-like head of a hairy young girl, by the artist and engraver Giacomo Franco. The caption states that this is the portrait of Tognina, the young daughter of the hairy man from the Canary Isles. Her brother, who was just as hairy as herself, was given as a present to Signor Farnesi, a wealthy nobleman. Tognina was herself staying at the ducal court of Parma. Another remarkable portrait of a hairy girl residing at the court of the Duchess of Parma was painted at about the same time, by Paulo Cagliari; it is very likely another painting of Tognina Gonzales. This portrait is in the collection of the Earl of Haddo, at Haddo House. A third drawing of one of Petrus Gonzales' daughters, probably Tognina, is now at the Pierpont Morgan Library in New York; it was the work of the celebrated portrait painter Lavinia Fontana. It was reproduced and described in the Hood Museum of Art's catalogue *The Age of the Marvelous*, and dated around 1583; this would imply that Tognina was the eldest daughter of Petrus Gonzales. The girl looks about eight years old, indicating that Tognina was born around 1575. Lavinia Fontana also did a fine oil portrait of Tognina, which is today at the art gallery of the famous Château de Blois in France. It is said to depict 'Antoinetta Gonsalvus'; both 'Tognina' and 'Antoinetta' are diminutive forms of 'Antonia' and 'Gonsalvus' is a Latinised form of Gonzales. This portrait is said to date from the early 1580s, adding further evidence that Tognina was indeed the eldest daughter of Petrus Gonzales. The New York drawing is probably

one of Lavinia Fontana's sketches for this fine portrait. A note in
Ulysses Aldrovandi's *Monstrorum Historia* tells us that Tognina later
married during her stay at the ducal court in Parma, and that she
lived there for many years and had several children of her own,
at least some of whom were as hairy as herself.

A few years later, another portrait of a hairy man, most likely
a member of the Gonzales family, was painted by Agostino
Carraci. It depicted Arrigo the Hairy, Pietro the Fool, Amon
the Dwarf and a group of 'other animals': two dogs, two apes
and a parrot, all belonging to Cardinal Odoarda Farnese just
like the humans. An *Avis de Rome* of 1 July 1595 tells us that the
Duke of Parma had given Cardinal Farnese a costly present: a
savage man eighteen years of age, whose face and brow were all
covered with long blonde hair. It is likely that this Arrigo was the
same individual as the twenty-year-old son of Petrus Gonzales
depicted by Aldrovandi. Arrigo Gonzales stayed at Cardinal
Farnese's establishment for many years, and was included in an
inventory of his house staff made in 1626. The final memorial of
the Gonzales family is an engraving given to a certain Mercurio
Ferrari after the death of his particular friend, the hairy man
Horatio Gonzales, in 1635. It is accompanied by a Latin poem,
which can be translated as:

> Here you see Gonzales, once famous in the court of Rome,
> Whose human face was covered with hair like an animal's.
> He lived for you, Ferrari, joined to you in love.
> And in this portrait he lives on, still breathing although he is dead.

This engraving is dated 1635, and it is not known whether this
Horatio was the same person as Arrigo, or possibly another son
of Petrus Gonzales.

THE HAIRY FAMILY OF BURMA

It was a long time before the world saw another hairy phenomenon like Barbara Urslerin or Petrus Gonzales and his

family; indeed, from the 1630s to the 1820s, no novel instance of
excessive hairiness was described either by scientists or by lovers
of curiosities. Had these two famous sixteenth- and seventeenth-
century cases not been detailed by the leading medical scientists
of the world, and painted from life by several celebrated artists,
there would definitely have been a risk that these hairy celebrities of yesteryear would have been considered as yet another
figment of imagination of the old monster medicine. Even so,
many were confused by these extraordinary descriptions of hairy
'wild people'. In Everhard Happel's *Relationes Curiosae*, published
in 1729, the Forest People from the Canaries are depicted in a
remarkable illustration. Standing in a sylvan glade, they are lis-
tening, in rapt attention, to a *concerto* played by the Hairy Maid
at the Harpsichord. Two other hairy savages come crawling out
of the undergrowth, enchanted by her music. In the *Eccentric
Magazine*, published in London in 1813, there is an engraved
portrait of Barbara Urslerin taken from an old print. According
to the caption to this illustration, great doubts were entertained
as to whether she was really a human being. The Editor of
the *Eccentric Magazine* had managed to resolve this controversy,
however. He had seen an old print of Barbara Urslerin, which
was formerly in the collection of Mr Frederich, a bookseller in
Bath. It had the following brief but telling note written on it:
'This woman I saw in Ratcliffe Highway, in the year 1668, and
was satisfied she was a woman. John Bulfinch.'

In 1826, a mission of the Governor-General of India, led by
John Crawfurd, visited the court of the King of Ava, a province
in Burma. In a published account of this mission, Crawfurd
described meeting a thirty-year-old hairy man named Shwe-
Maong. At the age of five, he had been given to the king by the
local chief of his district and, since then, had lived within the
palace as a curiosity and court entertainer. He was very clever
in acting the buffoon, dancing and making the most terrible
grimaces. Shwe-Maong stated that his parents were perfectly
normal and that none of his tribesmen were hairy. When he
was aged twenty-two years, having attained puberty only two

years previously, a wife was chosen for him by the king from the beautiful women in his retinue. There were four children, all girls, of this union. Two of them died at an early age, and a third was the very image of her mother; only one was abnormal, a girl named Maphoon, who was covered with hair just like her father and resembled an elderly bearded man. Crawfurd stated that the father never had more than two incisors and the two canines in the upper jaw, and four incisors and one canine in the lower jaw. Importantly, because it seems to eliminate the possibility that the other teeth simply failed to erupt, he says that where teeth were missing, the alveolar process was missing also.

In 1855, a second mission visited Ava, and Captain Henry Yule described the now thirty-one-year-old Maphoon, who was married to a normal Burmese and was the mother of two boys. Her father had been murdered by robbers, and she had been brought up in the king's household. The story told of her marriage was that the king had offered a reward to any man who was willing to marry her. Finally, an individual who was bold enough or avaricious enough ventured forth. Yule's description of Maphoon deserves to be quoted more or less verbatim:

> The whole of Maphoon's face was more or less covered with hair. On a part of the cheek, and between the nose and mouth, this was confined to short down, but over all the rest of the face was a thick silky hair of a brown colour, paling about the nose and chin, four or five inches long. At the alae of the nose, under the eye, and on the cheekbone, this was very fully developed, but it was in and on the ear that it was most extraordinary. ...The hair over her forehead was brushed so as to blend with the hair of the head, the latter being dressed (as usual with her countrywomen), à la Chinoise. It was not so thick as to conceal altogether the forehead. The nose, densely covered with hair as no animal's is that I know of, and with long fine locks curving out and pendent like the wisps of a fine Skye terrier's coat, had a most strange appearance. The beard was pale in colour, and about four inches in length, seemingly very soft and silky.

Maphoon's manners were modest, her voice soft and feminine, and her expression not unpleasing. Captain Yule thought her more like a pleasant-looking woman at a masquerade than a brutal, horrible monstrosity. Her dentition consisted of a few incisors only; the canine teeth and molars were absent, and the back parts of the gum merely a hard ridge. Maphoon's elder son, about four or five years of age, was not abnormal, although it is notable that in his teens he became more hairy than his younger brother. This brother, aged fourteen months, had tufts of long silky hair growing from his ears, a description which corresponds closely to the childhood state of the grandfather who later became so hairy.

In 1875, when the hairy family of Burma were discussed before the Anthropological Society of Paris, a photographic record of them appeared in the French journal *La Nature*. The French teratologist Boullet identified the hairy Burmese as Maphoon, her son Moung-Phoset, and her daughter Mah-Mé. Moung-Phoset would have been about twenty-one to twenty-five years of age at this time, depending on which of Maphoon's two sons he was. No other account of this time refers to more than one son; it seems likely that one of them had died between 1867 and 1875. According to Yule and others, Maphoon did not have a living daughter. Instead, there is good evidence that Moung-Phoset had a daughter named Mah-Mé, who would have been seven years old at the time of the photograph. It thus seems highly probable that the members of the family depicted in this photograph are Maphoon, her son Moung-Phoset, and her granddaughter Mah-Mé. Several other photographs of Maphoon, alone or in a family group, were taken by L. Allen Goss in 1872. One of them, showing Maphoon, two other hairy people and a normal Burmese, resembles the 1875 picture. Goss refers to the lively little girl in this picture, thus adding further evidence that Mah-Mé was really the daughter of Moung-Phoset. Two other excellent photographs in the Goss collection depict Maphoon and Moung-Phoset in detail.

In 1885, there was a revolution in Burma, leading to the so-called Third Burmese War; the king's palace was set on fire, and its inhabitants were driven away or killed. The hairy family managed to escape into a forest, Moung-Phoset carrying his fragile mother, Maphoon, on his back, followed by his wife and children. An Italian officer, Captain Paperno, who had been a military advisor to the Burmese court, was sent out to rescue them. When Paperno found them, he was astounded by their extraordinary appearance. He suggested that the hairy Burmese should make a tour of Europe, to be exhibited for money. Together with a fellow countryman, Mr Farini, the captain, who was himself without employment after the gutting of the Burmese court, decided to act as their impresario. Before the hairy Burmese left for Europe, Moung-Phoset's daughter Mah-Mé died at the age of eighteen. During the summer of 1886, the family appeared at the Egyptian Hall, Piccadilly, where they were seen by Mr J.J. Weir. He described Maphoon as a blind old woman, but lively and full of fun, and an inveterate chewer of betel in spite of her few teeth. He suspected that her hairy growth had thinned somewhat due to age, as Moung-Phoset had much more hair on the face and ears. He certainly presented a grotesque appearance, his entire features being hidden by the hair, which he combed over his face. Moung-Phoset's entire body was clothed with soft hair some inches in length, which he had cut from time to time; furthermore, he was tattooed from below the waist to above the knees. In spite of his bizarre exterior, Weir described Moung-Phoset as a well-educated and decent man. Importantly, he also stated that the hair of both Maphoon and Moung-Phoset was soft, wavy and of a brownish colour, quite unlike the hair of an ordinary Burmese. Captain Paperno, the family's impresario, informed Weir that although the dentition of all the hairy people was deficient, their non-hairy relatives all had perfect teeth. Mr Weir examined a cast of Moung-Phoset's mouth, finding in the upper jaw two canines and two large incisors, and in the lower jaw two canines and four small incisors; the molar and premolar teeth were all absent.

From London, the Burmese went on to Paris, where they appeared at the Folies Bergère. The French anthropologist M. Guyot-Daubès saw them there in 1887 and obtained an interview with their impresario, who told a remarkable story about Shwe-Maong's marriage. A beautiful young Burmese lady of high birth, a lady-in-waiting to the queen, had committed a crime against religion and was sentenced to be tortured to death in the most horrible way, at the churchyard of her dead ancestors. Just when the dreadful ceremony was about to start, a courtier rode up to offer her a pardon if she agreed to marry the court buffoon. After due consideration, she accepted the offer. The marriage ceremony was a ludicrous and degrading spectacle, as Shwe-Maong was joined by a veritable congress of dwarfs, albinos, idiots and jesters. It is odd that Crawfurd's original account did not mention this remarkable occurrence; it may have been a figment of Captain Paperno's imagination in order to make his hairy charges' life stories even more interesting. Like his grandfather, Moung-Phoset had married one of the maids of honour at the court, this time one who chose him of her own free will. Mah-Mé was their only daughter. In 1888 or 1889, the hairy Burmese went to the United States during their world tour, and their stage name was the 'Sacred Hairy Family of Burma'. The ultimate fate of Maphoon and Moung-Phoset is unknown; probably they went back to Burma and died in obscurity there.

THE STRANGE STORY OF JULIA PASTRANA

'Twas a big black ape from over the sea,
And she sat on a branch of a walnut tree,
And grinn'd and sputter'd and gazed at me
As I stood on the grass below:
She sputter'd and grinn'd in a fearsome way,
And put out her tongue, which was long and grey,
And hiss'd and curl'd and seem'd to say
'Why do you stare at me so?'

> Her ears were pointed, her snout was long;
> Her yellow fangs were sharp and strong;
> Her eyes – but surely I must be wrong,
> For I certainly thought I saw
> A singular look in those fierce brown eyes:
> The look of a creature in disguise;
> A look that gave me a strange surmise
> And a thrill of shuddering awe.

These are the first two stanzas of *Pastrana*, a remarkable poem by the Englishman Arthur Munby, published in his 1909 collection *Relicta*. After the long and detailed description of the grotesque, ape-like creature that is observed by the poem's narrator in the garden of a small German hotel, he describes his dinner in the hotel restaurant, where he is fascinated by a well-dressed lady of peculiar aspect:

> Sure, I remember those bright brown eyes?
> And the self-same look that in them lies
> I have seen already, with strange surprise,
> This very afternoon;
> Not in the face of a woman like this,
> Who has human features, and lips to kiss.
> But in one who can only splutter and hiss –
> In the eyes of a grim baboon!

The ludicrous conclusion of the poem is that the hotel waiters catch the apewoman after a desperate struggle, dragging her howling from the room in a large net, to the relief of the frightened narrator. When an admirer wrote to Munby to find out how he could have thought of such a bizarre subject for one of his poems, he replied that the poem had a certain background in reality. In 1857, he had seen a peculiar monster called 'Julia Pastrana, the Baboon Lady' being exhibited for money, and this had made a lasting impression on him, which had resulted in this thirty-two-stanza poem published fifty-two years later. When she was exhibited to the public in the United States, Canada and Europe in the 1850s, and long after her death in 1860, Julia Pastrana was one of the most famous human curiosities of her time. She was a Mexican Indian woman with excessive hairiness over large parts of the body, as well as an overdevelopment of the jaws that gave her an ape-like visage.

In July 1857, it was advertised in the London newspapers that 'a Grand and Novel Attraction' had come to the Metropolis: 'Miss JULIA PASTRANA, the NONDESCRIPT, from the United States and Canada, where she has held her levées in all the principal cities, and created the greatest possible excitement, being pronounced by the most eminent Naturalists and Physicians the Wonder of the World.' At this time, 'nondescript' was a term freely used about strange animals and monsters from beyond the seas. In the exhibition pamphlet, a good deal of information was given about her early history. Julia had been born in 1834 in a tribe of Mexican so-called Root-Digger Indians. It was luridly claimed that her mother had strayed into 'a region of country abounding in monkeys, baboons, and bears', and that she had later been found in a cave by some cowboys, nursing her hairy little daughter. Julia's new impresario, Mr Theodore Lent, claimed that Julia was 'a hybrid, wherein the nature of woman predominates over the ourang-outangs'. After her mother had died, Julia had been taken into the family of Pedro Sanchez, Governor of the State of Sinaloa, who wanted to study her as a curiosity. Brought up to be a serving-girl, she had stayed in the governor's house until April 1854, when an American showman had observed her extraordinary hairy exterior and persuaded her to accompany him to the United States to be exhibited for money. In a triumphal tour of Boston, Baltimore, Cleveland and New York, Julia Pastrana had attracted a good deal of attention both from the public and from men of medicine and science.

Julia Pastrana could speak the English and Spanish languages as well as her native tongue, and had learnt to sew, cook, wash and iron during her sojourn in the household of Governor Sanchez. She delighted in travel, and her health was excellent. It was remarked that she learnt things and retained knowledge as avidly as an eight-year-old child. She was kindly and affable during the shows, and willing to submit to any examination made to demonstrate that her extraordinary appearance was not an imposture. In the pamphlet, she was stated to be always cheerful and perfectly contented with her situation in life. In short, Mr Lent, who might well have written or at least supplied material for the pamphlet, seems to have considered her as a model freak; a house-trained monster that behaved well in front of the audience. It was stated without irony that she did not see the necessity of making money, but 'there are hopes that she will acquire in time the money-getting faculty, equal to that of the rest of the family of man'. Mr Lent himself did not lack this faculty: 'the Nondescript' attracted a good deal of publicity in the newspapers, and the exhibition soon became one of the most popular in town. During the shows, Julia entertained the audience by singing romances in English and Spanish, and dancing the Highland Fling, the schottische, and other 'Fancy Dances'. Most of the accounts of Julia agree that she was a good dancer and sang well in a mezzo-soprano voice. After the entertainment, those who wished could get to know her better: 'Miss Julia is pleased when the Ladies and Gentlemen ask her Questions, and examine her pretty Whiskers, of which she is very proud.'

In the *Lancet* of 1857, Julia was described by a certain Dr J.Z. Laurence. He stated that she was 4 foot 6 inches in height, thick-set and well proportioned in body; he thought her 'intelligent and quick'. Her body was hairy except for the palms of the hands and the soles of the feet, 'especially on those parts that are ordinarily covered with hairs in the male sex'. The hair was very thick and jet black, and had no disposition to curl, not even in the long beard and whiskers. The naturalist Frank Buckland also saw and spoke to Julia Pastrana when she was exhibited, and described her in the second volume of his *Curiosities of Natural History:*

> Her features were simply hideous on account of the profusion
> of hair growing on her forehead, and her black beard; but her

figure was exceedingly good and graceful, and her tiny foot and well-turned ankle, bien chaussé, perfection itself.

In his *A Terrible Temptation*, the novelist Charles Reade – who had probably seen Julia Pastrana when she was exhibited in London – had one of the characters describe her:

> Julia Pastrana, a young lady who dined with me last week, and sang me 'Ah perdona', rather feebly, in the evening. Bust and figure like any other lady, hands exquisite, arms neatly turned, but with long silky hair from the elbow to the wrist. Face, ugh! forehead made of black leather, eyes all pupil, nose a[n] excrescence, chin pure monkey; briefly, a type extinct ten thousand years before Adam.

After a very lucrative tour of London and the provinces, Mr Lent and Julia Pastrana left England late in 1857 and went to Berlin, where she attracted much publicity. The German authorities discouraged degrading monster shows such as this one, but Lent managed to secure permission to exhibit her through emphasising that Julia Pastrana only performed as a singer and dancer. When they reached Leipzig, a play called *Der curierte Meyer* was written especially for her participation and performed at the Kroll Theatre. The plot of the play concerned a stupid German dairyman who fell in love with a woman who always wore a veil; when he was not on stage, Julia lifted the veil, to the great amusement of the audience. This burlesque fun continued for several acts before Julia showed her face to the dairyman, who was instantly 'cured' of his infatuation. The German police had spies present at the first night, however, and the theatre was closed after only two performances of the play on the grounds that it was immoral and obscene. Thus, Mr Lent had to make do with having Julia dancing Spanish pepita dances and singing English and Mexican popular songs. Soon after the scandal with the closed play, the weekly magazine *Gartenlaube* published an extensive interview with Julia Pastrana, illustrated with a fine original drawing of her by the artist Herbert König. The journalist was impressed by her fluent conversation: she spoke of her triumphs on the stage during her tour of America and England. She said that she had had more than twenty offers of marriage during her American tour, but she had turned all these suitors down since they were not rich enough; the interviewer suspected that her showman had told her to repeat this in order to attract wealthy admirers.

The profits from Julia's German tour were excellent, and soon several rival showmen and circus managers wanted to put her on contract. However, Mr Lent managed to evade their designs on his protégée by marrying her, thus securing her services in a more permanent way. Naturally, he had no scruples in continuing to exhibit her, and early in 1858 they went on to Vienna. The exhibition was as popular as ever, and several medical men also attended. Herr Sigmund, professor of anthropology in Vienna, had never seen anything remotely like her, and considered her type of hairiness to be unique. Sigmund also had the opportunity to speak to her in private, and he found that she was certainly no semi-human monster trained to perform a few tricks, as the exhibition pamphlet maintained. In fact, Julia was intelligent, happy and pleased with her position in life. In view of her being unable to read and write, Sigmund was impressed by the range of her knowledge on various subjects. Julia never left her apartment during daytime, since her manager thought that her drawing power would be diminished if she was seen by nonpaying spectators, but in the evenings Lent often took her to the circus after she had put on a heavy veil. The German circus man Hermann Otto, who also appears to have met her during her stay in Vienna, agreed that Julia was clever and eager to learn, and that she was kind-hearted and a good judge of people. Her abnormal appearance gave her much pain, and she felt ashamed to be shown as a freak of nature. When her impresario instructed her to carry a flower in her hand during the shows, and to wear an elaborate headdress, it was only to emphasise further the difference between her and the rest of her sex. According to Otto,

Julia was an avid reader, and knew the world through books only. A popular Austrian singer and actress named Friederike Gossmann knew Julia Pastrana well and visited her many times, being deeply touched by her tragic fate. After her sojourn in Vienna, Julia Pastrana and Mr Lent toured Germany together with Rentz & Hinné's troupe of equestrian performers, and there is some evidence that she actually performed some acrobatic tricks on the back of a horse. She also sang, danced and played the guitar and mouth organ. In late 1858, Julia visited Poland, and seems to have caused quite a sensation in Warsaw. The dancing shows were regarded as a slightly obscene and scandalous public amusement, as evidenced by the caricature drawing of her by the artist Kostrzewski.

In late 1859, Lent and Julia Pastrana went on to Moscow, where they made more money than ever. After some months, Julia noticed that she was pregnant. She had hoped that her baby would be like its father, but its body was hairy all over and deformed in the same way as herself. The child died after having lived only thirty-five hours. The distraught mother herself died on the fifth day after the delivery, according to the romanticists from a broken heart, but according to the pathologist from 'metro-peritonitis puerperalis'. As usual, Lent was highly aware of the situation's commercial possibilities, and it seems as if a crowd of titled spectators actually visited Julia's deathbed and heard her purported last words: 'I die happy; I know I have been loved for myself.' The macabre Mr Lent was of course highly put out, having lost his prime source of income, but he managed to retrieve some further capital by selling the corpses of his wife and child to Professor Sukolov of Moscow University. The professor embalmed them through injection of a decay-arresting mixture of secret composition. According to Frank Buckland, there was 'great rascality connected with the whole business', and it is possible that the corpses were shown to visitors or otherwise indelicately treated. Professor Sukolov placed the embalmed bodies of Julia Pastrana and her child in the Anatomical Museum of the University of Moscow, where they became quite an attraction. But when Lent

saw how extremely lifelike they had become, he wanted them
back into his own custody. He had to pay Professor Sukolov the
equivalent of £800 for the mummies, having previously sold the
corpses to him for £500. In February 1862, the world's most
famous bearded lady again appeared before her many admirers
in London. The price of entrance was a shilling, which was considerably lower than during Julia's lifetime, but Mr Lent could
instead keep the exhibition open longer hours. Furthermore,
there was the added attraction of the child mummy, set up next to
its mother on a small pedestal. The exhibition of 'the Embalmed
Female Nondescript' was much noted in the popular press, and
had no shortage of interested spectators. When Frank Buckland
saw the mummy, he exclaimed 'Julia Pastrana!' The showman,
probably Lent himself, assured him that it really was the famous
'Nondescript' that had returned to her London admirers, and
he let Buckland examine the mummies closely:

> The figure was dressed in the ordinary exhibition costume used
> in life, and placed erect on the table. The limbs were by no
> means shrunken or contracted, the arms, chest, &c. retaining
> their former roundness and well-formed appearance. The face
> was marvellous; exactly like an exceedingly good portrait in wax,
> but it was not formed in wax. The closest examination convinced
> me that it was the true skin, prepared in some wonderful way;
> the huge deformed lips and the squat nose remaining exactly
> as in life; and the beard and luxuriant growth of soft black hair
> on and about the face were in no respect changed from their
> former appearance.

When the novelty of 'the Embalmed Female Nondescript' began
to fade, the mummies were lent to an English travelling museum of
curiosities. The abominable Mr Lent was now searching for some
new 'artist' to exploit, and when he passed through Karlsbad he
found out that a young lady in this town had a considerable beard.
Although she was kept locked in the garden of her family's town
house, Mr Lent managed to get acquainted with her and some

weeks later he asked her parents for her hand in marriage. After some time for consideration, her father permitted the marriage, but only on the grounds that Lent promised never to exhibit his wife for money. The cunning showman agreed to these demands, but soon after the wedding he took away his wife's shaving tools and made plans for a grand tour through Europe. He announced his new bearded wife under the name Miss Zenora Pastrana, in order to exploit her predecessor's notoriety. The exhibition handbills stated that she was Julia's sister, and sometimes Lent even tried to start rumours that they were one and the same person. Again, the talented Theodore Lent succeeded beyond all reasonable expectations: for more than ten years they signed lucrative contracts with Europe's finest circuses and gave private performances for several royal families. Initially, the mummies were also on tour with them, but not for long; perhaps Zenora did not want to see her mummified predecessor's ghastly, stiff grin and feel the cold stare from the black glass eyes. At any rate, the mummies were lent to the Präuscher Volksmuseum at the Prater in Vienna, a large fairground where various shows of giants, dwarfs and deformed people were an important part of the entertainments.

In the early 1880s, Mr Lent and Zenora retired from show business and went to St Petersburg, where they purchased a small waxworks museum. After the lucrative tours with his two bearded wives, Lent was a wealthy man, and he allowed the Präuscher Museum to keep the mummies for a considerable annual payment. However, in 1884 Lent went stark raving mad and danced about in the streets, tearing up the bank notes and stock certificates that he had earned in such a peculiar way and throwing them into the river Neva. He was taken to a Russian asylum, and it is unlikely that he survived long within its walls. In 1888, Zenora Pastrana left Russia for Munich, fetching the two mummies, which like the rest of Lent's estate were now her property, on the way. In 1889, she gave the mummies to a German impresario named J.B. Gassner, who ran an anthropological exhibition in Munich. In 1921, they were purchased by the Norwegian fairground owner Haakon Jaeger Lund, who was building up a 'chamber of horrors' at his large amusement park near Oslo. The mummies of Julia Pastrana and her son were exhibited along with many other bizarre preparations: half a man's corpse in a glass box, a human skin including the scalp, and numerous monsters in glass bottles, as well as a large collection of wax moulds illustrating various diseased conditions. Early in 1943, during the German occupation of Norway, the medical director of the German forces in Oslo, Dr Müller, ordered that the wax moulds and other exhibits in the Lund chamber of horrors were to be confiscated, and for the wax to be used in the war production. But the fairground owner's son, Hans Jaeger Lund, managed to save the preparations, suggesting that they should be taken on an extended tour of neutral Sweden, and that the profits from the exhibitions should benefit the treasury of the Third Reich. Dr Müller agreed to this scheme, and the old fairground director went to Sweden with three railway cars full of preparations, including the mummy of the 'Apewoman', as Julia Pastrana was now called. In 1953, Haakon Jaeger Lund stored the chamber of horrors, including the mummies of Julia Pastrana and her child, in a warehouse in Linköping, Sweden. It was soon rumoured that the warehouse was haunted by ape-like, monstrous creatures, and some daring youths broke into it to investigate. They were struck with horror when they saw Julia Pastrana's mummy staring at them from its dusty, cob-webbed sedan-chair and they fled the building in panic. The most intrepid of them later returned to take a photograph of the mummy, the first for more than eighty years. In 1954, Haakon Jaeger Lund died and his son Hans took over the fairground. In 1959, the chamber of horrors was exhibited at a large agricultural fair in Oslo, where it was seen by more than 700,000 people.

In September 1969, the name Julia Pastrana struck the head-lines again after more than 100 years. A wealthy American collector had found out that the mummies still existed, and was very eager to purchase them for his collection. But Hans, the fairground director, considered the American's offer – $10,000

– to be insufficient. Although the American collector increased his offer several times, Lund still declined to sell the mummies; he instead took them on tours of both Sweden and Norway during 1970. They were quite a public attraction due to the publicity in the newspapers and the objections against such a degrading monster show from various religious organisations. However, the American collector suffered a stroke and, instead of receiving $500,000, which was his last offer, Lund had no prospective buyer for his mummies. In 1971, the mummies were exhibited all over Norway and Denmark, and the next year they were hired by an American travelling amusement park that took them on tour throughout the United States. They were placed in a cage made of unbreakable glass to prevent them being stolen, and this contraption was carried on an enormous circus caravan. In 1973, Lund again planned to have Julia Pastrana exhibited in Norway, but there was a public outcry against this and the Bishop of Oslo objected to the use of a dead body in such a sordid commercial way. The mummies were instead rented to a Swedish travelling amusement park. During her grand tour through Sweden in the summer of 1973, Julia Pastrana became a public attraction equal to the most popular entertainers and pop stars: people thronged to see the world's only mummified apewoman. Julia stood in her Russian sedan-chair, with the mummy of her little son beside her, perched on a high pedestal like a parrot. Just as when Julia Pastrana was on show in London in 1857, the exhibition hand-bills declared her to be a hybrid between human and ape. But when the amusement park arrived at Hudiksvall, a small town in central Sweden, the local board of health closed the 'Apewoman' exhibition and a petition was sent to the Swedish Home Office that exhibition of dead bodies should be prohibited by law. Julia Pastrana and her son had made their last tour, and the caravan was stored at the fairground's winter quarters near Oslo. Three years later, Hans Jaeger Lund died and his son Bjørn Lund took over the fairground; he did not want to exhibit the mummies in public, but he felt that they should be kept for posterity. In August 1976, the fairground was broken into and the burglars forced the lock of the mummies' caravan. Julia Pastrana's dress was torn open and the child mummy's arms and lower jaw were knocked off. The damaged child's mummy was later eaten by mice, and Julia Pastrana was now standing alone in her glass cage in the large caravan. During the summer of 1979, the fairground was again broken into and Julia Pastrana's mummy was among the objects that went missing. However, the police were notified that some children had found a mummified human arm at a dump in one of the suburbs of Oslo; Julia Pastrana's mummy was found by the police in an abandoned caravan nearby. For many years, the Norwegian authorities debated what to do with the mummy: should it be cremated, sent back to Mexico, or buried in state in Oslo Cathedral? After lengthy deliberation, they made the wise decision to keep it for posterity at an anatomical institute just outside Oslo; it is still there today, although never shown to the public.

JO-JO, THE DOG-FACED BOY

Julia Pastrana's career coincided with the advent of Darwinism. Actually, Charles Darwin himself described her in one of his books, but he made no attempt to link her strange appearance with the theories about the descent of humankind. Some of his more radical followers went much further than that and postulated that Julia Pastrana and other hairy people shared primitive characteristics with mankind's early ancestors. According to the so-called recapitulation theory of embryology, advanced creatures like humans repeated the adult stages of their ancestors during their embryonic development. The study of anatomy and teratology was, according to this theory, a useful tool in unravelling the secrets of the evolution of mankind. A tailed or hairy child was thus considered to have reverted to a lower stage of development, and these characteristics were relics of the primate ancestors of human beings. The great majority of people in the 1860s and 1870s knew very little about these embryological theories; their definition of Darwinism was that they themselves were the descendants of an ape. This inferior level of understanding did not impede them from visiting Julia Pastrana and other hairy phenomena on show, particularly if these human curiosities were ostentatiously advertised as 'The Missing Link' and lurid parallels were made about their various ape-like or beast-like characteristics.

In 1873, thirteen years after the death of Julia Pastrana, the European public had an opportunity to make the acquaintance of two other hairy 'missing links': the Russian Adrian Jeftichejev and his son Fedor. The public attitude towards a hairy man or woman had not changed much since the sixteenth century; if anything it had become even more saturated with superstition and fanaticism. After all, Joris Hoefnagel and others had treated Petrus Gonzales with some respect and acknowledged him as a learned man. In 1857, Julia Pastrana had been advertised as a hybrid between baboon and human; in 1873, Adrian was presented by the showman as 'The Wild Man from the Kostroma Forest', the loathsome product of a short-lived and illicit *amour* between a bear and a Russian peasant woman. The French anthropologist Madame Clémence Royer saw Adrian and Fedor Jeftichejev being exhibited in Brussels in 1873. This learned lady told Adrian's impresario, in no uncertain terms, that she did not believe for a moment that a woman could give birth to a child fathered by a bear; the shameless showman replied that nor did he, but that it was good advertisement! He then gave Madame Royer and her friends a private showing of the Russian phenomenon.

At the time he was exhibited, Adrian Jeftichejev was fifty-five years old. He was a native of the Kostroma province of Russia. His memory of his parents was somewhat hazy, but he believed that his father had been a soldier; he could not recollect either parent being overtly hairy. Adrian also had two normal siblings, a brother and a sister, who had both been alive when he left Russia. Adrian had himself married in his youth, he said, and had sired two children in this marriage: a normal boy who died young and a girl, also deceased, who was hairy just like her father. Young Fedor, who was on show with him, was actually Adrian's illegitimate son, the impresario said, although many of the female visitors to the exhibition must have experienced a *frisson* of horror that even a sex-starved Russian peasant woman had once consented to copulate with such a monster. Adrian was like a man half changed into an animal, a spectacle destined to strike horror into nineteenth-century people. His face was entirely covered with hair, like that of a Skye terrier. A French doctor likened him to a Griffon dog of Flanders; exactly the same simile had been made about little Petrus Gonzales more than 300 years earlier. On Adrian's body were isolated patches of hairy growth, with hair between 1½ and 2 inches in length. The hair was said to be a dirty yellow in colour, but this was probably influenced by Adrian's reluctance to wash. Just as with Petrus Gonzales, Barbara Urslerin and the hairy Burmese, Adrian's hair was very soft and fine. The celebrated Dr Berthillon, who had taken some hair samples from the Russian phenomenon, found that a hair from Adrian's chin was three times as thin as a very fine hair from a man's beard, and that a hair from Adrian's head was half as thick as an ordinary man's head hair. The hairy-faced man was of medium height, strongly built, and dressed in not very clean-looking Russian garments. His eyes were a curious yellow, and his skin an unhealthy grey.

The showman said that as a young man, Adrian had fled into the woods to escape the derision and rough usage of his fellow villagers. For a time, he had lived in a cave and eaten the nuts and berries of the Kostroma woods. He also developed a taste for drunkenness during this period of solitary life and consumed strong vodka in quantities considered excessive even by his fellow Russian peasants. A German journal stated that even when surrounded by all the delicacies of Berlin, Adrian lived chiefly on sauerkraut and schnapps. A doctor was impressed to see Adrian drink a pint of undiluted vodka with relish, as he carved his beefsteak at the exhibition. A German authority told that Adrian was kindly and affectionate, in spite of his degraded intellect. He was incapable of learning any foreign language, and even his Russian dialect was difficult to understand. He showed little affection for his son Fedor, and Madame Royer and her friends saw that he much resented it when some visitors to the exhibition spoke to the lively young Fedor and tipped him handsomely, and then passed by the smelly, unprepossessing father with horror. After observing Adrian and speaking to him through an interpreter, Madame Royer concluded that he was by no means idiotic, and was certainly a human being; he was in fact a good representative of the moral and intellectual development among the inferior, savage tribes of Russia. The showman said that ever since he had first put Adrian on show before the curious in St Petersburg the year before, the hairy man had vowed to return to his native village as soon as his tour of the European capitals was over, and to spend all the money he had earned entirely on strong drink. According to another, slightly more prepossessing version, Adrian was a devout member of the Russo-Greek Church. Others in that faith had told him that he must surely have been cursed by the Devil, and poor Adrian spent all his money on the purchase of prayers from a devout community of monks near Kostroma, 'hoping one day to be able to introduce his frightful countenance in the court of heaven', as the exhibition pamphlet flippantly expressed it.

If many visitors to the exhibition were disgusted or horrified by the debauched, unkempt spectacle of Adrian, all were charmed by his little son Fedor. Although just three years and four months old, he was more intelligent and much more sprightly and vigorous than his wretched father. The growth of down on his face was not yet so heavy as to conceal his features, but the medical men who saw him did not doubt that he would one day become just as hairy as his father. Fedor's hair was white and as thick as that of an Angora cat, and he had long whiskers and a tuft of long hair at the outer angle of either eye. He liked to travel and to meet new people, and was already getting spoilt and petulant. He spoke French and, in spite of his tender age, gave rational replies to questions from the audience. He did not share his father's bestial and vicious facial expression, wrote Madame Royer, but otherwise the two were as alike as a young orang-utang and an adult orang-utang. After surveying Adrian and Fedor, she believed them to be the product of some strange atavism, or reversion to characteristics of a long-lost ancient race of man. Fedor's higher intelligence and less thick hairy coat was explained by the fact that he was a cross-breed between a hairy savage and an ordinary Russian woman, she wrote, just like a cross-breed between a white man and an American Indian woman showed some of the superior characteristics of the white race.

During their tour of Europe, Adrian and Fedor were examined by some of the leading anthropologists and medical scientists of the time. In Berlin, they were seen by Professor Rudolf Virchow, who left a thorough description of them. In Paris, they were more popular than ever, and Adrian was billed as 'L'Homme-Chien du Tivoli Vaux-Hall'. He was examined there by Dr E.R. Perrin in 1873. Adrian had for some time been feeling weak and nauseated, and had been troubled by persistent diarrhoea. The doctor found a considerable swelling in the gastro-hepatic region, the origin of which he did not hazard to guess. But considering the yellow discoloration of Adrian's eyes and his habit of drinking several pints of vodka every day, it is reasonable to suggest that the wretched man was suffering from quite advanced alcoholic cirrhosis of the liver. If the story of his purchase of prayers was true, these prayers were not wasted, and Adrian may well have guessed his fate. According to Dr Perrin, he still drank pints of vodka with every meal, breakfast included. While impervious to other European customs, he had embraced that of using tobacco and was never without a length of coarse chewing-tobacco. Perhaps as a result of Madame Royer's objections, Adrian was no longer exhibited as a hideous product of bestiality, but it was instead alleged, before the cultured French nation, that the two hairy men were members of a tribe of savage 'missing links' living in the Kostroma region.

In March 1874, Adrian and Fedor came to London. Their exhibition pamphlet was entitled 'The Story of Adrian and

Fedor, the Hirsute or Hairy-Faced People, found in the woods of Kostroma in Russia. The First of their Kind ever discovered. The Darwin Theory established'. They were seen by Professor C.S. Tomes and Mr Oakley Coles, two noted dental practitioners, who examined them closely and took casts of their teeth. The reason for this was that, as Rudolf Virchow and others had already discovered, the dentition of both Adrian and Fedor was very defective. Adrian had only the stump of a tooth in the upper jaw and four rotten teeth in the lower jaw. Fedor had a perfectly edentulous upper jaw, with no alveolar processes, and only four incisors in the lower jaw.

After their triumphal tour of Europe in 1872–4, Adrian and Fedor completely disappeared, and some authors have presumed that they either died or returned to obscurity in Russia. It is notable, however, that just a few years later, a Russian boy billed as Theodore Petroff, and later as 'Jo-Jo, The Dog-Faced Boy', or 'The Human Skye Terrier', began his career in show business. He was active for many years and probably one of the most successful human curiosities ever. With a singularly inapposite comparison, the French teratologist Jean Boullet, who was writing in the 1960s, called him 'la Brigitte Bardot des merveilles de la Nature'! Another French source, the book *Les Velus* by Le Double and Houssay, states that at the age of eight, Jo-Jo was engaged by an impresario named Forster, and later exhibited all over the world. The story of Jo-Jo's origin, repeated many times in the exhibition pamphlets, was that he had been found at a tender age by huntsmen in the Kostroma forest of Russia. He was accompanied by some kind of strange monster, hairy just like himself, who served him as father. The huntsmen took these two hairy savages with them to the civilised world, where the 'father' soon died. The boy was named Jo-Jo from some sounds he first made when he was found, and the huntsmen took care of him. He was sent to school, where he learnt to read and speak both Russian and English, and then set out to tour the world. All these circumstances hint that Fedor and Jo-Jo were one and the same, but what clinches the matter is that, in 1884, when Jo-Jo was exhibited in Berlin, he allowed Dr Max Bartels and Professor Rudolf Virchow to demonstrate him before the Anthropological Society of Berlin. He was introduced as Fedor Jeftichejev! Many of the Berlin anthropologists were delighted to see him again, since they had made his acquaintance eleven years earlier. Fedor, alias Jo-Jo, was now fourteen years old. He was a sturdily built, clever lad, completely normal except for his extraordinary hairy growth and his defective dentition. His impresario, the Russian Nicholas Forster, said that Adrian had returned to Kostroma after the successful tour of 1872–4, and that he had rapidly drunk himself to death there. Fedor had then been taken to St Petersburg, where he was exhibited at the waxworks museum owned by Theodore Lent, the former husband of Julia Pastrana. The German dentist Julius Parreidt took new casts of Fedor's teeth and found that he had only two canine teeth in the upper jaw and two incisors and a canine in the lower; the discrepancy between this observation and that by Coles and Tomes in 1874 is accounted for by the replacement, in the intervening years, of the deciduous by the permanent dentition.

Later in 1884, Jo-Jo was exhibited in Liverpool by his Russian agent, and plans were made to take him to London. One of P.T. Barnum's agents spotted him, however, and invited him to come to the United States to join Barnum & Bailey's circus. Nicholas Forster was soon persuaded that far greater profit could be gained on the other side of the Atlantic. They all boarded the steamer *City of Chicago*, which arrived in New York on 12 October 1884. Nicholas Forster, his young wife and Barnum's agents immediately set up a press conference for Jo-Jo at Astor House. He was advertised as 'The most prodigious paragon of all prodigies secured by P.T. Barnum in over 50 years', and billed as the ward of the Russian Government, who had come to the United States by the express desire of the Czar; Forster and his wife acted the part of a noble Russian couple, to whom the Czar had entrusted the guardianship of this valuable *lusus naturae*. The assembled newspapermen looked on aghast when the dog-faced boy came to greet them; never in their entire lives had they seen anything remotely like him. Barnum's reputation as a hoaxer meant that no human or animal specimen exhibited by him could be taken at its face value, however. After a polite question to the impresario whether the dog-faced boy might bite was answered in the negative, the entire press corps took turns to pull his facial hair to make sure it was not fastened by artificial means, and to examine his four teeth as a farmer surveys the mouth of a horse on exhibition. In spite of this ludicrous treatment, Jo-Jo remained polite and affable, and the press did much to help advertise him. He was as full of play as a puppy, they wrote, and although he could speak both Russian and German, they thought that his voice resembled the barking and growling of a dog. *The New York Herald* described him as 'the most extraordinary and absorbingly interesting curiosity that has ever reached these shores'.

In the 1880s, Jo-Jo was widely famous, and he was photographed many times. For some reason, he used to wear the clothes of a trapper and carry a long rifle. Other photographs depict him dressed in Russian garb or wearing a cavalry uniform. In 1885, the fifteen-year-old Fedor, alias Jo-Jo, was examined by a certain Dr G.T. Jackson in New York, as Barnum & Bailey's Greatest Show on Earth was passing through this city. In 1887, an advertisement in the *Avant Courier* newspaper depicted him with the head of a dog, but claimed that behind this canine visage there was a prodigious intellect, and that Jo-Jo could speak four languages. He later toured the world, and went to Australia, Europe and then back to the United States to rejoin Barnum & Bailey's circus. In their *Book of Marvels*, issued in 1899, he is advertised as 'The Human Skye Terrier'. He was an intelligent man and an avid reader, but according to some historians of the American sideshow, Jo-Jo sometimes used to act the part of a dog on stage and snap, growl, bark and chew bones. In 1901 and 1902, Barnum & Bailey's Greatest Show on Earth toured Europe, and Jo-Jo was one of the star performers. In Paris, he was billed as 'L'Homme-Caniche', or the 'Poodle-Man'. It was said on the handbill that he seemed to represent all that was shocking and

repulsive: the soul of a man in the guise of a woolly poodle...
the mouth of a dog speaking four languages. Jo-Jo did his usual
act in front of the astonished Frenchmen, and the circus was
as successful as ever. He died from pneumonia during a tour
of Greece in early 1904, and was mourned by many American
sideshow enthusiasts. He was a particular favourite also of the
French nation, and the paper *L'Illustration* published a photograph of him on his deathbed, as if he had been a prominent
statesman or magnate.

KRAO, THE HUMAN MONKEY

The record of the memorable sitting of the Berlin Anthropological
Society in 1884, when Max Bartels and Rudolf Virchow
demonstrated Fedor Jeftichejev, alias Jo-Jo, was entitled 'den
Affenmenschen und den Bärenmenschen' – 'The Ape-people
and the Bear-people'. Adrian and Fedor belonged to the latter
category; the former was represented by Julia Pastrana and
another hairy celebrity of the time, the little girl Krao, who had
been taken from her home in Siam by the German explorer
Carl Bock. In 1884, at the age of eight, she was exhibited in
the Berlin Aquarium as the 'Ape-girl'; Rudolf Virchow briefly
mentioned that the German police did not allow her manager
to put her in the same cage as four anthropoid apes, as was the
original plan.

In January 1883, Krao had first appeared before the curious at the
Royal Aquarium in London. Mr Farini, her manager, presented her
as the 'missing link' between human and ape and the living proof of
Darwin's theory of evolution. He claimed that the explorer Bock
had also captured Krao's parents, and that all three belonged to a
hairy tribe of people living in the interior of Laos. Her father's
body was completely covered with a thick hairy coat, exactly like
that of an anthropoid ape. His long arms and rounded belly added
further to his simian appearance. He was incapable of speech when
caught, but before his death, from cholera, before Herr Bock could
get him on board ship, he was able to utter a few words in Malay.

The mother was, for reasons unexplained, detained at Bangkok by the Siamese Government, but these authorities apparently had no objections to little Krao being taken from her parents and transported to the other side of the globe.

In no less a publication than *Nature* magazine, Krao was described by the anthropologist Dr A.H. Keane, who was one of the many Darwinists searching for the 'missing link' between human and ape. Both Africa and Asia were given attention by the zealous evolutionists, who were searching for atavistic signs, like tails or abnormal hairiness, in what they termed inferior races of mankind. Dr Keane had previously published a paper on the Aino tribe in Yesso and Sakhalin, and postulated the existence of a primitive hairy race in Further India. These preconceived notions made him a willing dupe to the showman's spiel. With rapt attention he examined little Krao, who had then been in London for ten weeks. She had already acquired several English words, which she used intelligently, and Dr Keane had to conclude that her intellect was equal to that of a normal human child. Her entire body had a coat of rather thick, black hair, but its growth was nowhere close enough to conceal the skin. She was remarkably supple and agile, and Dr Keane was interested to note that her feet had particularly long toes, with which she could actually grasp objects, and that her hands were so flexible that they could bend back over the wrists. He could detect no simian characteristics in the shape of her face, although the showman assured him that she used to stuff food into her cheeks just like a monkey, and that her lips could protrude so far as to give her 'quite a chimpanzee look'. She was given to terrible outbursts of rage when denied something, Mr Farini said, and the only thing that could suppress her unruly behaviour was the threat that she would be sent back to her own people. With these observations in mind, Dr Keane concluded that Krao was the living proof of a hairy race in Laos, and thus a phenomenon of exceptional scientific importance.

In 1884 and 1885, Krao toured Germany and Austria. She was exhibited at the Frankfurt Zoological Gardens, and the usual ostentatious advertising ensured a record audience: the zoo was so crowded that a twentieth-century German writer pronounced these shows the most memorable in its 150-year history. On the handbills and posters, a distinctly simian-looking Krao was portrayed dressed in a loincloth only; her hairy growth was exaggerated, and she stood grasping the branch of a tree in front of a jungle background. Several medical men examined her, among them the German dentist Julius Parreidt. He was interested to note that, unlike the hairy Burmese and Adrian and Fedor, Krao did not have a diminished number of teeth. In 1885, a certain Herr Bastian announced that the explorer Bock's dramatic account of how Krao had been captured with her 'wild' family was nothing but a pack of lies; in fact she had been born in Bangkok, the child of two normal parents, both of whom were still living.

In 1886, Krao and Mr Farini came to Paris. Here, she was examined by the French anthropologist Dr Fauvelle, who was as eager as Dr Keane in his search for her supposed primitive and ape-like characteristics. Krao was lively and agreeable throughout the interview and did not object to being examined. Apart from her hairy growth, Dr Fauvelle noted that her ears were rather large, that her nose was flat, and her joints very supple and flexible; all these observations were given a sinister interpretation. The impresario, always eager to make his charge appear even more interesting, assured him that she had thirteen ribs and the same number of thoracic vertebrae, that she had double rows of teeth, and that her behaviour was often quite ape-like. In all earnestness, Dr Fauvelle wrote that he had unfortunately been unable to assess the intelligence of this strange 'ape-girl', since her command of the English language was far superior to his own! When Dr Fauvelle's paper was read before the Société d'Anthropologie de Paris, it was commented on by Madame Royer, the forthright French lady anthropologist whose observations of Fedor and Adrian have previously been quoted. She began a lengthy lecture of her own, reviewing her observations of the hairy Russian father and son, and also drawing parallels between Krao and Julia Pastrana. Independently from the German dentist Parreidt quoted earlier, Madame Royer had examined some casts of Julia Pastrana's teeth taken by the Frenchman Magitot in 1857. She was clever enough to make the correct deduction, from a study of these, that Pastrana certainly did not have double rows of teeth, but instead a considerable overgrowth of the gums, which had led to some parakeratinised nodules of gum being mistaken for extra teeth. Krao had exactly the same disorder, but to a much lesser degree. Madame Royer then reverted to her own pet theories of anthropology, with the startling conclusion that poor Adrian, 'L'Homme-Chien de Kostroma', might well be the image of the Precursor of Mankind, the missing link between civilized man and the Neanderthals. Probably dismayed that Madame Royer had completely dominated the meeting, and that his own observations had been somewhat overshadowed, Dr Fauvelle's only retort was that, 'Le terrain sur lequel Mme Royer vient de s'aventurer est le champ des conjectures!'

Krao spent all her life in show business. Throughout the 1890s she toured Europe with her manager Mr Farini, who had become her adopted father, and her English governess. In 1893, a certain Herr Maass saw the now seventeen-year-old Krao being exhibited in Berlin. The prudish German considered her short dress somewhat *risqué*, although not unbecoming. She was quite a young lady, he wrote, and her manner was decent and friendly. It was clear to him that all the stories about her supposed ape-like characteristics were just inventions to make her even more interesting to the gullible public. Krao later became one of the stars of Ringling Bros and Barnum & Bailey's circus in the United States. One would not have supposed that a young girl who spent her adolescent years being exhibited as 'The Human Monkey' in various zoos and monster museums would grow up to be a harmonic and well-adjusted individual, but it is claimed that Krao became one of the most popular 'old troupers' of the circus. She was an educated, well-read woman who spoke many languages. Krao died in New York in 1926.

According to D.P. Mannix's book *Freaks: We are not as Others*, Krao was succeeded by another hairy celebrity, Percilla Bejano, who looked remarkably like her. In the true tradition of the American sideshow she was billed as Percilla the Monkey Girl, and exhibited together with her pet chimpanzee. Her showman, Carl Lauther, was also her adopted father. The French writer Martin Monestier added a remarkable story about her in his *Human Oddities*. When the sideshow came to Havana, a wealthy lady was quite taken with the seventeen-year-old Percilla and offered to adopt her as her own child and give her a superior education. Lauther was quite tempted to accept this offer, but he became somewhat worried when he found out that the Cuban lady lived in a large, high-walled estate with no other companions than a flock of apes and monkeys. Surely this lady had an unhealthy fascination for the simian tribe, and Lauther had misgivings about would become of poor Percilla if he accepted her offer. The stalemate was broken by Emmett the Alligator Man, another of the sideshow performers, who offered to marry Percilla, and was accepted by her. The newly-weds were billed as 'The World's Strangest Married Couple'; they both became old troupers within the sideshow business and were still active in the late 1970s. Percilla died in 2001, aged more than eighty; Emmett had died some years earlier.

LIONEL, THE LION-MAN

Stephan Bibrowski, later to be known as Lionel the Lion-Man, was born near Warsaw in 1891. Even at birth he was covered with fine, soft hair about 1 inch long. His mother was so upset and frightened by his appearance that at first she wanted to get rid of him. He grew up to be a lively, intelligent boy, however. His parents and six sisters had no abnormality of the hair whatsoever. As a four-year-old child, Stephan entered the world of show business. He was 'discovered' by a German impresario named Meyer, and appears to have been on permanent display at a large German amusement arcade, the Panoptikum in Berlin, for some years. A certain Professor Minakow examined him in Moscow at the age of five. His face and body were covered with fine blonde hair, up to 8 inches long on his face and 2–3 inches long all over the rest of his body. His dentition consisted of a solitary canine tooth in the lower jaw.

In 1901, the ten-year-old Stephan was taken to the United States to succeed Jo-Jo at Barnum & Bailey's Greatest Show on Earth. Stephan's mother had probably never even seen a lion, but the exhibition posters claimed that the boy's father had been torn to pieces by an escaped circus lion before her very eyes; this horrid sight had of course 'marked' her unborn child in this sinister way. In 1904, he toured large parts of the world with the circus. After this tour, he returned to the Panoptikum in Berlin. The German anthropologist von Luschan saw him there in 1907, at the age of thirteen. With his tremendously long facial hair, like a mane down his neck, he had a distinct resemblance to a big cat; at the Panoptikum he was known as 'Der Löwenknabe' – 'The Lion-Boy'. In 1910, when he was seen by Dr Paul Sarasin in Basle, his artist's name had been changed to Lionel the Lion-Man. He was exhibited at the Spring Fair in Basle and was immensely popular. This was as much due to his merry and jovial nature, and his impressive grasp of languages, as to his hairy face and long mane. The next record of him is from 1921, when the German pathologists Aschoff and Mense examined him thoroughly. They took hair samples from various parts of his body and X-rayed his jaws.

In 1923, Lionel went back to the United States. He had received a very good offer from the Coney Island amusement park: the authorities there had agreed to pay him $500 a week for taking up permanent residence at the park during the summer seasons. He liked the United States and remained at Coney Island for quite a few years; millions of Americans must have seen him there. Several accounts agree that his shows were far removed from the degrading spectacles around Julia Pastrana and Adrian Jeftichejev: Lionel spoke five languages, was a well-read and intelligent man, and quite an entertainer. He was something of a body-builder and very strong; he sometimes gave demonstrations of his gymnastic and athletic skills. One ribald newspaper account tells us that he was also something of a ladies' man: in spite, or perhaps rather because, of his extraordinary hairy face and body, he never had any difficulty getting admirers among the female visitors. After his successful stay in the United States, Lionel went back to Germany; in 1931, he died at a hospital in Berlin.

FROM THE ANNALS OF CONGENITAL HYPERTRICHOSIS

In his famous essay *The Elephant Man*, Sir Frederick Treves described how he had first come across, in the Mile End Road near the London Hospital where he worked, a canvas poster depicting John Merrick, the original Elephant Man. On the poster, his transformation into an elephant was by no means complete; it had only just begun, and there was still much more of the man than of the beast, only 'the loathsome spectacle of a man being changed into an animal'. The perpetual popular fascination of hairy people has the same rather sinister explanation. Singled out by their extraordinary appearance, and enhanced by their extreme rarity, they were exhibited as 'wild men', man-animal hybrids or 'missing links'. Interestingly, the oldest case, Petrus Gonzales, fared reasonably well, and is likely to have had a far more interesting life touring Europe with his family, and reading Latin to kings and princes, than if he had been a non-hairy peasant in the Canaries. The callous exploitation of Barbara Urslerin and Julia Pastrana is sad to contemplate. Their lives had many parallels, but the macabre tours with Pastrana's mummy for many years, even 110 years after her death, is fortunately without precedent in the annals of human deformities. The exhibition of little Krao as 'The Human Monkey', which occurred as late as the 1880s in the most degrading forms, is an equally unsavoury phenomenon.

The exhibition of the chronically ill, debauched Adrian Jeftichejev before the unfeeling crowds must also have been a repulsive spectacle. In contrast, his son Fedor, alias Jo-Jo, who had spent all his life in show business, was an extrovert character and intelligent enough to take advantage of his abnormal condition to make an almost unprecedented success in the international sideshow. He willingly played the buffoon, and both frightened and amused the spectators by barking, snapping and growling in the ring. Some advertisements actually depicted him with the head of a dog, standing on stage with a number of Skye Terriers, before an admiring audience. According to one account, the novelty of his act finally palled, and, after thirty years on the road, Jo-Jo died a bitter and disillusioned man. Perhaps his spirit was broken the thousandth time some rapier wit among the American sideshow 'rubes' asked him where he had mislaid his razor, or inquired whether he had paid the dog-tax. Lionel the Lion-Man appears to have had a rather more pleasant existence. In his heyday he was almost as famous as Jo-Jo, and earned considerable sums of money; he was a celebrated star of the American sideshow and the favourite of many emancipated American ladies who visited Coney Island. It is not unlikely that a photograph of Lionel might have inspired an American TV series from the 1980s, entitled *Beauty and the Beast*. The hero of this odd, sentimental melodrama is a leonine-looking, hairy man who lives in an underground community in the sewers of New York.

Some parts of nineteenth-century anthropology are today categorised as pseudo-science, particularly the race theory with the white man at the top of the pyramid, and the sometimes ludicrous by-products of early Darwinism. One of the more fruitful consequences of the great interest in anthropology in nineteenth-century Germany was that many of the cases of congenital hypertrichosis (inherited excessive hairiness) were well described. The anthropologists not only attended the exhibitions of Julia Pastrana, Krao and Jo-Jo and left valuable descriptions of them, but also carried out considerable research, which has been largely ignored by later writers, to find sources of the historical cases, like Barbara Urslerin and the Gonzales family. The more gifted anthropologists, like Rudolf Virchow and Max Bartels, were themselves fully aware that individuals like Jo-Jo and Krao really had no sinister ape-like or primitive characteristics, as more ostentatious commentators had claimed. They knew that this kind of excessive hairiness was an inherited disorder, and although they discussed the possibility that it might be an atavism, the reappearance of a lost character typical of the remote ancestors of mankind, they remained undecided on this issue. It was they who gave this disease its name: congenital hypertrichosis lanuginosa (inherited excessive hairiness with lanugo hair).

During the next 100 years, from 1890 until 1990, very little advance was made, however. Few novel cases of congenital hypertrichosis were described, and the commentary around the older ones was often confused and muddled. Several influential dermatologists and geneticists, like the Englishman Cockayne and the German Salaman, divided the individuals with congenital hypertrichosis lanuginosa into one 'dog-faced' and one 'monkey-faced' group: the former containing the Gonzales family, Barbara Urslerin, Adrian and Fedor, and Stephan Bibrowsky, alias Lionel; the latter consisting only of Julia Pastrana and Krao. As even the scientists were faltering to explain, or even classify, the hairy people of yesteryear, it is not at all surprising that the popular opinion about them was as much steeped in ignorance and bigotry as it was 100 years earlier. When Julia Pastrana's mummy was exhibited in the United States and in Scandinavia in 1971–3, she was still advertised as a hybrid between baboon and human. A similar message was repeated by the Ku Klux Klan in the 1970s; this body published photographs of Julia Pastrana in their loathsome pamphlets, with the caption that she was a hybrid between Negro and ape. At least one other American racist organisation followed suit, and another used the lurid nineteenth-century photographs of Krao for a similar purpose. An Internet search on Pastrana and Krao turns up a racist publication called *The Liberty Bell*, in which a scholar claims that Pastrana was a baboon-human hybrid. Another homepage, concentrating on the elusive Bigfoot, suggests that both Krao and Pastrana may well have been hybrids between Bigfoot and human. Similarly ludicrous is the suggestion that the hairy people may have inspired the werewolf legend; there is no evidence for this whatsoever in the original sources. The recent books on human malformations have provided little support for those wishing to dispel these silly fantasies and racist lies. In Barry Humphrey's *Bizarre*, Julia Pastrana is referred to as the Gorilla Woman, a unique freak of nature and the most hideous creature of all times; in Martin Monestier's *Human Oddities*, Krao is accepted as a unique 'missing link' with simian characteristics.

In 1990, I was the first medical scientist to examine Julia Pastrana's mummy. It was possible to secure hair samples from it and to have the jaws radiographed using up-to-date techniques. The results were not a little surprising. It turned out that Julia Pastrana had terminal hair, not lanugo hair. Since replacement of lanugo with terminal hair never occurs in a person with true hypertrichosis with lanugo hair, it could conclusively be stated that she did not have this disease. The radiographs showed that unlike the hairy toothless people like Adrian and Lionel, she had a complete set of permanent teeth. When my colleague, Professor A.E.W. Miles, examined a set of plaster casts of her jaws, kept in the Odontological Museum of the Royal College of London, he found evidence that she had suffered from gingival hyperplasia, a form of overgrowth of the gums. With these findings in mind, it was possible to diagnose Julia Pastrana as an extreme case of congenital hypertrichosis (with terminal hair) and gingival hyperplasia, an established, autosomally dominant syndrome. From the good examinations of her by Julius Parreidt and Madame Royer, it seems very likely that Krao had the same disorder. The old classification into a 'monkey-faced' and a 'dog-faced' subgroup of congenital hypertrichosis lanuginosa is thus not only uncouth, but also completely erroneous: the patients belong to two completely different genetic syndromes, with excessive hairiness as the only common denominator. This classification is today accepted in the standard textbook on this subject, Professor McCusick's *Mendelian Inheritance in Man*.

In 1984, Dr M.A. Macias-Flores and co-workers described a large Mexican family with congenital hypertrichosis running in five generations. In all, seventeen family members have been affected, many of whom have earned their living as circus or sideshow performers. Two young boys belonging to this family

were active as circus acrobats, under the artists' name of 'The
Werewolf Boys'. Their pattern of hairiness was somewhat
different from the classical European cases, with shorter and
somewhat coarser hair. The pedigree and the mode of inheritance, coupled with the fact that males were much more severely
affected than females, suggested an X-linked mode of inheritance. Some scientists doubted this, but in 1995 Dr L. Figuera and
co-workers actually mapped what they called 'the congenital
hypertrichosis locus' to a certain part of the X chromosome
(Xq24-q27.1) using multiple blood samples from the Mexican
family.

In an X-linked disease, an affected father marrying a normal
mother has normal sons and affected daughters. Since the historical accounts agree that Shwe-Maong, the ancestor of the
hairy Burmese, had at least one normal daughter and at least one
affected daughter, his variant of congenital hypertrichosis cannot
have been X-linked. Nor is the pedigree of Petrus Gonzales,
with an affected father siring affected children of both sexes,
consistent with X-linked inheritance. The historical cases thus
provide vital evidence that the mode of inheritance in congenital hypertrichosis lanuginosa is autosomally dominant, and that
the 'hypertrichosis locus' described by Figuera and co-workers
is not the genetic defect responsible in these cases. In 1993, Dr
F.A.M. Baumeister and co-workers examined one of the rare
modern cases of congenital hypertrichosis lanuginosa, and found
a slight chromosomal abnormality, what is known as a balanced
pericentric inversion, in the eighth chromosome. Intriguingly, a
group of Italian scientists recently made exactly the same finding in another child with congenital hypertrichosis lanuginosa,
speaking in favour that this balanced structural chromosomal
aberration may well have been causative; such an aberration is
of course perfectly compatible with an autosomally dominant
mode of inheritance.

These recent advances imply that there are (at least) three
major subgroups of inherited excessive hairiness. Firstly, there
is the traditional congenital hypertrichosis lanuginosa, which

affected many of the historical cases like Barbara Urslerin, the Gonzales family, the hairy Burmese, Adrian and Fedor, and Lionel. The inheritance is autosomally dominant, from a locus on the eighth chromosome. Although most cases are sporadic, and the result of spontaneous mutations, there is one example of a three-generation pedigree (the Gonzales family) and one example of a four-generation pedigree (the hairy Burmese). Secondly, there is the syndrome of excessive hairiness with terminal hair and overgrowth of the gums, which affected Julia Pastrana and Krao. This syndrome is also autosomally dominant, and clearly has variable expression. Some individuals have only mild gingival hyperplasia, others more severe overgrowth of the gums and also excessive hairiness; only the very extremes, like a Mexican girl described in 2002, have any resemblance to Julia Pastrana, with massive gingival hyperplasia, coarse faces and excessive hairiness. In 2003, Mexican scientists described yet another case of hypertrichosis with terminal hair, gingival hyperplasia and facial deformity very much resembling Julia Pastrana. They quote my 1993 paper on this subject, proposing this syndrome to be a distinct new entity. Thirdly, there is the X-linked hypertrichosis without gingival hyperplasia, recently described from Mexico; this syndrome cannot be implied in any of the historical cases.

The question regarding whether excessive hairiness is an atavism is still debated today. An atavism is defined as the reappearance of a lost character, either morphology or behaviour, which is typical of remote ancestors and not seen in the parents or recent ancestors of the individual in question. Examples of such an ancestral phenotype are hind limbs in whales and three-toed (polydactylous) horses; in humans, supernumerary nipples, the presence of a tail, and excessive hairiness have been quoted as examples of atavisms. The model used to explain them is that the genetic and developmental information originally utilised in the production of these characteristics has not been lost during evolution, but lies dormant within the genome and can still be 'turned on' by a mutation. Although the majority of earlier

writers have accepted the concept of congenital hypertrichosis
as an atavism without questioning, it seems reasonable to raise
a few objections to it. The fact that there are (at least) three
separate genetic defects, some of them X-linked, others autosomal, causing congenital hypertrichosis would weaken the case
for this condition being the result of the re-activation of an
ancestral pattern of development. The associated defects – tooth-
lessness or overgrowth of the gums – cannot be considered as
ancestral qualities. Many of the historical cases, like Jo-Jo and
Lionel, have had an extremely hairy nose, something that is
untypical of primates. Nor is there any evidence of any sinister
primitive or 'animal-like' characteristics in the individuals with
congenital hypertrichosis. Most of them have been of normal
intellect; some, like Petrus Gonzales and Lionel, were remarked
upon as 'learned' or particularly clever. The claims that Jo-Jo
was 'dog-like' in his behaviour were just a hoax to make him
appear more interesting to the sideshow 'rubes'. It is more serious that the alleged 'ape-like' characteristics of Julia Pastrana
and Krao are still widely believed by credulous and careless
authors, even in recent books published by university presses.
For any person who has examined a chimpanzee, it is apparent that the shape of its face is due to the protuberance of the
jaws, and not to any abnormality of the gums. The radiographs
of the head of Julia Pastrana's mummy indicated that her jaws
were of a normal shape, and the casts of her jaws indicate that
her prognathic appearance was entirely due to overgrowth of
the gums. It is impossible to directly disprove that congenital
hypertrichosis is an atavism, since the concept of an atavism is
in itself an arbitrary one, but there are several arguments against
it. The sinister interpretation of the word atavism, implying that
the affected individuals, like a hairy child or a baby with a tail,
are generally 'primitive' or 'ape-like', thus opening the door to
racist and bigoted interpretation, is completely unfounded. This
unsavoury relic of nineteenth-century anthropology should be
left to moulder in the murky old tomes of libraries.

3

Some Words
ABOUT
HOG-FACED
Gentlewomen

This lady was neither pig nor maid,
And so she was not of human mould;
Not of the living nor the dead.
Her left hand and foot were warm to touch;
Her right as cold as a corpse's flesh!

Thus begins a 'quaint Bretagne ballad' intoned by the ghastly Madame de la Rougierre in Joseph Sheridan Le Fanu's famous novel *Uncle Silas*. Nominally the governess of the young Victorian girl Maud Ruthyn, this sinister hag is secretly in the employ of Maud's wicked uncle, who tries to lure her into marrying his own boorish son. The ballad continues:

And she would sing like a funeral bell, with a ding-dong tune.
The pigs were afraid, and viewed her aloof,
And women feared her and stood afar.
She could do without sleep for a year and a day;

> She could sleep like a corpse, for a month and more.
> No one knows how this lady fed –
> On acorns or on flesh.

One of the first to acknowledge Sheridan Le Fanu as one of the nineteenth-century masters of horror was the distinguished antiquary Montague Rhodes James, who was also a ghost story writer par excellence. M.R. James recognised, as have some perceptive modern literary critics, that Le Fanu was no mere horror-monger, but a writer of considerable depth and hidden meaning. In his introduction to a new edition of *Uncle Silas*, M.R. James wrote that he had been greatly intrigued by the 'Breton ballad of the lady with the pig's head, which is introduced with such sinister effect'. He had valiantly tried to trace its original source, but without success. Nor have later researchers managed to locate a source for this poem. To do so, one must disregard, at least for the moment, its immediate literary context in Le Fanu's writings, and investigate the hoary myth that lies beyond it: the tale of the Hog-faced Gentlewoman and her avaricious suitors.

> Some say she's one of the swine possessed,
> That swam over the sea of Genesaret.
> A mongrel body and demon soul.
> Some say she is the wife of the Wandering Jew,
> And broke the law for the sake of pork;
> And a swinish face for a token doth bear,
> That her shame is now and her punishment coming.

❧

In the Grenville Library of the British Museum is a slender volume bound in pigskin, formerly the possession of the Right Honourable Thomas Grenville, like so many others, and carrying his seal. It is unique only in its astounding title emblazoned on the spine: 'Hog-Faced Gentlewomen'. Its no less remarkable contents are a lengthy pamphlet, published in London in 1640, giving 'A Certaine Relation of the Hog-faced Gentlewoman called Mistris Tannakin Skinker'; in Grenville's collection, it was bound along with Mr Fairburn's portrait of the Pig-Faced Lady of Manchester Square (6th Edition, with additions; Price 1s coloured) and a pamphlet entitled 'A True Description of the Young Lady born with a Pig's Face, now living in London'.

It is the first mentioned of these pamphlets that provides some valuable information about the origin of the legend of the Hog-faced Gentlewoman. She had come from Holland, all accounts agree, and was in London looking for a husband. When, in December 1639, the Hog-faced Gentlewoman first made her curtsy to the London public, her fame spread rapidly. In one week's time, no fewer than five ballads about her were registered; they were respectively entitled: 'The Woman Monster', 'A Maiden Monster', 'A Strange Relation of a Female Monster', 'A New Ballad of the Swines-faced Gentlewoman' and 'A Wonder of these Times'. None of these ballads is today in existence, but Samuel Pepys preserved, in his collection of black-letter broadside ballads, a copy of the astonishingly titled:

A Monstrous Shape.

Or

A shapelesse Monster.

A Description of a female creature borne in Holland,

compleat in every part, save only a head like a swine,

who hath travailed into many parts, and is now to be seene in LONDON,

Shees loving, courteous, and effeminate,

And nere as yet could find a loving mate.

According to the Grenville pamphlet, the hog-faced Miss Skinker was born in 1618, the only child of a wealthy Dutch couple residing in Wirkham, a town on the border of Holland and the German Empire. Her parents were much ashamed of their daughter's monstrous appearance and brought her up in a private chamber. She always wore a veil, and was fed and taught by her parents only. They pondered over the cause of her deformity, and strongly suspected that she had been bewitched within her mother's womb. When Madame Skinker had been pregnant, a witch-like old woman had approached her begging for alms. She turned the crone away with petulance, and the sinister old witch was seen to skulk away, 'muttering to her selfe the Divells pater noster, and was heard to say; "As the Mother is Hoggish, so Swinish shall be the Child shee goeth withall"'. It was considered very likely that the 'malitious Spells, and divelish murmurations of this wicked woman' had caused poor Tannakin's deformity. The witch was tried and convicted, but even when at the stake she refused to reverse the spell, either because of perverse obstinacy or simple lack of power.

When she was seventeen years old, the strange deformity of Tannakin Skinker's face had become well known in Wirkham and its surroundings. People who saw her eat were astonished that she fed from a silver trough 'to which she stooped and ate, just like a Swine doth in his swilling Tub.' They were no less amazed to hear her speak: her only language was the Dutch hoggish 'Hough' and the French piggish 'Owee! Owee!' The anti-Dutch author of the ballad *A Monstrous Shape* wrote:

> And to speak further for her grace,
> She hath a dainty white swines face,
> Which shews that she came of a race
> that loued fat porke and bacon.

The more Tannakin was mocked and laughed at by these heartless visitors, the more diligently did her parents seek a cure for their poor daughter. Finally, her father consulted an astrologer and mathematician named Vandermast, who was well known to dabble in the black arts. He pondered her case at length, and finally recommended that the only way to cure her was to marry her off, the sooner the better. As long as she remained 'in the estate of a Virgin', there was no hope at all of her recovery,

but if she was married, not to a 'Clowne, Bore, or Pesant; but
to a gentleman at least', there might be some chance that she
could escape her semi-porcine guise; the learned astrologer did
not digress on exactly how this strange transformation would
take place. The parents, seizing on their only hope, purchased
a very rich and costly dress for their daughter, who was then
about seventeen years old. Her face, or rather snout, was still kept
veiled. They then announced that any gentleman who married
her would receive a dowry of £40,000. The front page of the
Grenville pamphlet is decorated with a curious woodcut, in
which a gallant in gentlemanly dress greets Tannakin with the
words 'God save you sweet mistress': her only reply is 'Ouch!'

As could be expected, there was no shortage of suitors: 'His
Gates were thronged as at an Outcry, or rather as a Lottery, every
one in hope to carry away the great Prize of forty thousand
pound; for it was not the person, but the prize at which they
aimed.' The suitors' comments were probably as amusing to the
rowdy Londoners at the alehouses as they will be abhorrent
to women of the present age. 'Put her head but in a blacke
bagge, and what difference betwixt her and any other woman',
queried one of them. Another gallant comforted himself that
he would at least never have a scold for his wife, since 'if shee
cannot speake, shee cannot chide.' A parsimonious individual
congratulated himself that since the monstrous girl only ate
gruel and pig food, she would not 'be very chargeable to him
for her Dyet'. The suitors to the Pig-faced Lady came from
all over Europe: from Italy, France, England and Scotland. First
came a Scottish captain, who had spent the greatest part of one
month's pay on a fine suit of clothes. Tannakin's parents were
much impressed and thought that he was some great laird from
the Highlands. They introduced him to their daughter, and the
captain paid her many compliments on her elegant dress and
handsome proportions. But as soon as she lifted her veil, the captain ran out of the room saying that they must pardon him, since
he could 'indure no Porke'! Next came a sowce-man (cook)
from England, who comforted himself that his familiarity with

the members of the porcine race and their habits would make him an excellent husband to the monstrous girl. But as soon as he saw her face, he exclaimed: 'So long I've known Rumford, I never saw such a Hogsnout!' He did not know whether his stomach was strong enough for such a dish, since he preferred his pork well boiled or roasted and never took it raw. A tailor and several other suitors came to see her, but retired in disarray the moment she unveiled her face. The author of the ballad *A Monstrous Shape* wrote that:

> Great store of suters euery day,
> Resort vnto her as they say,
> But who shall take this girl away,
> as yet I doe not know:
> But thus much dare I undertake,
> If any doe a wife her make,
> It is onely for her moneys sake
> he loues her.

Tannakin Skinker's parents, having failed dismally in their attempts to get their daughter married on the Continent, decided to set out for London, the capital of folly, where they took up residence in either Black Friars or Covent Garden (the pamphlet writer was not sure which). The parents did not wish to announce their address, since the house might be stormed by the multitude of the curious and pulled down about their ears. Some people had already seen Tannakin in London, and were much impressed by her courteous manners and elegant dress, and even more by her fortune of £40,000. The sneering, anti-Dutch author of the ballad *A Monstrous Shape* solemnly warned those young gallants who wanted to seek her out, with the words:

> If any young man long to see
> This creature wheresoere she be
> I would haue him be rul'd by me,
> and not to be too forward,

Lest he at last should fare the worse,
Although she haue a golden purse,
She is not fit to be a nurse
in England.

The legend of the Pig-faced Lady became part of seventeenth-century culture, and is several times alluded to in the
contemporary literature, much more often in England than in
Holland or France. The 'Swines-fac't Lady' is the subject of an
epigram in Robert Chamberlain's *Jocabella*, and she is again alluded
to in *Ad Populum, or a Low-Country Lecture*, published in 1653.
The *Mercurius Democritus* newspaper of the same year speaks of
a monstrous giant exhibited by an English merchant in America,
and jokes that 'The Hogges-fac't Gentle-Woman is sent for out of
Holland to be his godmother.' Another newspaper, the *Mercurius
Fumigosus*, mentions that in 1654 one of the signs at Bartholomew
Fair was 'the Signe of the Hoggs-fac'd Gentlewoman'. 'The Long-
Nos'd Lass', a popular song of the 1670s, began with the lines:

O did you not hear of a Rumor of late,
Concerning a person whose Fortune was great;
Her portion was seventeen thousand good pound,
But yet a good Husband was not to be found:
The reason for this I will tell to you now,
Her visage was perfectly just like a Sow,
And many to Court her came flocking each day,
But seeing her, straight they run frightened away.

The song was a coarse satire on various London tradesmen:
tailors, millers, tinkers, tanners and glovers, who went out in
force to see the Pig-faced Lady, but were so frightened by her
beastly countenance that they swiftly withdrew. Another popular
song, commonly sung in the music halls by a character in the
dress of a country yokel, began with the words:

Your zarvant all round and you zee I be here
And what I left plough for will soon make appear,
For I's come to Lunnon an outlandish place,
To marry the lady that's got the Pig's face!

In the eighteenth century there were many pig-faced ladies, all shapely and elegant except for their deformed faces, and all eagerly seeking a husband. The prolific pseudo-gothic novelist Thomas Peskett Prest described one of them in his *Magazine of Curiosity and Wonder*. His account was stated to have its origin in a German book published in 1704, but Prest was sometimes unreliable with regard to his source material, and I have not been able to trace any original source. The tale of the Hog-faced Gentlewoman is embellished by a woodcut stated to have been taken from this same German book; it has a suspicious similarity in style to Prest's other woodcuts in his magazine, however. At any rate, the lady was thirty-four years old and lived in Amsterdam. Her figure was perfection itself, and she had beautiful long dark hair, but her face exactly resembled that of a pig. She could not venture outdoors, due to 'the curiosity of the spectators, who followed her in vast crowds, and excessively annoyed her with their rude remarks.' Confined to her own town house, she was waited upon by a devoted, elderly servant. She talked fluently, and could converse elegantly upon the most difficult subjects, but she laughed just like a grunting pig. Unlike Tannakin Skinker, she ate normally, and did not use a silver trough. The German writer concluded his account with the words: 'I called upon her several times, during my stay in Amsterdam, and by her own permission took her likeness, and had her consent to publish this account, which the reader may depend upon it is strictly true.' Another hog-faced gentlewoman was described in a German broadsheet published in 1717. She was of Dutch origin, and her parents were extremely wealthy. She sat in her castle, awaiting her suitors, but when they saw her deformed face, they ran away.

James Paris du Plessis, a writer on monstrosities active in the early eighteenth century, described yet another hog-faced gentlewoman, who was not a native of Holland, but resided at St Andrew's Parish, Holborn, in the heart of London. She belonged to a wealthy, noble family, and was well built, with beautiful black hair, although her face resembled that of a sow or cow. When travelling, her face was covered with a large black velvet mask. She spoke distinctly, but in a grunting voice. James Paris du Plessis is usually a reliable observer, but unlike the majority of his teratological case studies in his manuscript *History of Prodigies*, he does not claim to have seen the woman himself.

A contributor to Chambers' *Edinburgh Journal* was informed by a venerable and clear-headed old lady of ninety that her mother had been well acquainted with a noble lady of Scottish ancestry, who was called the Pig-faced Lady due to some 'peculiar conformation of her features.' This lady had been at large in the 1750s, and the elderly informant asserted that her mother had frequently visited this lady at her home in Sloane Square.

In the winter of 1814–15, there was a widespread rumour in London that a pig-faced lady was actually living in the metropolis. She was reported to be young, immensely rich, and the daughter of a noblewoman residing in London; there were hints that she lived in a closely guarded, fashionable town house in Manchester Square, and sometimes took exercise in a carriage, protected by a heavy veil. There were several letters in the more fanciful newspapers of the day, submitted by excited or horrified Londoners who claimed to have observed the veiled silhouette of a pig's head in a passing, elegant carriage, or seen a snout emerge from its window.

In early 1815, an elegant hand-coloured portrait of the Pig-faced Lady of Manchester Square, by Fairburn (Senior) was published, and went into several editions. On this engraving, some additional information about this phenomenon was provided, allegedly from the source of 'a female who attended on her'. She was about twenty years old, a native of Ireland, of high family and fortune, 'and on her life and issue by marriage a very large property depends'. Like the earlier pig-faced ladies, she was flawless in body and limb, but her head and face were those of a pig. She spoke only in grunts, and ate her victuals from a silver trough. In spite of being paid the princely salary of 1,000 guineas per annum, her female attendant was too frightened by the less ladylike habits of her monstrous mistress. She resigned from her position, and apparently felt free to tell the press all about her strange employer afterwards.

The Pig-faced Lady was stated to have been the general topic of conversation in the metropolis at this period of time. Thousands, particularly those living in the West End of town, believed in her existence. An article in the *Times* of 16 February 1815 deplored the credulity of Londoners in general, and the Pig-faced Lady craze in particular. A few days earlier, an earnest young woman had put an advertisement in the *Times*, offering herself as the Lady's paid companion. She made it perfectly clear that she requested both a handsome yearly income and a premium for residing with her for seven years. This scheming prospective swineherdess may well have read the statement that the earlier attendant of 'her Sowship' had received 1,000 guineas per annum, and hoped for a similar salary.

An even more ridiculous advertisement was submitted to the *Times*, along with a £1 note, by a young London gallant hoping to become the husband of the Pig-faced Lady. Enraged already by the previous idiotic addition to the Pig-faced Lady section of the *Times'* Lonely Hearts column, the Editor decided to burn the advertisement and give the money to some charity. The *Morning Chronicle* had no such censorial aspirations with regard to its contents, and published the following bizarre advertisement:

SECRECY. A single Gentleman, aged thirty-one, of a respectable Family, and in whom the utmost Confidence may be reposed, is desirous of explaining his Mind to the Friends of a Person who has a Misfortune in her Face, but is prevented for want of an Introduction. Being pefectly aware of the Principal Particulars, and understanding that a final Settlement would be preferred to a temporary one, presumes he would be found to answer the full extent of their wishes. His intentions are sincere, honourable, and firmly resolved. References of great Respectability can be given. Address to M.D. at Mr Spencer's, 22 Great Ormond Street, Queen's Square.

It is unknown whether this earnest young suitor to the Pig-faced Lady had any success, and if any scented letter with the noble crest of a boar's head was dropped by a trembling hand into the letterbox of 22 Great Ormond Street.

The Editor of the *Times* wrote a further article to point out that the story of the Pig-faced Lady was an old one. Some elderly people of good memory could well recall that in 1764 exactly the same tale had been current in London. A man had offered to make the Pig-faced Lady an ivory trough to feed from. The Editor deplored the credulity of the Londoners, remarking that if there had been just one actor in this first folly, there were now twenty, and a man had just written to the *Times* offering to make the Pig-faced Lady a silver trough. A letter writer seconded the Editor's article the day after, and ridiculed the Pig-faced Lady craze further by comparing it to the scandalous activities of the prophetess Joanna Southcott. The pig-faced woman was probably the daughter of Joanna, he wrote, and the 'Swinish Lothario' who had sent a letter to the *Times* was advised to 'woo her in grunts'. When faced by this onslaught, the Editor of the *Morning Chronicle* saw it proper to defend the Pig-faced Lady. He stated that for several months there had been a story of a young lady of family and fortune, on whose issue by marriage a very large estate depended, who had a head of such deformity as to resemble that of a pig. Although the doctors he had consulted declared such a deformity to be unknown to them, the Editor boldly declared that it might well be true that such a female existed, but that her deformity had been exaggerated by the credulous people. As to the letter from the 'desperate fortune-hunter', the Editor had not found it immoral or indecent enough to decline it for publication. It was his decided opinion that when any respectable newspaper deemed an advertisement improper for publication, it should also return the money.

ஒ

Despite the efforts of the Editor of the *Times* and other sceptics, the Pig-faced Lady craze continued. During the illuminations that took place to celebrate peace between Britain and France, a great crowd assembled in Piccadilly and St James' Street, and the carriages moving by could only travel very slowly, as in the present-day traffic jams in these parts. From one of them, an enormous pig's snout was seen to emerge, protruding from beneath a fashionable-looking bonnet! The startled crowd called out 'The Pig-faced Lady! The Pig-faced Lady! Stop the carriage! Stop the carriage!', but to no avail. The coachman whipped up his horses and drove through the crowd at a dangerous pace. It was later stated that the coach had been seen to put down its monstrous load in Grosvenor Square, the home of a well-known lady of fashion; it was presumed that the Pig-faced Lady was her daughter or ward.

Several satirical caricature prints were inspired by the Pig-faced Lady craze of 1815. One of these, 'Waltzing in Courtship', suggested that the short and hunchbacked Lord Kirkcudbright was one of the Lady's suitors. He is depicted waltzing with the tall, elegant lady with a pig's head. In another caricature, also published in March 1815, the Pig-faced Lady stepped into foreign politics. In an amusing drawing by George Cruikshank, the Pig-faced Lady of Manchester Square sits playing the piano. She is elegantly dressed and her snout is covered by a transparent veil. The back of her chair is topped by a coroneted pig; the title of her music is 'Air-Swinish Multitude set to Music by Grunt Esq.'; and on the wall is a portrait of Lord Bacon, a man with a pig's head. Below the title are the words:

> This extraordinary Female is about 18 years of age – of High
> rank & great fortune. Her body & limbs are of the most perfect

& Beautiful Shape, but, her head & Face resembles that of a Pig – she eats her Victuals out of a Silver Trough in the same manner as Pigs do, & when spoken to she can only answer by Grunting! her chief Amusement is the Piano which she plays most delightfully.

In another image, next to her, is a caricature of King Ferdinand VII of Spain as 'The Spanish Mule of Madrid', complete with a mule's head. An insert, designed as a picture on the wall entitled 'Amusement at Madrid', depicts a friar pointing towards two men on a gibbet full of hanging corpses, saying, 'Here's some more Patriots'; the king with a mule's head replies, 'O! that's right Kill'em Kill'em.' The text underneath this image parallels that of the Lady, parodying the monster handbills of the time and doing an excellent job of it:

This wonderful monster (to the great grief of his subjects) is a King!!! He was caught 7 years ago by Buonaparte, & during his confinement in France, amused himself by singing Anthems & Working a Robe in Tambour for the Holy Virgin! but since his liberation, he has amused himself, by Hanging his best Friends!!!!!

Another amusing Cruikshank caricature, published on 22 March 1815, was entitled 'Suitors to the Pig-faced Lady'. Various tradesmen and upstarts court the Lady, who rejects them all eloquently: 'If you think to *gammon* me, you'll find you've got the wrong *sow* by the ear – I'm *meat* for your *masters*, so go along, I'll not be plagued by any of you.' Another drawing was entitled 'The Wonderful Miss Atkinson' and based on a drawing by the artist George Morland. Since Morland had died in 1804, it cannot have been directly inspired by the craze in 1815. The original drawing, in the possession of Morland's nephew, merely stated that this prodigy was 'Born in Ireland, has £20,000 fortune, and is fed out of a silver trough'. A later, undated version of the same hand-coloured print in my collection, tells quite another story: 'The

Wonderful Mrs Atkinson is Born and Married to a Gentleman in Ireland of that Name, having 20,000 fortune. She is fed out of a Silver Hog-Trough, and is called to her Meals by Pig-Pig-Pig.' According to a note on the print, the original source of this information, and the description of the Lady's appearance, was Morland's servant George Simpson, 'who will swear to the truth of it, having heard it on board the *Vesuvius* Gun Boat, from some Irish Sailors who he says cannot tell lies'.

Another story told that Sir William Elliot, a young baronet, was once visiting a lady of fashion in Grosvenor Square. He was ushered into the drawing room, where he saw an elegantly dressed lady standing with her back turned to him. Intrigued, he walked up to her, but recoiled when she turned round sharply and revealed a hideous pig's face. Sir William gave a shout of horror and rushed for the door. The Pig-faced Lady obviously thought him quite impolite, since she gave a furious grunt, ran after him, and bit him on the back of the neck. This very credible story ends by stating that Sir William's wound had proved a severe one, and that he was under the care of Mr Cesar Hawkins, surgeon, in South Audley Street. A caricature, in the same manner of those mentioned previously, was made to celebrate Sir William's misadventure; it was entitled 'Beware of the Pig-stye!'

An unexpected postscript to this strange Pig-faced Lady craze of 1814–15 is provided by some correspondence in the *Notes and Queries* magazine of 1861. A gentleman signing himself M.A. inserted a query as to whether there was any further information about the Pig-faced Lady who had lived in London about forty years earlier. He knew of two authentic observations of her, one by a gentleman still living. He earnestly inquired whether there had been any more recent cases of pig-faced ladies, since 'in spite of the natural horror of the phenomenon, its interest, both physiological and psychological, is so considerable that I am surprised to find so little information afloat on the subject'. He was answered by a certain George Lloyd, who had seen a pig-faced lady exhibited in Wakefield in 1828 or 1829; he had been too young to take a note of this phenomenon 'further than a mental one, which has haunted me ever since'. Another correspondent to the *Notes and Queries*, Mr F. FitzHenry, provided a more sinister reply. He knew a certain lady, whom he termed Lady H.W., who was much admired as a beauty in the 1820s. When at a dinner party forty years earlier, all the party were solemnly cautioned not to say a word about pigs, out of delicacy to Lady H.W., since it was widely believed that her sister, Lady C.B., had been the original Pig-faced Lady.

The Pig-faced Lady of Manchester Square makes her final appearance, albeit not in the flesh, in Mr Elliott O'Donnell's curious book *Ghosts Helpful and Harmful*. In the 1920s, a house near Chelsea was reported to have been haunted by a pig-faced phantom, appearing at night and frightening several gentlemen out of their wits. One of them left an eloquent description of this singular ghost:

> The body, beautifully formed, and gleaming like polished ivory in the moonbeams, resembled that of a woman, but the face was the face of some very grotesque and repulsive animal. In the place of human cheeks were huge collops of white, unwholesome fat; the nose was snoutlike, the mouth a great slit, full of hideously crooked tusks; and whilst the whole conformity of the features suggested the face of a distorted and horrible-looking pig, the animal, in contrast to the human, was made all the more poignant by the hair – unmistakably a woman's – which fell in a bright mass of rippling gold around the neck and shoulders.

In eighteenth- and nineteenth-century Ireland, speculation was rife about Madam Grizel Steevens, the Pig-faced Lady of Dublin. She was said to be fabulously rich and had financed the building of a large hospital, where she spent the remainder of her days hiding from the rough and insensitive populace who wanted to gawp at her. Her malformation was believed to have been a result of her pregnant mother having refused a beggar woman carrying several children alms with the words 'Take away your litter of pigs!' Many Irishmen had seen the large silver trough from which she used to feed every day. For many years, there were also people who claimed to have seen Madam Steevens in person, during fairs and markets; they willingly asserted that she really had the head and face of a pig.

Sources agree that, unlike Tannakin Skinker and the Wonderful Miss Atkinson, Grizel Steevens was undoubtedly a real person. She was the daughter of the Revd John Steevens, a wealthy clergyman. In 1710 her twin brother, Dr Richard Steevens, died and she was left a considerable fortune; she was to have £650 a year, and the remainder was to be used for the erection of a hospital in their hometown of Dublin. Madam Steevens, who was well known for her zeal in working for various charities, decided to go one better: the hospital was to be built in her own lifetime. The philanthropic lady succeeded in this enterprise, and Dr Steevens' Hospital still remains as a memorial of her benevolence.

In her youth, Grizel Steevens suffered from some disorder of the eyes, which forced her always to wear a veil. She was a lady of retiring disposition, and during her charitable rounds to the poor districts of Dublin, she preferred to remain seated in her carriage while her servants doled out the various alms to the needy. It has been supposed that her veiled countenance, seen through the carriage window, had given rise to the rumour about her monstrous appearance, which soon spread like wildfire through Dublin. Grizel Steevens was of course much dismayed by this ludicrous rumour, particularly since she had not the slightest deformity of the face. Although there is no record of her receiving any impudent offers of marriage from impecunious Dubliners, it must have been quite an ordeal for a shy, nervous lady to have rude boys grunting at her in the streets, and drunken Paddys jumping up on the footstep of her carriage to try to catch a glimpse of her snout through the window. To scotch the rumour of her pig-faced countenance, she used to sit in an open balcony near the hospital, allowing all and sundry to see her. When she tired of this, she had her portrait painted, and ordered it to be hung in the hospital main hall for the inspection by curious visitors. It is still there, and although it depicts a far from handsome old lady, there is no hint of the porcine in her features.

The visitors to Dublin preferred to go to a neighbouring public house, however, which had a silver trough and a portrait of Madam Steevens with a fine pig's head on show to impress the customers. Poor Grizel Steevens must have despaired of human vulgar credulity, and the representation of her with a pig's head may well have added to her determination to become a hermit inside her own hospital, where she died in 1746, at the ripe old age of ninety-three. Her memory, and that of her many charitable acts, were revered by the hospital governors and doctors, but the ludicrous legend of her having a pig's face was equally revered by a large proportion of the Irish nation; even today, it remains the major claim to fame of this pious, charitable lady.

When, in 1832, William Wilde, the father of Oscar, arrived at Steevens' Hospital as a medical student, one of the memorabilia he was shown was a silver trough, which was presumed by many curious visitors to be the one from which Madam Steevens had eaten her gruel. He had already seen an engraving of her feeding from it in a penny peep show, one of many that upheld this unfortunate lady's undeserved notoriety. To visit the hospital and see this silver trough seems to have been quite a fashionable pastime in early nineteenth-century Dublin. Dr T.P.C. Kirkpatrick, author of the *History of Doctor Steevens' Hospital,* wrote that in the early nineteenth century, several hospital officers were in the habit of telling the story of the pig-faced Madam Steevens to credulous visitors, and of showing them a silver trough. It even appears, according to the same work, as if a plaster cast of a human face with a large pig snout was on show at that time. Later, the hospital governors seem to have doubted that this spectacle had the *gravitas* suitable for an establishment dedicated to the healing arts, and forbade this ludicrous practice, on pain of dismissal for the individuals involved.

In 1864, the *Dublin Medical Press* mentioned that it was still a popular legend among the poor in Dublin that Madam Steevens had a pig's face. This belief was by no means confined to those Irish people living in Dublin. An American sailor of Irish descent wrote a letter, dated 'Jan. 30th, 1864, On board U.S. Ship of War Portsmouth, off New Orleans', directed to Madam Steevens senior, whom he believed still to be alive. The letter contained a proposal to marry her pig-faced daughter, since the sailor had heard that she would 'give any Man A fortune to any one who will Marry her'. The *Dublin Medical Press* published this letter to ridicule the poor sailor, who had probably not intended his earnest, badly written missive for publication in a medical journal.

In the 1880s, an Irish lady correspondent of Mr Richard Chambers, Editor of the *Every-Day Book*, wrote that when she was a girl, everybody believed that Madam Steevens had the face of a pig, and the idea was still prevalent. Many people went to the hospital to see the silver trough and a painting of her with a pig's head which were said to be on show there; the matron of the hospital received them graciously, but said that she was currently not allowed to show these treasures. She never denied that they existed, and never refused the tips that were offered to her. According to another account, a Dublin gentleman used to show a large silver punch bowl, wearing the noble crest of a boar's head, as Madam Steevens' silver trough. Dr T.G. Wilson, the biographer of Sir William Wilde, writing in the early 1940s, commented that even in his own time many Dubliners still believed Madam Steevens to have had a pig's face.

❦

In the eighteenth and nineteenth centuries, pig-faced ladies were hot property in British show business. There had been exhibitions of pig-faced ladies moulded in wax or papier-mâché, and such was the perpetual fascination of this subject among the Irish that even a print of the Wonderful Miss Atkinson was one of the prime exhibits at an early nineteenth-century fair, visited by the afore-mentioned William Wilde. At the Hyde Park Fair, in the year of Queen Victoria's accession, Madam Steevens, the Wonderful Pig-faced Lady, was advertised to be *living*! This Irish celebrity, who was eager to get married, and who grunted to give replies to questions from the audience, had many visitors, and was several times mentioned in the newspapers. There is evidence that a live pig-faced lady appeared at Bartholomew Fair in 1828, and probably also in previous years. The living pig-faced lady seen by the impressionable Mr Lloyd in Wakefield in 1828 or 1829 may well have been the same one.

The *modus operandi* was that the showmen procured a fine black bear, and proceeded to shave the hair off its snout, neck and front paws. The beast, which had previously been drugged with a tub of warm, strong ale, or with some concoction of Mickey Finn, was then lugged into a comfortable armchair, and dressed in an elaborate lady's costume with a padded bosom, frills and ribbons. Elegant shoes were fastened to the bear's rear paws, and stuffed satin gloves to the shaven front paws, to hide the claws and give the resemblance of human fingers and toes. Finally, a large wig with elaborate blonde ringlets was stuck on its head, and a large fashionable hat on top of the wig.

As soon as these brutal stylists had made 'Madam Steevens' ready to make her bow to the audience, the yokels were admitted into the tent to admire Her Sowship, who was reclining benignly in her easy chair. It was explained to them that 'Madam Steevens' could not speak to her court of visitors, but only grunt, once for yes and twice for no. Then the interrogation occurred: Are you the heiress to a great fortune? One grunt. Do you feed from a silver trough? One grunt. Are you yet betrothed to any man? Two grunts. If one of the visitors was still unsatisfied, the Pig-faced Lady was treated to a meal of ale, gruel and apples, all served in a silver trough. Towards the end of the fair, the situation must have become precarious indeed: the alcohol had worn off, and the bear was becoming restive; it had taken exception to being surreptitiously prodded by a stick to provoke the answers to the questions, and was generally unamused by its situation. When its bonds were eventually released, it is not unlikely that some of the knaves got a resounding box on the ear for their trouble – I rather hope so.

Gangs of rowdy Dublin medical students were adept at this game, and delighted to exhibit 'Madam Steevens' before the crowds of wide-eyed Paddys who had come to visit the manifold curiosities of the Irish capital. It is recorded that the many Irish exhibitions of pig-faced ladies were all uniformly successful; nor was any charge of fraud made against the 1828 Bartholomew Fair exhibition, or that held in Hyde Park in 1843. During a fair in Plymouth some time in the 1880s, a quarrel broke out and a mob broke into the Pig-faced Lady's tent and tore her wig and cap off. The showmen were not treated gently; nothing is known about how the bear fared in this encounter.

In two papers published in the journal *Volkskunde*, the Dutch antiquary G.J. Boekenoogen attempted to trace the earliest sources of the legend of the Pig-faced Lady. After searching various Dutch and British archives, it was clear to him that the legend had first appeared in 1638 or 1639. In ballads, handbills and pamphlets, the Pig-faced Lady was celebrated in Holland, France and Britain, and it is clear that something of the legend's universal popularity was due to its novelty. It is of par-ticular interest that one early Dutch print reproduced by Dr Boekenoogen contains a version that may well be the original one. A wealthy Dutch lady named Jacamijntjen Jacobs, living in Amsterdam, was one day approached by a filthy beggar woman, who asked her for alms. The lady did not want to give her any, however. The mendicant was carrying three unprepossessing children, and pleaded that her poor children were starving, but the hard-hearted Jacamijntjen Jacobs just said 'Take away your filthy pigs, I will not give you any thing!' The beggar woman wept bitterly, and said 'Are these my children pigs? May the Lord

God then give you such pigs as I have here!' Jacamijntjen Jacobs was pregnant at the time, and she later gave birth to a daughter with the head and face of a pig. This took place in 1621, and at the time of writing, this daughter was twenty years old. She ate from a trough, and spoke in a grunting voice like a pig.

It is not fanciful to link this very early version of the Pig-faced Lady legend to another Dutch legend, that of Countess Margaret of Henneberg, who was cursed after turning away a beggar woman with twins, and who later gave birth to 365 children, as many as there were days in the year. This was a very widespread medieval legend, occurring in many variations, one being that the gentlewoman insulted the female beggar with the taunt that her children were like a litter of pigs. In the French version of the 'Porcelets', the noblewoman who likens the beggar woman's children to a litter of squeaking piglets herself gave birth to nine little pigs. In this transitory version, the mother is punished both by the great number of 'children', and by their deformity. The added horror of the child's pig face had great power and considerable popular appeal; in the mid-seventeenth century, it actually eclipsed the original version. It is thus very likely that with regard to the origin of the legend, the Pig-faced Lady is the Countess Margaret's 366th godchild.

There have been several other theories as to the origin of the Pig-faced Lady legend. One of them has assumed that the birth of some severely malformed child at the time, with a pig-like visage and incapable of speech, might have given rise to a rumour that gradually got wilder and wilder, with colourful details like the silver trough and the immense dowry added to make the tale more interesting. The old annals of human monstrosities list an ape-woman, an elephant-man, a turtle-boy, a fish-boy, a bear-boy, a cat-woman and several porcupine-men, but no instance in which the unfortunate individual in the monster show was likened to a pig. In late nineteenth- and early twentieth-century Britain, there were several newspaper stories that a pig-faced child had been born at some (named) hospital, but no further particulars of this unfortunate child were ever published, and the whole thing has many characteristics of the contemporary newspaper *canard*. A case report published in the *American Journal of Obstetrics and Gynaecology* of 1952 described a stillborn foetus with a snout-like face and many other malformations. But although the authors of this report were audacious enough to draw parallels with the nineteenth-century prints of the Pig-faced Lady, they wholly fail to convince the reader of any link between the malformations in question. In particular, while the 'pig-face foetus' was incapable of extrauterine life, the traditional legend of the Pig-faced Lady presents her as being in the prime of health, her malformation notwithstanding.

There have also been, in otherwise healthy individuals, instances of facial deformity making the individual's face resemble that of a member of the porcine tribe. My early military service was in a small Swedish town. In certain isolated areas nearby, the deleterious effects of inbreeding were only too evident when one surveyed the intellectual ability and exterior appearance of the recruits who were natives of these parts. An extreme example of this was one of the enlisted sergeants, generally known (but never in his presence!) as the Pig-man. He was a remarkable sight with his large, snout-like facial configuration, which was further adorned with an unkempt handle-bar moustache. The collar of his untidy, spotted uniform nearly choked him as he strode out to inspect his platoon through bulging, bloodshot eyes. His loud grunting voice, uneven tusk-like teeth set in narrow jaws, and large floppy ears all added to the overall impression. For a short while he had been a cab driver, but few people had wanted a ride with such a sinister-looking creature. Perhaps the military authorities had hoped that the Pig-man would have a similar deterrent effect on invading Soviet stormtroopers, or at least that he would be capable of scaring some discipline into the young National Service recruits. As second in command of his platoon, I witnessed the latter objective being achieved to perfection.

In her earliest, mid-seventeenth-century incarnation, the Pig-faced Lady was treated as an object rather than a person; in spite of her costly dress and various ladylike accomplishments, she was just a malformed wooden dummy. No one ever felt sorry for the Pig-faced Lady, whose fate it was to be ridiculed, insulted and surreptitiously rejected by her horrified suitors. The real objects of the satire in the ballads and pamphlets were the vainglorious upstarts, the tailors, captains and sowce-men, people with whom the readers could identify: their ludicrous attempts to secure her hand in marriage, and their ignominious retreat. In the eighteenth and nineteenth centuries, the origin of the tale as a garbled version of the legend of Margaret of Henneberg gradually became forgotten. The persona of the Pig-faced Lady was still treated with the same jocularity and cheerful unconcern, however, during the 1815 craze in London and the nineteenth-century exhibition of 'Madam Steevens'. A switch of gender would have been as unthinkable in 1815 as it was in 1639, and the story would have lost its entire fascination if it had dealt with a Hog-faced Gentleman. Today, the legend of the Pig-faced Lady is of course almost completely forgotten, although it may not be entirely fanciful to draw a parallel to Miss Piggy in the *Muppet Show* and her desire to marry her reluctant suitor, Kermit the Frog.

Joseph Sheridan Le Fanu was by no means a typical nineteenth-century horror novelist. He was a writer of consider-able hidden depth, who delighted in subtle hints and devious sub-plots. He used the standard Victorian sensation novel as his medium, and accepted the obvious limitations this put on the artistic side of his work. Furthermore, his novels were of a very variable quality, and some of them were dashed off quickly due to pecuniary adversities. In contrast, the plot of *Uncle Silas* had been left to mature for twenty-six years. As 'Chapters in the History of an Irish Countess', a short version had been pub-lished in the *Dublin University Magazine* of 1838, and later, as 'The Murdered Cousin', in his 1851 collection *Ghost Stories and Tales of Mystery*. M.R. James was quite right that *Uncle Silas* was Le Fanu's best work by far, and it is still acknowledged as such by literary historians, including Le Fanu's biographer Dr W.J. McCormack. *Uncle Silas* is very carefully plotted, and it is clear that Le Fanu must have had some particular reason for including the poem about the lady with the pig's head. Neither M.R. James nor any other literary historian has ever found the original of this 'Bretagne ballad'; the reason is probably that Le Fanu, a published poet in his youth, had written it himself with the purpose to add yet another of his clever puzzles to the complex narrative of *Uncle Silas*. The legend of the Pig-faced Lady was well known in mid-nineteenth-century Dublin, and Sheridan Le Fanu must have heard of it, particularly as his house at Merrion Square in Dublin was not far from Doctor Steevens' Hospital. He may well have read one of the earlier pamphlets or poems about the Hog-faced Gentlewoman and her suitors, and must certainly have been aware of the metaphorical meaning of the avaricious suitors to the Pig-faced Lady. Its meaning is likely to be that, in the eyes of Madame de la Rougierre, Maud Ruthyn is the Hog-faced Gentlewoman. Although she is described as a beautiful young girl rather than a deformed monster, her situation in life resembles that of the original Pig-faced Lady. Her family is very rich, and she leads an isolated life in a large country house, along with her father, a retiring misanthrope who barely speaks to her. She is the sole heiress to his vast fortune. A certain Captain Oakley, a foppish young military man, has shown her attention and wishes to marry her for money. Her wicked Uncle Silas is also after her money, and as the scheming Madame de la Rougierre sings the ballad about the pig-faced lady, she is actually leading her naive charge to a concealed rendezvous with another avaricious suitor, her cousin Dudley, Silas' son. Can it be doubted that these two individuals, one a fortune-seeker and the other the boorish, ill-mannered son of a murderer, are to symbolise the suitors to the Pig-faced Lady?

The inclusion of the wife of the Wandering Jew in Le Fanu's poem again testifies to his knowledge of Pig-faced Lady lore. Just as in the case of the marvellous 'children' of Margaret of

Henneberg, there were several garbled versions of the legend of the Hog-faced Gentlewoman. One, allegedly immortalised in a sculpture in a Belgian cathedral, tells that a Christian man had converted to Judaism, but that shortly after, his wife gave birth to a girl with the face of a pig. The distraught man consulted a priest, who of course advised him to return to the faith of his fathers. He did so, and at the same moment, his daughter's porcine face changed into a divinely beautiful human face. Just like this version of the legend of the Pig-faced Lady, Le Fanu's *Uncle Silas* has a happy ending, although it is somewhat contrived. In the original concept of the story, outlined in 'The Murdered Cousin', the ending is that Dudley Ruthyn murders his own sister, using a pickaxe, since he mistakes her for Maud in the dark. Maud herself later becomes a gloomy old maid, who sits pondering her joyless and miserable life, saying that she would have preferred her cousin's fate for herself. Sheridan Le Fanu thought this ending a bit too dismal for a popular novel, and changed it when parts of the novel had probably already been written: it is not Maud's cousin, but Madame de la Rougierre herself who is killed by mistake by the brutal Dudley. The novel leaves it unexplained how even a blood-crazed murderer could have made such a mistake: while Maud is described as shapely and slender in build, her former governess is a tall, strongly built woman with feet almost the size of a *pain riche*. At any rate, Maud is saved from the clutches of the villainous Uncle Silas, who later takes poison and dies. She marries a distinguished nobleman, and thus also avoids the fate of the Pig-faced Lady: to live surrounded by wealth, but unmarried, unloved and alone.

4

Horned
HUMANS

In Herman Melville's novel *Whitejacket*, the reader encounters the somewhat sinister Surgeon of the Fleet Cadwallader Cuticle and his private museum of pathological specimens. The prize of his collection is a plaster cast of a human face, expressly stated to have been taken from life. Melville describes this cast in such an eloquent way as to indicate that he had seen its original himself:

> It was the head of an elderly woman, with an aspect singularly gentle and meek, but at the same time wonderfully expressive of a gnawing sorrow, never to be relieved. You would almost have thought it the face of some abbess, for some unspeakable crime voluntarily sequestered from human society, and leading a life of agonized penitence without hope, so marvellously sad and tearfully pitiable was this head. But when you first beheld it, no such emotions ever crossed your mind. All your eyes and all your horrified soul were first fascinated and frozen by the sight of a hideous, crumpled horn, like that of a ram, downward growing from the forehead, and partly shadowing the face; but as you gazed, the freeing fascination of its horribleness gradually waned, and then your whole heart burst with sorrow, as you contemplated those aged features, ashly pale and wan.

A rather less well-known writer, W.H. Davies, an eccentric Welshman who was a friend of George Bernard Shaw and who wrote the popular *Autobiography of a Super-tramp*, describes a no less sinister encounter with a *homo cornutus* (horned human). In his youth, long before he set out touring the world as a tramp, he knew an old woman who always, indoors and out, was in the habit of wearing a cap that fitted her head very closely. One day, as she was sleeping in a chair before the fire, the mischievous young Davies crept up behind her and pulled her cap off. He was horrified to see that she had a pair of horns growing out of her head.

The literary imagination of the author of *Moby Dick* is undeniable, as is that of the globe-trotting Super-tramp, and many readers have probably considered their tales of these strange horned women as mere dramatic excesses. But it is an established fact in medical science that horned people have always existed, and neither Herman Melville nor W.H. Davies need to have exaggerated. In fact, both their accounts are likely to have been inspired by famous real-life cases of *homo cornutus*.

In early times, horns symbolised wisdom and supernatural power. Both Moses and Alexander the Great were sometimes depicted with horns to show their omnipotence. Even Michelangelo's famous sculpture of Moses sports a pair of horns. Sorcerers and shamans wore headdresses with antlers, and the worship of a horned god, known as Pan or by other names, was widespread at the time when Christianity emerged. In England, worship of a horned god was particularly long-lasting, and at one time, in the seventh and eighth centuries, formed such a serious threat to early Christianity that bishops and archbishops anathematised the old rites severely. It was not until the attributes of Pan, including his horns, were attributed to the Christian Satan that the idea of a humanoid figure with horns acquired a wholly negative image.

The medieval chronicles have a good deal to say about horned human beings, but unfortunately little that belongs in the realm of reality. Conradus Lycosthenes tells us that, in the year 1225 in Raustadt in Germany, a child was heard to cry loudly in the womb before birth, to the terror of the mother and all around her. When the child was finally born, it had a pair of horns on its head. The learned Lanfrancus, writing towards the end of the thirteenth century, had once seen a man with seven horns on his head. He wanted the largest of them cut off, but Lanfrancus refused to perform such a hazardous operation, and told the man that he should not waste time and money consulting other physicians, since he was completely incurable. Gilbert Nozerenus once saw a child with the face backward, a horn on the head, and the paws of a bear. Fincelius, in his aptly titled *De Miraculis*, told of a farmer's wife near Wistock who gave birth to a monstrous horned child, purple in colour, with huge eyes, a wide mouth reaching from one ear to the other, and a cloven tongue.

Ambroise Paré, the founder of French surgery, several times mentions horned humans. In his *De Monstris*, he records that a woman near Turin had given birth to a five-horned child. He probably never saw this child himself (if it ever existed), and does not seem to have come across any other instance of *homo cornutus*. His collected case reports contain a no less startling observation, however: having *imaginary* horns was quite a common disease in sixteenth-century France, and Paré had seen several patients 'who stubbornly persuaded themselves of having horns'. This delusion could not be eradicated by any means from 'the melancholy and bizarre brains' of the patients with this singular ailment. To effect a cure, Ambroise Paré blindfolded the patient and scratched him on each side of the forehead with a sharp cow's horn; the resulting effusion of blood often succeeded in persuading the patient that his horns had been torn out with force.

Mrs Margaret Gryffith, an elderly Welshwoman who appeared in London in 1588, has the dubious honour of being the earliest horned human being to be more thoroughly described. This was not due to the exertions of any member of the medical profession, however, but to a cunning showman successfully advertising his most recent 'artist'. In a pamphlet laboriously entitled *A Miraculous, and Monstrous, but yet most true, and certayne discourse, of a Woman (now to be seene in London) of the age of threescore years, or there abouts, in the midst of whose fore-head (by the wonderfull worke of God) there groweth out a crooked Horne, of foure ynches long*, her attractions were fully described. Margaret Gryffith was the widow of a husbandman named David Owyn, and the mother of three children, who lived in Llhan Gaduain in the County of Montgomery. The cause for the horn was supposed to be that in her youth her husband had suspected her of 'some light behaviour' and chided her severely. She had denied with as much vehemence, and rejoined that if she had given her husband the horn, she wished that a horn would grow from her own forehead. To her great mortification, a small hard knob soon appeared in the middle of her forehead, and although she tried to cut it off or to file it, it grew steadily, and no surgeon could cure her.

In her widowhood, Margaret Gryffith lived quietly, and she maintained herself on a small parcel of land. The pamphlet leaves it unsaid whether it was her own idea to go to London, or whether some itinerant showman had 'discovered' her in Wales; one would presume the latter. She appears to have been quite a success when put on show before the curious in London; it is recorded that even the Queen's Privy Council took time off from their preparations to receive the Spanish Armada to see the horned old Welshwoman being exhibited. Her horn was probably kept for posterity: in 1599, when Thomas Plater of Basle visited the repertory of a London magnate, Sir Walter Cope, he saw 'a round horn that had grown out of an Englishwoman's forehead.'

Interestingly, several Elizabethan poets and playwrights allude to Margaret Gryffith and her horn. Thomas Nashe, in *Have with You to Saffron Walden*, wrote that a certain gentleman, at an entertainment for Queen Elizabeth at Audley End, had danced with a woman 'thrice more deformed than the woman with a horne in her head.' In John Marston's *The Malcontent*, published in 1604, the fool Passarello says that 'the horn of a cuckold is as tender as his eye, or as that growing in the woman's forehead twelve years ago, that could not endure to be toucht'. Thomas Dekker made even more direct use of the horned Welshwoman in his *Olde Fortunatus*, published in 1599. The plot is that the English princess Agripyne is tricked into eating the fruit of the Tree of Vice by her rival Andelocia. She then grows two horns from her forehead! When she complains to Andelocia that she has lost a magic purse, the wicked sorceress replies: 'Sigh not for your purse, money may be got by you, as well as by the little Welshwoman… that had but one horne in her head, you have two.' It is curious that both Marston and Dekker seem to have accepted the showman's tale that the horn had grown as the result of unchastity and vice, and used this imagery in their own plays.

In 1598, ten years after Margaret Gryffith had been exhibited in London, a party of French gentlemen were hunting in the forest near Mezières. They saw a group of rustic-looking mountain men standing nearby and engaged them in conversation. All the mountain men respectfully doffed their caps, except one surly-looking fellow. A certain Monsieur de Laverdin reproached him for his insolence, but the man, a coarse character dressed in a jacket and trousers made from fox's furs, obstinately refused to remove his headgear. Enraged, M. de Laverdin then rode forth and tore the hat from his head. The gentlemen gave a great outcry of horror and surprise when they saw that the man had a large horn growing from the upper part of his bald forehead! It was curved like a ram's horn, and of considerable length and thickness.

After M. de Laverdin and his companions had recovered their *sangfroid*, they spoke to the horned mountain man and examined him further. His name was François Trouvillou, he said, and he was thirty-five years old. He was a native of the village of Firmi. Since the age of seven, he had been aware of the horny growth on his forehead and had tried his best to hide it. But the horn grew at an alarming rate and had reached the length of a human finger when he was seventeen years old. One day, someone caught sight of it, and there was a great uproar in the village. Sorcery and witchcraft was of course suspected, and poor François was expelled from his village. Since then, he had earned a meagre living as a huntsman and coaler up in the mountains. He kept his own company, and always wore a hat. The horn grew in a curve, and bent backward as far as the coronal suture. The sharp tip of the horn would have embedded itself in the scalp, had François not filed it regularly.

Although François Trouvillou was a morose, unprepossessing character, and his behaviour altogether rustic, his discoverers knew at once that they had come on to a good thing. Although many human and animal curiosities had previously been exhibited before the Parisians, a horned man would become quite a sensation. M. de Laverdin went to Paris and succeeded in obtaining an audience before King Henri IV. He gave such an eloquent description of his horned charge that the king immediately expressed a desire to see him. In a house near Saint-Eustache, François Trouvillou was introduced to the king. The reaction of either party has unfortunately not been preserved for posterity, but it is known that certain irreverent courtiers remarked that with his reddish beard, bald head and grotesque, curved horn, the mountain man was certainly the image of one of the satyrs of ancient legend. As a reward for this singular audience, Henri IV gave M. de Laverdin a signed permission to put François Trouvillou on show before the Paris townspeople. With this valuable help from the king, the enterprising showmen soon earned quite a fortune from their horned charge. The upkeep of this coarse country bumpkin cost them little,

since he turned away the Parisian delicacies in favour of a rustic
meal of gruel, cabbages and lard. He stubbornly refused to wear
modern clothes, and wore his strange costume made from fox's
furs at all times, even in bed. A profound misogynist, he wanted
nothing whatsoever to do with women. An excellent engraving
of François Trouvillou, by Garnière, was sold at the exhibition,
together with a brief account of his life.

During the two months he was on exhibition in Paris, François
Trouvillou was seen by several scholarly observers, some of whom
had travelled to Paris on purpose to see him. In the company
of Dr Jacob Fesch and his pupil Johannes Echenstein, Professor
Emmanuel Ursitius had occasion to examine Trouvillou in 1598.
Ursitius had read a tall story about a horned Benedictine monk
who ruminated, and he wanted to examine Trouvillou's teeth,
but the horned mountain man refused, in no uncertain terms.
Another notable visitor was the philologist Isaac Casuabon, who
left a thorough description of him. François Trouvillou told him
about his sad childhood and how he had been banished from
his village. He always kept his head covered during his stay in
the mountains, since he was certain that if any person had seen
his horn he would have been killed or imprisoned as a monster. His forehead, where the horn was situated, was completely
bald. The horn was hard as a ram's horn and yellowish brown
in colour. Isaac Casuabon was apparently much impressed by
this strange horned man, and wrote that after seeing him he no
longer doubted the old legends of horned satyrs and aegipans.

After his successful stay in Paris, François Trouvillou was taken
to Orléans, where he suddenly died in 1599, after previously
appearing to be in good health. According to one account, he
died from a broken heart after being exhibited like a wild beast
before the coarse, unfeeling crowd, but this is probably an invention by some sentimental French writer. He was buried in the
Saint-Côme cemetery in Paris, where his gravestone could still
be seen in 1820, according to Dr A.P. Dauxais, the author of a
doctoral thesis on horned people. It had the suitable epitaph:

Dans ce petit endroit à part
Gît un très-singulier cornard;
Car il le fut sans avoir femme,
Passans, priez Dieu pour son âme.

This can be translated as:

A strange horned man departed this life,
And lies buried under this grave stone.
Since he got his horn without a wife,
Pray for his soul, passer-by, ere you're gone!

❧

The engravings of François Trouvillou were widely disseminated all over Europe, and several medical men described the
horned Frenchman in their scholarly tomes. Since it was now
definitely proved that horned people really existed, many savants
searched for other instances, and tried to figure out what natural
and supernatural causes could explain this anomaly. No one
was more eager to do so than Thomas Bartholin, the Danish
anatomist who saw Lazarus Colloredo and examined the Hairy
Maid twice. Throughout his long career, Bartholin kept a sharp
lookout for horned human beings. In 1642, he was reading
Judge du Thou's historical anecdotes and found an account of
François Trouvillou. He suspected that the other descriptions
of Trouvillou were taken from du Thou's work, but his old
friend and tutor Olaus Wormius wrote to tell him that Johannes
Ursitius had himself seen Trouvillou in Paris and touched the
horn. An elderly Dane, Dr Christian Fabritius, had also been
in Paris at the time, and could well remember seeing François
Trouvillou being exhibited.

The year after, Thomas Bartholin sent Wormius a picture of
Trouvillou's horned 'son', who was also shown in the market-
place as a curiosity. Olaus Wormius scented knavery, however.
He knew that it was possible to cut the comb and spurs off a

cock, and transplant the spurs into the remnant of the comb to make them appear like horns, and suspected that both François Trouvillou and his 'son' had been subjected to some strange operation to make them into horned 'curiosities' for the lucrative freak show industry. Thomas Bartholin had heard from his friend Johannes Rhodius about the horned Benedictine monk who ruminated, and was amazed to find out that Trouvillou's alleged son was also reported to ruminate: had his father transmitted this character to the son, by virtue of the ruminant character both carried so conspicuously on their heads?

In 1646, Thomas Bartholin finally fulfilled his ambition to see a horned human being with his own eyes. In the northern parts of Holland, he saw the seventy-year-old woman Margaretha Mainers, who had a long, curved horn growing from the right temple. The appearance of the horn was, by some strange reasoning from the old woman herself, attributed to the bitter quarrels she had had at the time with her prodigal son. The horn appeared like a goat's horn and grew curved almost in a bow. Interestingly, Bartholin noted that it grew from a reddish skin tumour, which the woman said was itching abominably; when she scratched it, it bled freely.

Thomas Bartholin later collected several other cases of horned humans. His friend, the famous anatomist Johann Caspar Bauhin, had seen a tailor who had a painful fleshy tumour behind the right ear. From this tumour grew a horn resembling a ram's horn, although of course smaller. It was possible to move it somewhat, but this caused the man much pain. Since the tumour from which the horn grew was a considerable one, no attempt was made to remove it. A sixty-year-old nun who consulted the anatomist Johann Vesling for a small horn growing from an encysted tumour on her forehead, was more fortunate. The surgeon cut it off in the presence of Thomas Bartholin, and tried to prevent its recurrence by etching with blue vitriol. The horn re-grew, however. Although the poor nun objected to such a brutal method of treatment, Vesling then burned away the skin tumour with a red-hot branding iron. The eloquent Thomas Bartholin tells us that this operation was a complete success, thus verifying the words of Hippocrates: 'What is not cured by fire, is incurable.'

Thomas Bartholin's work inspired the German savant Georg Franck to write the earliest treatise entirely devoted to human horns. His thirty-one-page *Tractatus Philologico-Medicus de Cornutis*, published in Heidelberg in 1676, promised to cover all possible theological, legal, philosophical, historical, mathematical, ethical, philological, political, medical and pathological aspects of horned human beings. It was a worthy review, although much devoted, in the manner of the time, to repeat the statements on the subject from all possible sources, the older the better. The reverence he felt for the old chroniclers prevented him from offering much in the way of a critical discussion, however, and some of his arguments belong in the age of superstition. Nevertheless, Georg Franck managed to draw up a list of twenty-five cases, several of them from the old monster chronicles, but others from Bartholin, Ulysses Aldrovandi and other medical luminaries of the time.

In 1680, just a few years after Georg Franck's thesis had been published, another horned woman made her curtsy on the London stage. Her name was Mary Davies and she was quite old at the time: one source says that she was born in Great Saughall near Chester, in 1594, another that she was born in Shotwick in 1604. According to a letter from the Squire Owen Salus Evett, of Brereton, to Sir Joseph Banks, she was born in 1591 and lived on the Squire's family estate in Cheshire. Mary Davies was exhibited by the sign of the Swan, in the Strand, and a pamphlet entitled *A Brief Narrative of a Strange and Wonderful Old Woman that hath a Pair of Horns growing upon her head* was published to promote her career in show business. It contained the poem:

Ye who love wonders to behold,
Here you may of a wonder read:

The strangest that was ever seen or told;
A Woman bearing Horns upon her head.

Mary Davies was stated to be a wonder greater than any in Mr
Tradescant's famous cabinet of curiosities, and exceeding all the
marvels the greatest travellers could affirm to have seen. She was
the widow of Henry Davies, who had died twenty-five years
previously, and a midwife by profession. In her youth, she was
much troubled by a soreness in her head, occasioned, the old gossips thought, by wearing a straight hat. This soreness continued
for twenty years, and then ripened into a 'wen' the size of a hen's
egg. Five years later, solid and wrinkled horns of a texture like a
ram's horn began to grow from this 'wen', and 'sadly grieved the
old woman, especially upon changes in the weather'. She shed
her first pair of horns after four years, and they were preserved
by the vicar of Shotwick. The second pair, shed four years later,
was purchased by Sir Willoughby Aston. The third set of horns
grew together to reach a length of not less than 9 inches, but
was broken off one day when Mary Davies slipped and fell
backwards. This pair was purchased by a wealthy nobleman, who
later presented it to King Louis XIV of France.

Mary Davies was still going strong in London late in 1680, and
the advertisement promised that her fourth pair of horns would
outgrow all the others. What finally happened to the wonderful
horned old woman is not known, but one of her horns, and a
portrait of her, were preserved in the British Museum in the
mid-eighteenth century. In the van Rymsdyk brothers' *Museum
Britannicum*, published in 1778, the portrait of Mary Davies is
mentioned, but not her horn; this volume instead described an
11-inch horn taken from a woman named Mrs French, living
near Tenterden. In 1685, another of Mary Davies' horns was demonstrated by Dr Robert Plot before the Philosophical Society of
Oxford. Mr Elias Ashmole, the famous collector and antiquary,
ordered that it should be put in his repository. It was seen there
in 1710 by the German Zacharias Conrad von Uffenbach, who
wrote that it had been shed by the then seventy-one-year-old

Mary in 1668. It was of a blackish colour, not very thick, but well proportioned. The same museum also had two horns taken from the forehead of a man, and Uffenbach rather imprudently deduced, from this slender patient material of two, that the men generally had their horns on the forehead, and the females theirs on the back of the head. He illustrated Mary Davies' horn, which had a long and graceful curve just like her others, and postulated that England must have a climate specifically predisposed to the formation of horns. He had never seen goats and rams with such huge horns before he came to England, and was not amazed that even the human beings sprouted horns in this *terra maxime cornifera*. According to the Revd John Pointer's *Oxoniensis Academia*, published in 1749, Mary Davies' horn could be seen in a room adjacent to St John's College Library. The 1836 printed catalogue of the contents of the Ashmolean Museum mentions the horn. Dr Erasmus Wilson, writing in 1844, confirmed that both Mary Davies' horns were still in their respective repertories. Neither of these horns is in existence today, however: they could have been lost through carelessness, or scrapped by some rationalist Victorian museum keeper lacking in reverence toward these early curiosities.

Mary Davies was described in several antiquarian works of the time, particularly in Charles Leigh's *Natural History of Lancashire*. A plate depicted her in 1668, aged seventy-two, and another plate showed Alice Green, the Horned Woman of Whalley Abbey, who had two long horns growing out from the back part of her head. Leigh's portrait of Mary Davies was probably engraved from the British Museum portrait of her; another curious engraving of her, in Ormerod's *History of the County Palatinate and City of Chester*, was probably made from another portrait, also now lost, that had been in the Ashmolean Museum. Scotland has its own horned celebrity: Elizabeth Lowe, who was a contemporary of Mary Davies. In May 1671, when she was fifty years old, the surgeon Arthur Temple cut off a 4-inch horn growing from her skull, 3 inches above her right ear. It had been growing for seven years. An added note states that Elizabeth

Lowe was still living in 1682, and had another horn growing
from the same site. The amputated horn was 4½ inches long,
hard, and dark brown in colour, in the shape of a stretched-out
letter 'S'. It was kept in the Anatomical Museum of Edinburgh
University for many years, and was thoroughly described in
Bennett's *Clinical Lectures* in 1858. The Scottish anatomists have
been more reverent towards their horned celebrity than their
colleagues in London and Oxford, and Elizabeth Lowe's horn
is still in the Anatomical Collections of the Department of
Biomedical Science, University of Edinburgh Medical School.
It is kept in a cylindrical glass jar and held in place by a silver
chain; an inscription on an oval silver plaque tells the story of
the operation in 1671 by 'Arthur Temple Chirurgion'.

It took a long time before the first systematic study of horned
human beings was published, and well into the eighteenth century the odd treatise of Franck von Franckenau remained the
standard work on this subject. It was not until 1791, when the
surgeon Everard Home read a paper on horny growths before
the Royal Society of London, that the question was reviewed by
a trained observer with up-to-date medical knowledge. Everard
Home was the brother-in-law of the great John Hunter, and
served as his assistant surgeon at St George's Hospital. Hunter
was at this time the leading surgeon in London, and a scientist
of great talent and versatility. Hunter and Home were interested
to note that the exhibition of horned 'human curiosities' was still
going strong in London 200 years after the demise of Margaret
Gryffith; at the time Everard Home was writing, two horned
women were on show in the metropolis. One of them, fifty-six-
year-old Mrs Lonsdale from Horncastle in Lincolnshire, had four
horns growing from encysted scalp tumours. The other, a certain
Mrs Elizabeth Allen from Leicestershire, had a considerable horn
growing from an encysted tumour. She was younger and more
attractive than the horned old women described earlier, and

became known as 'the Female Satyr'. Mrs Allen achieved a brief notoriety before the Londoners, but her neighbours back in Leicestershire were appalled by her brashness in putting herself on show, and her husband came to London and took her back home.

It is well known that John Hunter and Everard Home collaborated closely, and it is interesting to note that a newspaper article in the *British Mercury* stated that Elizabeth Allen had been presented to John Hunter, without even mentioning Home. It may well be that, as in some other instances, Home had been provided with his busy master's notes on a certain subject, with instructions to write them up for publication. The article is certainly well ahead of its time. Home and Hunter had noted that in both Mrs Lonsdale and Mrs Allen the horns grew from encysted tumours on the head. This was apparently the case in many of the older instances of horned people, including the celebrated Mary Davies and the 'wens' on her head, and had in fact been noted already by Thomas Bartholin 150 years earlier. Horny growths could occur all over the body, although those on the head and face had of course been particularly noticed. They had a perfectly natural explanation: a skin tumour, or repeated local trauma, changed the normal growth of the skin and caused it to produce a horny substance. Human horns were thus just another skin disease, like a birthmark or a wart. Although unsightly, most of them were not cancerous in nature, and the individual could live for a prolonged period of time, as showed by Mary Davies and her horns, which grew for more than ten years.

This clear demonstration of the natural cause of human horns was published in the *Philosophical Transactions* of the Royal Society of London, a prestigious journal that was disseminated all over the world. The great German pathologists of the early nineteenth century agreed with Hunter and Home that human horns had a perfectly normal explanation, that they could arise not only on the head but on any part of the body, and that they were caused by a diseased state of the skin. The acceptance of this theory among the medical scientists did not extend to the

common people, however, and for many years to come a horned
human being was regarded with superstitious awe. A worthy
example is the sad story of Mrs Burnby, originally presented in
the *Hampshire Telegraph* of 13 April 1812. This pious and worthy
lady had remained single and worked as a schoolmistress until
she was fifty years old. She then rather imprudently decided to
marry, and although some of her religious friends objected that
this sudden urge for matrimony might have arisen from impure
motives, her decision was firm. However, when she was walking back from church after the wedding ceremony, 'a mental
derangement took place', and for the rest of her long life, poor
Mrs Burnby never recovered. As a final *frisson* of horror, it was
added that during her prolonged residence in the local mad-
house, a 6-inch, crooked horn grew from her forehead.

Another strange story is that of Anna Schimper, the horned
nun of Filzen. She was born in 1747 and entered the Filzen
nunnery at an early age. In 1795, French revolutionary troops
occupied the area. One day, they suddenly charged the nunnery and chased the German nuns out of their cells and chapel,
shouting, breaking windows and singing irreligious songs. Poor
Anna Schimper's secluded life had not prepared her for such a
shock to her mental equilibrium: at the sight of the marauding
Frenchmen, she went completely insane, and had to be taken
from her cell in the nunnery to another cell in the local lunatic
asylum. Here, she spent most of the time banging her head
against a solid table. After a number of years, the asylum atten-
dants saw that a horn was growing from a large bump on her
head, just above the right eye, where she used to pound it against
the furniture. Miraculous to say, the longer and thicker this horn
grew, the more Anna Schimper's clouded mind improved, and by
the time she sported a thick, curved horn that almost obscured
the right eye, she was fit enough to move back to the Filzen
nunnery, which had by this time been restored by the German

authorities. The horned nun resided there for many years, in the odour of sanctity, and was promoted to abbess in due course. In 1834, her horn had grown to such a prodigious size that she felt ashamed of it; every time she went outside the convent she had to cover it up with her headdress. She consulted the surgeon W. Giese, who finally agreed to cut it off. It was feared that Anna Schimper might not survive this operation, but although the bleeding was quite considerable, the eighty-seven-year-old abbess soon recovered and went back to her duties at the nunnery. She died two years later, with a small horn re-growing from the thick, ulcerated skin tumour above the eye, from which the original horn had grown. A sentimental German poet wrote a lengthy epistle, entitled *The Finger of God*, to celebrate her strange life and miraculous recovery.

The largest human horn ever recorded belonged to a Mexican. Señor Paul Rodrigues was a strong, muscular fellow, who worked as a packer in a warehouse. He always kept his head covered with a large handkerchief. One day in 1820, a large barrel of sugar fell down from a pile and struck him on the head. When the bystanders removed the handkerchief from the head of the unconscious man, they saw to their horror that he had three enormous horny growths emerging from the upper and right sides of his head, not less than 14 inches in circumference. All three horns were curved, with a texture similar to that of a ram's horn. His ear could be touched through the opening between the first and second horns. The back horn had partially been knocked off by the blow from the barrel. The doctors and nurses at the Anderes hospital bandaged poor Rodrigues, and it appears as if he escaped this adventure with his life, but his secret had been exposed. Professor Cevallos, the chief medical officer at the hospital, published an account of the case, of which a translation was published in the *Medical Repository*, an influential early American medical journal, along with a discussion comparing Rodrigues with some earlier cases of local interest. Mr Scudder's Museum in Philadelphia contained a 7-inch horn taken from the head of an old woman. Not to be outdone, a certain Dr Chatard reported that he had once, in Baltimore, seen another old woman with a large horn on her nose, much resembling that of a rhinoceros.

An equally grotesque horn belonged to the Widow Dimanche, an elderly Frenchwoman who lived at No.12 Rue de Bercy in Paris. At one time, she was admitted as an inpatient at the Hospice de Perfectionnement of the Medical School of Paris. The Widow Dimanche was quite a celebrity in Paris: she was called 'Mère-la-Corne' or 'Mother Horn'. An enormous horny excrescence grew from the forehead, and extended downward, shadowing her face. It was 10 inches long and 2 inches in diameter at its base. It was not implanted in the frontal bone, and its weight was fatiguing to the poor woman, who had to wear a linen sheath around her horn to support it; this sheath was fastened to the band of the nightcap she always wore. The Widow Dimanche was seen by many surgeons during her stay in the hospital ward, and received many offers to have her horn removed by means of operation, but she always refused. One account tells, however, that at the venerable age of eighty-two, having carried her grotesque horn for many years, she finally consented to have it cut off. The operation was performed by the celebrated surgeon Joseph Souberbielle and was a complete success. Mother Horn died in 1840 aged eighty-four, without the horn re-growing. In the 1820s and 1830s, several wax or plaster casts had been made of the Widow Dimanche's face and the horn. In 1851, the Boston Society for Medical Improvement discussed a cast of the Widow Dimanche, quoting a description of the case given by Dr Souberbielle himself. The cast was described as belonging to the 'College Cabinet', and a certain Dr J.B.S. Jackson mentioned that casts of the head of Mother Horn could be found at several other American pathological museums. What has happened to these other casts is not known, but the wax cast at the College Cabinet is very likely to be the same one that can still be seen at the Mütter Museum of the College of Physicians of Philadelphia. The latter specimen was purchased by Dr Mütter somewhere in Europe between 1832 and 1857; it

came into the Mütter Museum as part of his original bequest in
1858. At his museum is also kept a 12-inch horn, removed from a
seventy-year-old woman who had had it for seven years. Several
casts of Mother Horn were kept at various French museums; one
of them was at the Musée Dupuytren in Paris in the 1930s.

Some modern debunkers and rationalists have tried to cast doubt
on the old cases of horned people, and implied that some of them
belonged in the realm of the fabulous. Already Olaus Wormius
doubted whether François Trouvillou's alleged 'horned son' was
genuine, perhaps with some right, since it seems as if this individual was merely profiting from Trouvillou's great notoriety. There
should be no doubt whatever about the genuineness of François
Trouvillou's own horn, however. The contemporary descriptions
agree perfectly well, and the trained medical men who saw him
would not have been deceived by a fake horn attached to his
head. In 1935, an almost identical case was described in the
Indian Medical Gazette: an eighteen-year-old man with a curved,
5-inch horn growing from the top of his bald head. This horn
very much resembled that of François Trouvillou. It gave him
no trouble, and the only reason that the young Indian applied to
Dr J.M. Richardson, of Bilaspur, was that his strange appearance
had given him an unwelcome notoriety in the village, and it
was impossible for him to persuade any of the local maidens to
marry him! Dr Richardson performed the operation without
difficulty, and the large horn, which sprang from the aponeurosis
of the occipitofrontal bone, was removed.

The exhibition of horned people for money has continued
well into the twentieth century. In 1930, newspapers related
that a Chinese peasant with two horns on his head had been
taken to Japan for the purpose of being exhibited. He was given
the princely salary of £2,000 per year. His biggest horn was
10 inches long and 6 inches in diameter at the root. Several
'horned men' have been active in the American sideshow,

although at least one of them seems to have been exposed as a fraud. I have seen a photograph of a Chinese man named Wang, billed as 'The Human Unicorn', who had a 14-inch horn growing from the back of the head. His strange appearance certainly matched that of François Trouvillou.

Modern dermatology agrees with John Hunter and Everard Home that human horns can arise all over the body and not only on the scalp; in fact, only 30% of them are located on the face or scalp. They consist of concentric layers of keratinised epithelial cells; unlike true animal horns, they have no bony core. They are caused by a variety of skin diseases. According to a recent pathological study, 65% of all cutaneous horns are benign, and caused by skin warts or epithelial hyperplasia. Another group of human horns (20%) is due to premalignant conditions, mainly solar keratosis and Bowen's disease (basal cell carcinoma). Finally, 15% are caused by malignant skin tumours, mainly squamous cell carcinomata. It has several times been noted that individuals with large, broad-based horns often have squamous cell carcinomata. In 2002, a group of medical scientists reviewed four modern cases of gigantic cutaneous horns of the scalp, occurring in a twenty-year period. One of them had grown from the scalp of a fifty-five-year-old woman for thirty years and was 10 inches in length; it was curved and very much resembled that of François Trouvillou. It had never given her any pain, but she had concealed it out of a feeling of stigma and shame. The histology in all four instances was that of a so-called proliferating tricho-lemmal tumour, a form of very low-malignant squamous cell carcinoma. It is very likely that some of the historical instances of very large cutaneous horns of the scalp, like those of Margaret Gryffith, Mary Davies and the horned nun of Filzen, had a similar aetiology.

W.H. Davies' encounter with the horned woman could have been inspired by some odd family tradition; it could also be the result of reading some popular account of Mary Davies. The biography of this horned celebrity was frequently reprinted in various nineteenth-century anthologies of *biographiae curiosae*, one of which may well have been read by the young Davies. Some literary historians have proposed the sixteenth-century pamphlet about Margaret Gryffith as a source for Herman Melville's account of the horned woman in *Whitejacket*, but this is extremely unlikely to have been the case. This pamphlet was extremely rare, and her case little known even among the antiquaries. It is also notable that Surgeon Cuticle actually had a plaster cast of the woman in question, and that this cast was stated 'often to be met with in the Anatomical Museums of Europe'. Only one historical case of *homo cornutus* fulfils these characteristics: the enormous horn of the Widow Dimanche. It is apparent from his description that the plaster cast of Surgeon Cadwallader was identical to one of the several made of Mother Horn. It is just possible that he might have seen the wax model in Dr Mütter's collection, if it was there in 1849. More probably, he had seen the one at the Musée Dupuytren in Paris. This museum was open to the public in Melville's time, although 'to gentlemen only' due to its gruesome contents. It is interesting to note that according to Herman Melville's journal entry for 5 December 1849, he went to the Musée Dupuytren and saw 'Rows of cracked skulls. Skeletons & things without a name.' This date was just before he finished *Whitejacket*; indeed, one of the purposes of his journey to London and the Continent was to find a suitable publisher for this manuscript. The macabre sight of the plaster cast of Mother Horn is likely to have inspired him to incorporate a similar cast into his fictional narrative.

5

Daniel Lambert,

THE HUMAN
COLOSSUS

To become renowned as the most corpulent man of whom authentic records exist is not the kind of celebrity anyone would wish for, but this was the fate of the enormous Daniel Lambert, who lived between 1770 and 1806. Six men of normal build could be buttoned into Lambert's waistcoat, and his stockings were the size of linen sacks. Daniel Lambert's contemporaries were fascinated with this prodigy of nature, and in nineteenth-century Britain his name became synonymous with extreme bulk and heaviness. Although he is no longer the heaviest man in the world, the memory of Daniel Lambert is still revered, particularly in the area around Leicester, where several inns and public houses are named after him.

∞

Daniel Lambert was born on 13 March 1770, in Blue Boar Lane in Leicester, as the eldest son of the keeper of the Bridewell prison in that town. He had two healthy sisters and a brother who died young. Neither his parents nor his siblings were overweight, according to local sources, which noted, however, that his paternal aunt and uncle were both very heavy. As a boy and young man, Daniel Lambert was strong and healthy. He was heavily built, with a good appetite, but by no means corpulent. At the age of fourteen, he was apprenticed to Mr Benjamin Patricks' die-casting and engraving business in Birmingham. This business was a flourishing one in the early 1780s, but the buttons and buckles manufactured there rapidly went out of fashion, and hardly anyone wanted to buy them. According to another version, Daniel stayed in Birmingham until Mr Patricks' firm was completely demolished during the riots in 1791. In either case, Mr Patricks despaired of ever being able to resurrect the firm and Daniel had to return to Leicester, where he became assistant keeper of the prison, serving under his own father. When he reached the age of twenty, he began to suspect that he would one day become very heavy, and took pains to exercise regularly and to keep up his muscular power, which was extraordinary. He could lift up a heavy cartwheel, and carried five hundredweight with ease.

Like his father and uncle, Daniel Lambert was greatly addicted to country pursuits, and was particularly fond of otter hunting, horse racing, shooting and fishing. For quite a few years, he regularly taught the Leicester children to swim in the river Soar. Already in his teens, Daniel Lambert took a keen interest in the breeding of sporting dogs, mainly spaniels, setters, terriers and pointers. One day, Daniel was standing outside his father's house in Blue Boar Lane, watching a party of itinerant Savoyards perform in the street with their dancing bears. Suddenly, one of Daniel Lambert's dogs flew at a large bear and bit it viciously in the rear quarters. The bear was muzzled, but when the dog attacked again, the bear knocked it on the head and crushed it to the ground. The Savoyards were annoyed at this untoward interruption of their performance, and prepared to take the muzzle off the bear, in order for it to finish off the poor dog. Daniel Lambert came up and prevailed upon them to allow him to remove his dog, but a Savoyard ignored him and instead loosened the muzzle. Daniel snatched a pole from this man, and called out that he would kill the bear if it lay in his power. The moment the bear's muzzle was removed, Daniel struck it a tremendous blow. The bear was stunned for a moment, and the dog managed to escape. The bear then attacked Daniel instead, and he had to fight for his life. The weather was frosty, and he fell heavily just in front of the infuriated animal, but rose again just in time to strike the bear a resounding blow with his left hand. The bear was nearly knocked out cold, and declined further contest. The performers complained to the authorities that Daniel Lambert had interrupted their performance and beaten one of their animals severely, but the local magistrate was no friend of these foreign jugglers and merely ridiculed them.

In the early 1790s, Daniel Lambert's father retired as keeper of the prison, and Daniel succeeded him. For many years, this huge, rotund figure became a familiar sight to the Leicester people as he sat outside the prison gates, smoking his pipe. The sedentary life at the prison did not agree with him at all, and as the years went by, Daniel's weight steadily increased. In 1793, he weighed 448 pounds but was still strong and active. He once walked from Woolwich to London without showing signs of fatigue, and during the swimming lessons in the river Soar, his powers of floating enabled him to swim with two men of ordinary size sitting on his back. It was a source of grief to him when, in 1801, he had to give up hunting, since both he and the poor horse he rode were too out of breath to keep up with the rest of the hunt.

All sources agree that Daniel Lambert was a competent keeper of the prison. His attitude towards the prisoners was more humane than was expected at the time: far from establishing a regime of terror at the Bridewell prison, he often gained friends among the prisoners, and made every exertion to help them when they went up for trial. It was said that few criminals left the prison without expressing their gratitude to him and that many shed tears when the time came for them to leave their cells! In the early 1800s, Daniel's weight had increased to about 560 pounds and there was apparently some concern about whether he was fit to remain in charge of the prison. He was certainly fortunate that the contented prisoners in his charge did not try to escape; any attempt to pursue them would have been futile owing to his extreme bulk. A certain James Neale, who visited the Bridewell prison in 1803, ironically wrote that 'had this fat man studied a thousand years, he would not have thought on a *profession* better calculated to suit his constitutional propensity to ease'. Although Daniel Lambert had a very good reputation locally, Neale thought him a very improper person to be the keeper of a prison.

At Easter 1805, the Bridewell prison was closed and the prisoners moved to a new institution for forced labour. Daniel Lambert liked his work at the prison, and would probably have preferred to stay on, but the magistrates were firm in their decision. They granted him an annuity of £50 for life, as a declaration of the universal satisfaction he had given in the discharge of his duties. After he had left the prison, Daniel became little more than a recluse in his own house. Nor could he visit horse races or cocking matches any more, due to the interest in his person from the impudent populace. The reputation of this prodigiously fat man had spread throughout England, and many travellers wanted to see him as a curiosity. Lambert was quite sensitive about his grotesque appearance, and he detested such visits. Once, a gentleman from Nottingham who knew Lambert's interest in horses, was admitted into his house under the pretence of asking his advice about the pedigree of a certain mare. Daniel Lambert, who was shrewd enough to perceive from his manner the real nature of his errand, brusquely told him that the mare in question 'was by *Impertinence* out of *Curiosity*.' Another stranger tried to entice the great man from his house by pretending to ask him about some fighting cocks. Daniel Lambert's servant knew that his master never saw strangers, but the man persisted. Lambert overheard their conversation, opened a window and instructed his servant to 'tell the gentleman that I am a *shy-cock*'.

Daniel Lambert was not only very averse to putting himself on show, he also steadfastly refused to weigh himself, although jocose and unfeeling friends offered to let him have the use of one of their cattle weighing machines. Finally, these same friends took him to a cocking match in Loughborough. Poor Daniel had to go sideways into the carriage, but finally managed to squeeze through the door. While they were on the way, the others went out under some pretence or other, and the carriage was driven over a large weighing machine. After they had subtracted the weight of the carriage, which had previously been ascertained, they could tell Daniel Lambert, to his great mortification, that his weight was now nearly 700 pounds (50 stone). His extreme corpulence prevented him from doing any work, and in spite of the annuity from the Leicester magistrates, he was soon facing dire financial straits. With the greatest reluctance, he decided to travel to London and exhibit himself for money there. Several friends had previously suggested this ignominious way of earning his living, but he had always refused. In March 1806, he chose to profit from his extreme obesity, which had previously caused him only misery.

On 4 April 1806, Daniel Lambert left Leicester in a purposely constructed carriage and took up residence in the heart of London, at No. 53 Piccadilly. He was widely advertised in the newspapers and on handbills, and when he began to see visitors on 7 April, numerous spectators paid a shilling to see this human colossus, the heaviest man in Britain. This unenviable title had previously belonged to the grocer Edward Bright, known as 'the Fat Man of Essex', who was well known for his appetite and who drank a gallon of beer a day. He weighed 616 pounds at the time of his death in 1750. Among the runners-up were the 340-pound bookseller John Love and the enormous Dr Stafford, on whose gravestone the following words were inscribed:

Take heed, O good traveller! and do not tread hard,
For here lies Doctor Stafford, in all this churchyard.

A reporter from the *Times* wrote that:

> The concourse of fashionable visitors to the house of Mr
> Lambert... has been very great, during the last two days. To find
> a man of his uncommon dimensions (weighing no less than
> fifty stone, or 700 pounds) possessing great information, manners
> the most affable and pleasing, and a perfect ease and facility in '
> conversation, exceeded our expectations, high as they had been
> raised. The female spectators were greater in proportion than
> those of the other sex, and not a few of them have been heard
> to declare, how much they admired his manly and intelligent
> countenance.

A journalist from the *Morning Post*, who visited Daniel Lambert
on 13 April, was similarly impressed with his intelligence and
affable manner, and the politeness with which he answered the
numerous questions from the audience. No fewer than 400
people came to see this 'prodigy of human dimensions' from
twelve until five o'clock.

There was immediate interest also from the medical profession,
and the *Medical and Physical Journal* published an article giving 'the
correct particulars' of this human phenomenon. Daniel Lambert
was 5 foot 11 inches tall and weighed upwards of 700 pounds.
In spite of his extraordinary bulk, he enjoyed perfect health: his
breathing was free, his sleep undisturbed, and all functions of his
body in excellent order. Daniel Lambert ate ordinary food, he
told the doctor, and drank only water and no alcoholic bever-
ages. On examination, the doctor found that there was immense
accumulation of fat within the abdomen, and enormous tume-
faction of the thighs, legs and feet. Daniel Lambert never felt pain
or discomfort from the stretching of the skin, but he had had
four or five attacks of erysipelas of the legs, which had caused
a permanent scaliness and thickening of the skin. This account
agreed with the local sources that Daniel's weight had gradually
increased from the age of twenty, but disagreed in stating that
both his father and his uncle had been heavy men, although the

weight of either had not exceeded 420 pounds. Many people were amazed that Daniel Lambert's habits were very far removed from those usually associated with great corpulence: he ate only one course at meals (he claimed), drank no ale, and slept no more than eight hours per night, always with the window open. He was never heard to snore. He was mentally alert and active, read widely, and sang in a strong tenor voice.

Once his habitual shyness and aversion to putting himself on show had been conquered, Daniel Lambert had a gregarious, extroverted personality and the manners of a gentleman. At least at the beginning, this gave his apartments the air of a fashionable resort rather than a sordid freak show. Early nineteenth-century people did not share the present-day obsession with leanness, and Daniel was considered as a 'prodigy' or a wonder of nature, rather than a repulsive monstrosity. Among the Londoners, it became highly fashionable to have visited him, and even more fashionable to be his friend. His interests coincided with those of the upper and middle classes of society, and he could spend hours discussing horses and hounds with them. He had brought seven setters and two pointers with him to London, and sold these animals to Mr Mellish and Lord Kinnaird for not less than 218 guineas in all, a sum showing the high regard for his breeding among fanciers of sporting dogs. Daniel Lambert insisted on being treated with civility, and every man who entered his rooms, even Quakers, had to remove their hats. Once, a French impresario tried to persuade Lambert to accompany him back and tour France, but although the man assured him that Bonaparte would make his fortune when they entered Paris, 'Lambert, who had too much good sense to be the dupe of a designing Monsieur, declined in the most emphatic style of a true son of John Bull.' Daniel Lambert's greatest triumph during his season in London was when he was presented to King George III; unfortunately, the king's reaction has not been recorded.

Daniel Lambert was one day visited by a party of eight ladies and six gentlemen from Guernsey, who had travelled to London to see this prodigy after he had been eloquently described to them by a neighbour. Lambert suggested that they should remain in London for a few days and see the remaining sights of the town, but they declared that since they had now achieved the sole purpose of their journey, they had no desire to visit any other attractions. When Daniel Lambert had been in London a few months, he was visited by the famous midget 'Count' Joseph Boruwlaski, who had made a fortune touring Europe. He was by now seventy-four years old and lived in comfortable retirement in Durham. Boruwlaski was renowned for his excellent memory, and he could actually recollect that Daniel Lambert had several times come to see *him* in Birmingham, at the time when Daniel had been working as an apprentice at the die-sinker's business. Since poor Daniel had increased in weight at least threefold since that time, the witty Boruwlaski exclaimed: 'Ah mine Got, I have seen dis face twenty years before at Birmingham, but certainly it be anoder body!' Daniel Lambert inquired whether the count's wife was still living, but he replied that she was not, and that he was not very sorry, because this lady, who was of normal stature, used to put him on the mantelpiece, from whence he did not dare to jump down, during their domestic arguments. One of Lambert's sleeves would have provided enough cloth for Boruwlaski's coat. The elderly count then felt one of Lambert's legs, exclaiming: 'Ah mine Got! Pure flesh and blood – I feel de warm. No deception! I am pleased, for I did hear it was deception.' Those present when these two personages met were envied by all London's innumerable lovers of curiosities: as eloquently expressed in a newspaper: 'It was *Sir John Falstaff* and *Tom Thumb*, which must have afforded a *double* treat to the curious.'

A somewhat less appealing, and probably more trustworthy, description of Daniel Lambert on show is provided by the *Memoirs of Charles Mathews* written by his wife Anne. Charles Mathews was a popular actor who visited Daniel Lambert many times and found him a pleasant and intelligent man. Mrs Mathews wrote that Lambert, who was evidently becoming somewhat bored with being on show, received his visitors in a 'half-courteous, half-sullen manner'. It was distressing to Charles Mathews and his wife to hear the coarse observations made by some of the visitors, and they pitied Lambert's plight before a host of unfeeling individuals, who asked rude questions about his appetite. Another pet subject for these hecklers was the size and cost of Daniel Lambert's coat. One woman was particularly solicitous to find out the cost of this garment, but Lambert sullenly replied that if she made him a present of a new coat, she would then find out exactly what it cost. An obnoxious fellow was equally persistent in his attempts to have the same question elucidated, and rudely remarked that since he had contributed a shilling towards the cost of Lambert's next coat, he had the right to demand any information about it. 'Sir', rejoined Lambert, 'if I knew what part of my coat your shilling would pay for, I can assure you I would cut out the piece.' Daniel Lambert's wit made him a formidable foe to these hecklers, and when a young snob, who had walked around the great man for some time scrutinising his appearance through his quizzing-glass, finally asked Lambert whether it was true that he liked dogs, he received the deserved retort, 'Yes, Sir, all kinds of dogs, except *puppies!*'

The production of caricature prints was particularly prolific in the late eighteenth and early nineteenth century. In Daniel Lambert's time, the most popular topics for caricatures were the war with France, the controversial politician Charles James Fox and his proposals for peace, and the unpopular measures of taxation on tobacco and other commodities. The early nineteenth-century buyers of prints were easily amused, and in the caricatures John Bull was depicted beating Napoleon with a cudgel, refusing the crafty Fox's offers of peace, and objecting against the novel taxes, often using violence against the persons of the ministers involved. The traditional figure of John Bull was that of a stout, well-nourished countryman, and it took little inspiration for the draughtsmen to put Daniel Lambert in his place. Charles James Fox was also quite fat, and in one caricature,

'The two greatest Men in England', he is depicted as being the same size as Lambert, with a projecting paunch. Another caricature was entitled 'Fox feeding Daniel Lambert with Peace from a Barrel'. In 'Bone and Flesh, or John Bull in Moderate Condition', Daniel Lambert received Napoleon Bonaparte as one of his visitors. Astonished by the sight of Lambert, the emperor says, 'I contemplate this Wonder of the World, and regret that my conquered Domains cannot match this Man, pray Sir, are you not a descendant of the great Joss of China?' Daniel Lambert replies, 'No Sir, I am a true born Englishman from the County of Leicester, a quiet Mind and good Constitution nourished by the free Air of Great Britain makes every Englishman thrive.' In 'The English Lamb and the French Tiger', Daniel Lambert and Napoleon are sitting at a dining table. Lambert completely fills his chair, but the Emperor sits in the middle of his too-high seat. Daniel Lambert placidly carves a round of beef, with a huge tankard of brown stout in front of him. Napoleon eats only a bowl of soup, and he is regarding Lambert's roast beef with a sinister stare. In the caricature 'Two Wonders of the World, or a Specimen of a New Troop of Leicestershire Light Horse', Lambert is dressed in a militia uniform, and seated on the horse Monarch, the largest in the world at about 7 foot high. He attacks the tiny Napoleon, who drops his hat and sword and holds up his hands in terror, exclaiming: 'Parbleu! If dis be de specimen of de English Light Horse vat vil de Heavy Horse be? Oh, by Gar, I vil put off de Invasion for an oder time!'

Daniel Lambert's great success in London had exceeded his most sanguine expectations, and he returned to Leicester a wealthy man. He had been wise enough to remain his own master, and never became the dupe of some cunning showman who wanted to exploit his fame. In Leicester, he resumed his earlier occupations: visits to race meetings and cock-pits, and the breeding of sporting dogs and fighting cocks. The *Leicester*

Journal of 19 September 1806 could report that at the Leicester Races, 'Among the distinguished characters upon the turf we were glad to see our old friend, Mr Daniel Lambert, in apparent high health and spirits.' After his lucrative season in London, he was now able to build up a fine pack of coursing greyhounds; although he was unable to follow them on horseback, he enjoyed watching them from his carriage as they pursued a hare through the open landscape. In December 1806, Lambert went on tour to Birmingham and Coventry, among other cities; one newspaper marvelled that, in spite of all his attention to regimen, his bulk still increased steadily. In early 1807, he returned to London and took rooms in Leicester Square. Unfortunately, he fell ill after a few months in the metropolis and his physician, Dr Heaviside, suspected that the London air did not agree with his constitution. Daniel Lambert was advised to return to Leicester, but later the same year he recovered enough to make a series of tours in the provinces. In the summer of 1808, he again came to London for a shorter period, and sold a brace of spaniel puppies at Tattersall's for 75 guineas. Daniel Lambert received an offer of 100 guineas for a small terrier bitch, said to be the finest in England, but he refused to sell his favourite pet. This little terrier always slept by his bed, and remained his loyal companion until the day he died.

Throughout the years when he exhibited himself in London, Daniel Lambert was one of the sights of the town, and not a few foreign tourists visited this prodigy. One of those who saw 'the Human Colossus' was the Swedish artillery captain Johan Didrik af Wingård, who had been sent to London in 1808 to purchase a large quantity of English rifles for the Swedish militia. According to his memoirs, one of af Wingård's ambitions was to explore 'the filthy side of English street life'; his acquaintance with a man named Mathews, who may have been some kind of pimp, ensured that the Swede soon made giant strides towards achieving this purpose. Captain af Wingård's more edifying pursuits included visits to music halls, museums and exhibitions of natural curiosities. He saw a panorama of a recent battle between the British and French fleets, and went to Guy's Hospital to visit an American albiness. She demonstrated an automaton that could reply to questions and tell fortunes using a large glass ball, but the Swede exposed a conjurer skulking behind a screen, manoeuvring this 'automaton'. Johan Didrik af Wingård was much more impressed by Daniel Lambert, the sight of whom he eloquently described in his memoirs:

> This enormously fat man sat in a sofa wide enough for three or four people, and filled it well. He had a really quite handsome, small head, at least compared with his ungainly body. Had he been able to stand up, a feat that really must have been impossible for him to perform, he would have been quite a tall man. His wide cheekbones and huge double chin did not disfigure him very much, but his belly, dressed in a striped waistcoat, resembled a huge featherbed, and his legs, dressed in similarly coloured stockings, were the size of two large butter kernels. This unfortunate man, who was not destined to live long, had permitted his relatives to make a show of him for profit, since no company could be prevailed upon to insure his life. Maybe Count Carl de Geer still keeps a portrait of this hideous mass of flesh, since this noble gentleman certainly purchased one when we saw Lambert together.

In October 1808, the *Times* reported that Daniel Lambert was showing himself in York, probably during the course of another tour of the provinces. In June 1809, he travelled to Cambridge, and then to Huntingdon and Stamford. He often mixed business with pleasure during his tours, and his visit to Stamford coincided with the Stamford Races. One account actually states that Stamford was the last town where he intended to show himself for money, probably since he was now financially independent. On 20 June, he occupied an apartment on the ground floor of the Waggon and Horses inn (he could no longer walk up stairs). He was tired after his journey but still in good spirits: in the evening, he sent a message to the *Stamford Mercury* to order some handbills and advertisements. With the words 'as the Mountain could not wait upon Mahomet, Mahomet would go to the Mountain', he requested the printer to call on him to receive the particulars about these handbills. In the evening, the printer came to see him. Daniel Lambert was still in bed, and admitted to feeling fatigued, but he was as business-minded as ever and anxious that his handbills were delivered in time. The following morning, he rose as usual and seemed to be in good health. Just as he was about to start shaving, he suddenly complained of a great difficulty in breathing, and ten minutes later died. As quoted from his obituary in the *Stamford Mercury*:

> Nature had endured all the trespass she could admit; the poor man's corpulence had constantly increased until, at the time we had mentioned, the clogged machinery stood still, and this prodigy of mankind was numbered with the dead!

Just a few days before his death, Daniel Lambert had been weighed with Mr King's famous Caledonian Balance in Ipswich, where he turned the scales at 739 pounds. Since the putrefaction of this huge corpse was extreme, a coffin of suitable size was constructed with the greatest expedition, and an immense grave dug at the back of St Martin's church in Stamford. The coffin consisted of 112 square feet of elm, and was built upon two axle trees and four clog wheels, thus enabling the mourners to wheel Daniel Lambert to his final place of rest. It was 6 foot 4 inches long, 4 foot 4 inches wide, and in shape almost resembled a square box. On the day after Daniel Lambert's death, the corpse was put into this huge coffin with the greatest difficulty, and the window and wall of the room were pulled down to allow his exit. On the morning of 23 June, the coffin was wheeled towards the churchyard. A regular sloping descent had been constructed from the grave, but it still took twenty men nearly half an hour to pull the coffin into the grave. A huge crowd of people of all ages, many of whom had seen Daniel Lambert while he was alive, had gathered to pay the great man their last respects. His friends in Leicester paid for a handsome gravestone, with the inscription:

> In Remembrance of
> that PRODIGY in NATURE
> DANIEL LAMBERT
> a Native of LEICESTER
> who was possessed of
> an exalted and convivial Mind
> and, in personal Greatness
> had no COMPETITOR:
> He measured three Feet one Inch round the LEG
> nine FEET four INCHES round the BODY
> and weighed
> FIFTY TWO STONE ELEVEN POUNDS
> He departed this life
> on the 21st of June
> 1809
> AGED 39 YEARS
> As a Testimony of Respect
> this Stone is erected
> by his Friends
> in Leicester.

Shortly after Daniel Lambert's death, Mr J. Drakard of Stamford published his biography: *The Life of that Wonderful and Extraordinary Heavy Man, the late Daniel Lambert*. This was by no means the first account of Lambert's life that had appeared before the reading public. In 1808, a short biography of him had been incorporated into *Granger's Wonderful Museum and Magazine Extraordinary*. This amazing collection is one of several early nineteenth-century anthologies of *biographiae curiosae*: large, well-illustrated, multi-volume compilations of wonderful Occurrences, singular Events, heroic Adventures, absurd Characters, remarkable for eating, drinking, fasting, walking &c., memorable Exploits, amazing Deliverances from Death and various other Dangers, strange

Accidents, extraordinary Memoirs &c.' Daniel Lambert shares
the 3,000 pages of this wonderful museum with characters like
'Peter the Wild Boy', 'the Hairy Girl', 'Foolish Sam', 'Frederich
III King of Prussia' and 'the Kangaroo'; he is the only one of
them to be honoured by having his portrait as the frontispiece
of one of the volumes. *Granger's Wonderful Museum* and other
works of a similar nature easily found readers; none of these
dictionaries of curious biography, with names like Smeeton's
Biographia Curiosa, the *Eccentric Mirror* and the *Eccentric Magazine*,
could do without an illustrated account of the life and death of
Daniel Lambert.

Not long after his death, Daniel Lambert became something
of a cult figure. Everything connected with him was preserved
as a curiosity, and there were quite a few stories, real or invented,
about his exploits. The tale of his encounter with the bear is one
of them, and it is curious to note that an earlier version, dating
from the time Lambert was still alive, actually states that the bear
was the victor and that poor Daniel was completely shattered
by his narrow escape from the furious beast. Daniel Lambert's
friends arranged several auctions to sell his clothes and other
effects, including his specially made carriage; many of these items
went into the hands of collectors and lovers of curiosities and
have been preserved to this day. The Victorians actually started a
secondary production of Daniel Lambert memorabilia: his figure
in china or as a glazed inkwell, a metal inkstand showing him in
the act of carving up a goose, and a ceramic teapot which was
opened by taking Lambert's head and shoulders off.

A huge wax statue of Daniel Lambert had been made in 1806.
It later found its way to the United States, and was exhibited at
Mix's Museum in New Haven, Connecticut, in 1813. In 1828,
this statue was at the Vauxhall Gardens in Boston, whose proprietor was proud to announce that he had acquired, through
contacts in Leicester, a complete set of Lambert's clothes to dress
it in. This wax statue later came into the ownership of none less
than P.T. Barnum, and was exhibited at his American Museum in
New York. When the museum was ravaged by fire in 1865, some

workmen made a valiant attempt to save the Lambert statue. Staggering under its weight, they tried to carry it downstairs, but it started to melt from the heat and had to be left behind in the flaming inferno.

Throughout England, particularly around Leicester and Stamford, many inns and public houses were named after Daniel Lambert and had his portrait on their signs. Lambert's name seemed to imply that good food was provided in extremely generous helpings, with ale in proportion. Even in London, public houses were named after him, and in particular, the Daniel Lambert tavern on Ludgate Hill propagated the great man's fame for many years. A fine portrait of Lambert, by Mr Singleton, R.A., and a showcase containing his stout walking stick hung in the lobby. Mr James Dixon, proprietor of the Ram Jam Jam inn, Stamford, went one better in 1826. He actually bought the suit of clothes that Daniel Lambert had worn at the time of his death and exhibited it at his tavern, which was of course renamed the Daniel Lambert inn. Once, six stout labourers were buttoned up in Lambert's enormous waistcoat. In 1846, Daniel Lambert's clothes were seen by P.T. Barnum and his tiny protégé, the fourteen-year-old midget Charles Stratton, otherwise known as General Tom Thumb. Barnum donated one of Tom Thumb's own costumes to Mr Dixon, to be exhibited next to that of Daniel Lambert. General Tom Thumb was apparently quite fascinated by Lambert's wearing apparel. He again visited Stamford in 1859, when twenty-seven years old, and was tied up like a parcel in one of the great man's stockings. In 1866, Tom Thumb, in company with his equally diminutive wife Lavinia Warren, his sister-in-law Minnie Warren, and the competing midget Commodore Nutt, again saw Lambert's clothes; all four midgets could pass through the knee of Daniel Lambert's breeches at one time. Later in 1866, the clothes of Daniel Lambert and General Tom Thumb were purchased by Mr Thomas Tasker Wells, owner of the Old London tavern in Stamford. This gentleman continued to exhibit them for many years. In 1892, Mr Wells produced a thirty-two-page pamphlet, consisting of Drakard's biography of

Daniel Lambert, along with some newspaper cuttings, portraits of Daniel Lambert and Tom Thumb, and copies of letters proving that the clothes were the genuine article and not a fraud.

Several nineteenth-century authors mentioned Daniel Lambert and his extraordinary career. In William Makepeace Thackeray's *Barry Lyndon*, an old servant named Tim, who had stayed in Ireland during Barry's prolonged travels on the Continent, 'had managed to grow monstrously fat in my absence, and would have fitted almost into Daniel Lambert's coat.' In the early chapters of Thackeray's famous *Vanity Fair*, the corpulent 'Jos' Sedley, the brother of Amelia Sedley and once the suitor of Becky Sharp, recklessly drinks a huge bowl of punch when he and his friends visit Vauxhall. He gets exceedingly drunk and finally begins to sing and dance in front of the astonished guests: "'Brayvo, Fat un!" said one, "Angcore, Daniel Lambert!" said another; "What a figure for the tight-rope!" exclaimed another wag, to the inexpressible alarm of the ladies, and the great anger of Mr Osborne.' There are no hints in Thackeray's letters or notebooks that he actually sought information about Lambert, but stories about the great man from Leicester were probably still circulating when the young Thackeray was amusing himself in London during the 1830s. Charles Dickens delivered his thoughts on Daniel Lambert, and also the 'armless and legless wonder' Miss Biffin, in *Nicholas Nickleby*. The absent-minded Mrs Nickleby describes a neighbour with the following words: "'The Prince Regent was proud of his legs, and so was Daniel Lambert, who was also a fat man; he was proud of his legs. So was Miss Biffin: she was – no", added Mrs Nickleby, correcting herself, "I think she had only toes, but the principle is the same."' In his magazine *Household Words*, Dickens later added that after Daniel Lambert had become a wealthy man from putting himself on show, he had devoted his life to sporting pursuits: he had kept thirty terriers, and his only literature had been the *Racing Calendar*. Many other nineteenth-century writers used the well-known name of Daniel Lambert as a synonym for hugeness. The popular novelist Robert Smith Surtees often mentioned him, as in his *Young Tom Hall's Heart-Aches and Horses*: 'A couple of gigantic footmen threw back the portals, as if Daniel Lambert or the Durham ox were about to emerge instead of his slim antiquitated lordship.'

Thomas Carlyle's trenchant criticism of Hudson's proposed statue of Oliver Cromwell contained the words: 'This big swollen and gluttonous "spiritual Daniel Lambert" deserved a coalshaft from his brother mortals: let at least his column be ugly!' Herman Melville's *Mardi* describes a breach in a palisade with the words that it was 'wide enough to admit six Daniel Lamberts abreast'. Herbert Spencer speaks of a 'Daniel Lambert of learning' in his *Study of Sociology*, and in George Meredith's *One of our Conquerors*, London is described as the 'Daniel Lambert of cities'. Lord Macaulay also alluded to the great man from Leicester in one of his essays: 'To paint Daniel Lambert or the living skeleton, the pig faced lady or the Siamese twins, so that nobody can mistake them, is an exploit within the reach of the signpainter.' The poet Thomas Moore ridiculed the corpulent Prince Regent by pretending to write a letter from the prince's tailor, who begs his master's pardon for making too small a coat:

> ...my Wife, who's the Queen of all Slatterns
> Neglected to put up the Book of new Patterns
> She sent the wrong Measures too – shamefully wrong –
> They're the same us'd for poor Mr Lambert when young;
> But bless you! they wouldn't go half round the R*g—t –
> So, hope you'll excuse yours till death, most obedient...

Daniel Lambert is no longer the most corpulent man of whom authentic records exist. The free access to calorie-rich food for the over-consuming people of the Western world has led to an epidemic of obesity. The fact that 20% of Americans are obese, many of them grossly so, is soon apparent to any visitor to that country. In certain individuals with a psychological and/or physical predisposition to corpulence, the abundance of 'junk food' can lead to disaster. The highest undisputed weight for a

human being remains 1,069 pounds for the American Robert
Earl Hughes, born in 1926 and buried in a pianoforte-sized
coffin in 1958. For most of his adult life, Hughes was on exhibition in various fairs and sideshows in the Middle West. There
have been several later pretenders to the title of the human
heavyweight of all times, but some of them appear to have
been 'doctored' by unscrupulous dieting experts, who have
exaggerated the initial weights of their patients to draw attention to their own prowess; others rely on sensational newspaper
evidence alone. The hippy Francis John Lang weighed 1,187
pounds, according to the newspapers, and could not be admitted for treatment of gallbladder inflammation at the Veterans
Administration Hospital in Houston due to the impossibility
of getting him through the doors. He was instead treated inside
the caravan, parked in the hospital car park, in which he lived,
like a large fish in a rather small aquarium. In 1988, American
Walter Hudson claimed that he had weighed 1,400 pounds
(100 stone), thus nearly twice Lambert's weight, before he had
started dieting. He was a prisoner in his own house, since he
could not squeeze through the doorway. After being put on a
starvation diet, he claimed to have lost 900 pounds in weight;
the 500-pound Hudson emerged through the doorway of his
house for the first time in eighteen years and instantly became
an American media celebrity. It was later claimed that Hudson
was exploited by the company fabricating the diet nutrients
he took, and that the whole thing was a scam: Hudson did not
weigh more than 800 or 900 pounds to begin with, and lost
at most 150 pounds. In a 1988 newspaper article, an American
nutritionist claimed that Hudson had slimmed down from 1,204
pounds to 518. Another of his success stories, Mike Partelano,
had once weighed 1,022 pounds, but lost 280 of them with the
help of a diet consisting of vitamin and mineral drinks, and small
helpings of raw fruit and vegetables. Another newspaper story
told the sad tale of the American Michael Hebranko, who had
weighed 994 pounds, but lost 798 of them with help from a
nutritionist. He had a relapse, however, ate five hot dogs at the

airport and again became a food addict. He rapidly increased in weight to 798 pounds, but after lengthy treatment in hospital managed to lose 290 of them. In 1999, this same individual was again in the newspapers after it had been necessary for the New York emergency services to demolish a wall in order to forklift the 1,100-pound Hebranko to an ambulance.

In the British Isles, only one man, the publican William Campbell, has exceeded Daniel Lambert's weight. He was the landlord of the Duke of Wellington public house in Newcastle, and weighed 750 pounds at the time of his death in 1878. Like Daniel Lambert, he once exhibited himself in London, at the Egyptian Hall; also like his distinguished predecessor, he was said to have been a man of considerable wit and intelligence. When the heaviest woman in Britain, Nellie Lambert Ensall, exhibited herself in Birmingham in 1910, she claimed to be Daniel Lambert's great-granddaughter. This is probably untrue, however, since Lambert never married and is unlikely to have had any children, but she may still have been related to him in some way. Daniel Lambert still has relatives living in Leicester, and in 1970 they met to dine on the 200th anniversary of his birth.

During Daniel Lambert's lifetime, it was frequently observed that since he did not eat to excess, and never drank ale, his extreme corpulence could only be due to some unknown, obscure disease. Several later commentators have suggested that there must have been something seriously wrong with his 'glands', although they did not detail exactly what. Modern biology would not agree, however. Obesity can be separated into a primary form, which occurs without other disease being present, and a secondary form, where the corpulence has some external endocrine or genetic cause. For example, myxoedema (severe lack of thyroid hormone) may cause obesity, as may Cushing's syndrome of overproduction of the corticothropic hormone. More uncommon causes include Froelich's syndrome of hypothalamic insufficiency and certain rare genetic syndromes like the Laurence-Moon-Biedl syndrome and the Prader-Willi syndrome. Daniel Lambert had no symptoms of

either hypothyroidism or hypothalamic insufficiency, nor had he
the typical moon-face of the patient with Cushing's syndrome.
Patients with Prader-Willi or Laurence-Moon-Biedl syndromes
may become extremely corpulent, but are often quite feeble
both bodily and mentally, with a tendency towards diabetes and
severe eye disease that may lead to blindness. Sources agree that
in spite of his extreme corpulence, Daniel Lambert was a strong,
powerful man, and that until 1806 he had no complaints about
disease, except for erysipelas and venous insufficiency in both
legs. His intelligence was clearly above average. Thus, it is very
likely that Daniel Lambert suffered from primary obesity. Indeed,
the popular belief that very obese individuals have something
wrong with their 'glands' is very ill-founded; in fact, only a small
minority of them have an endocrine cause for their obesity. The
above-mentioned Robert Hughes used to blame his corpulence
on a singular accident: when three years old, he suffered from
whooping-cough and 'ruptured his thyroid gland'. This explanation, of course eagerly swallowed by the journalists, deserves a
place among the true greats of medical cock-and-bull stories,
along with the tale of the Irishman who tried to convince the
doctor that he had caught venereal disease from borrowing
another man's trousers.

Several of the grossly obese Americans discussed above seem
to have had troubled life stories, and to have been far from
mentally sound, with an addiction to food that can be likened
to that of an alcoholic for strong drink. If the contemporary
accounts are to be believed, Lambert did not overeat and never
touched a pint of beer in his life. It is true that some individuals with what is known as morbid obesity have an abnormal
tendency to gain weight. Their weight certainly increases more
than that of a 'normal' person when eating the same calorie-
rich diet. It has been speculated that they have a persistent
upregulation of the lipoprotein lipase enzyme, which regulates
the liberation of triglycerides from lipoproteins; these triglycerides are incorporated into the fatty tissue. This hypothesis is
supported by the fact that obese individuals have an upregulated

lipoprotein lipase activity, even after dieting, to a normal body weight; this is one of the very few metabolic abnormalities in a person with primary obesity that actually persist even when the individual loses weight. Nevertheless, the main cause of primary obesity is overeating of calorie-rich food in combination with a sedentary lifestyle. When a senior registrar in endo-crinology in 1995, I had occasion to see several obese patients who vehemently claimed that no matter how they tried to diet, they still steadily gained weight. This was investigated by means of treating them as inpatients for two weeks, and feeding them a very strict low-calorie diet. The patients were far from fond of this regimen, and the nurses sometimes had to stand guard to prevent expeditions to the hospital snack shop! In every single case, however, the patients lost weight during these trials, an experience (often, alas, vainly) intended to increase their enthusiasm for changing their diets in a more permanent way. Nearly all overweight people have a tendency to understate their intake of calories, and it is likely that Lambert was one of them. He would indeed have been unique in Leicestershire sporting circles if he had never had a second helping of roast beef and never tasted a tankard of brown ale. It is also very instructive that Daniel Lambert managed to keep his weight within reasonable limits as long as he led an active life, but that his corpulence increased very rapidly as soon as he sat down permanently in the prison-keeper's chair. If Daniel Lambert had lived today, he would probably have been surgically treated with either a gastroplasty or a gastric bypass. Briefly described, these operations remove or bypass the major part of the stomach pouch, and the remaining small gastric reservoir leads to the feeling of fullness being experienced even after quite a small meal. I have seen both operations performed with good effect, and they certainly seem to provide a more lasting benefit than the various fads of dieting, which may well be of benefit on a short-term basis, but allow the individual to regain the lost weight as soon as he or she cannot stand the meagre, low-calorie helpings of diet food any more.

Another unsolved problem is Daniel Lambert's cause of death. The *Dictionary of National Biography* proposed that he died of 'fatty degeneration of the heart', but this does not appear likely. It has been observed, in extremely corpulent individuals, that there is a gradual development of cardiac failure, for the reason that the peripheral resistance increases due to the immense mass of well-vascularised fatty tissue. The circumstances of his death again speak against cardiac insufficiency as the direct cause of death, however, since it was reported that he felt well that fatal morning, before *suddenly* complaining of acute difficulties in breathing. A letter from Elizabeth Gilbert to her sister Ann, kept in the Cambridge University Library, also points out that Daniel Lambert did not suspect his impending, sudden death. A more likely hypothesis is that Daniel Lambert died from a massive pulmonary embolism. It is certain that he suffered from venous insufficiency of the legs, with repeated erysipeloid infections. One of the best accounts of Lambert's life, that in the *Beau Monde and Monthly Register* magazine, mentions that in his later years he suffered very much from pain in his legs. Venous insufficiency of the legs predisposes for venous thrombosis, as does his corpulence and the fact that he had spent the entire day before his death in a recumbent position. Daniel Lambert's corpse was not autopsied, however, and the exact cause of death will never be known.

The morbidly obese twentieth-century Americans described above have all had tough lives. They have been regarded as repulsive 'losers', ridiculed by strangers in the street, and treated with disgust by all and sundry. Finally, their choice was either to become a recluse in their own house or to join the sideshow, just like Daniel Lambert in 1806. The public's expectations of the fat man on show were somewhat different in 1806, however, and the attitude towards him more forgiving than today. When reading contemporary accounts of Daniel Lambert, one is struck by the fact that he was viewed as a 'curiosity' and a 'human wonder' rather than a repulsive, deformed freak. Even though Daniel Lambert was forced by circumstance to join the rank of the early nineteenth-century 'freaks', his exhibition was a very superior one. To many people, he personified the true Englishman, the stout-hearted John Bull, in figure as well as in his rural and sporting interests. Otherwise, Lambert's time was not one noted for kindness to deformed individuals. An example is the massively steatopygous 'Hottentot Venus', Saartje Baartman, who was exhibited like an animal in front of a gawping audience, who made rude jokes and prodded her prodigious behind with their umbrellas to make sure there was no imposture. This happened in 1810, just after Lambert had breathed his last; his old friend Charles Mathews was not the only educated Londoner to find the exploitation of her too pitiful to bear in silence. But then she had the added disadvantages of being black (from the Cape Colony), female and hardly able to speak the English language, whereas Lambert was an affable, middle-class man.

The twentieth-century negative attitude to fat people has also struck Daniel Lambert. It is sad to have to relate that just a few years ago his gravestone was vandalised and the word 'FATTY' scrawled across it in huge letters. This disgraceful vandal represents a tiny minority, however, and Daniel Lambert remains a well-known and respected figure throughout the Midlands, particularly in Leicester and Stamford. His armchair, riding crop, prayer book, walking stick, waistcoat, breeches, shirt, gloves and stockings are at the Newarke House Museum in Leicester. The complete set of his clothes formerly exhibited at the Old London inn is now to be seen at the Stamford Museum, where a full-scale model of Daniel Lambert has been dressed in his coat, breeches, hat and stockings. The portrait and walking stick from the Daniel Lambert tavern at Ludgate Hill are now exhibited at the George Hotel in Stamford, where I saw them in 1998. Lambert memorabilia are valuable: in 1990, a pair of his socks was sold at auction for £270. Many people consider Daniel Lambert as a symbol for the city of Leicester, and in 1981 a play called *The Ghost of Daniel Lambert* chronicled the history of the town. Many visitors to the Leicester Museum, particularly the schoolchildren, are fascinated by the permanent exhibition about Lambert's life and death. Not long ago, there was an advertisement in the *Leicester Mercury*, with a large portrait of Daniel Lambert and the text, 'Think big! Leicestershire the location for the successful business!'

6

THREE

Eighteenth-Century
LONDON GIANTS

O n 5 February 1734, a large crowd of spectators had gathered to see *Cupid and Psyche* at the Drury Lane Theatre in London. Earlier performances of the same play had been little heeded, by critics and audience alike, but there had been rumours that something extraordinary was afoot, and that this particular show would indeed be worth seeing. The play was enacted just as usual until the character of Gargantua was to appear: at that instance a trapdoor opened and a gigantic figure, 7 foot 8 inches tall, suddenly appeared on the stage 'to the no small Admiration of the Spectators'. This was the theatrical debut of that legendary figure, Daniel Cajanus, the Swedish Giant. He had come to London early in 1734 in order to earn money by exhibiting himself. The theatrical directors got the bright idea of recruiting the giant to their show, and Cajanus was not unwilling to make his debut as an actor. On 22 February, a handbill announced that 'this is the last time of Mynheer Cajanus, the Tall Man's Appearance on the Stage', but the giant appeared in several further performances in February and March, to a total of twenty plays on the London stage. In his

Epilogue spoken by Monimia, the poet Aaron Hill gave the gigantic
Swede a fitting poetic tribute:

> What thinking face will any praise ordain us,
> Whose climbing eyes have scal'd – Mynheer Cajanus!
> Give place, Great Alexander! – Go, retire –
> We have enroll'd a Hero – Three foot higher!

Daniel Cajanus was born in Paldamo, Finland, in 1704. His
father, the curate Anders Cajanus, was a stubborn, difficult character, continuously at loggerheads with his clerical superiors.
When he was finally defrocked in 1710, it was an aggravating
circumstance that he had been caught red-handed when affix-
ing certain pagan, magic amulets to his fishing-nets, in order
to improve the catch! On learning the shocking news, the
bishop rightly decided that such a curate would not be the
right person to teach Christianity to the rough farmers and
trappers in the Finnish outback. The last official act of Anders
Cajanus was to curse, from the pulpit, his cousin and superior,
Eric Cajanus, rector of Paldamo; he solemnly wished that every
devil in Hell would infest the rector's house and make his life
an utter misery. Daniel Cajanus had five brothers, two of whom
became clergymen, and two sisters. He received a reasonably
good education and attended both 'low and high school', as
he later put it. His youth coincided with the time of the Great
Nordic War, waged by King Charles XII of Sweden against
Poland, Russia and Denmark. Finland bore the full brunt of this
lengthy war, which lasted from 1700 until 1718. In the 1710s,
the Russians invaded Finland and plundered and ravaged the
countryside. Daniel thus grew up during a great famine in
Finland, but nevertheless he attained a great height during his
teens. According to novelist Zacharias Topelius, the thirteen-
year-old Daniel Cajanus actually fought in the war, and was
one of the heroic defenders of the fortress of Kajaneborg when
it was attacked by the Russians in 1717, but this is probably
poetic licence on his part. In 1723, the records tell that Daniel

Cajanus paid the taxes along with his father Anders and their family and servants. The erring curate had been reinstated in 1713 and allowed to lead the life of an itinerant preacher, who roamed the Finnish villages just outside the territory of his cousin the rector. The year 1723 was the last time the giant's name appeared in the lists of Finnish taxpayers, however, and it is likely that he decided to leave his native country in the mid-1720s.

There was a tradition in Sweden and Finland that Daniel Cajanus went to the court of King Frederick Wilhelm I of Prussia. He intended to enlist in this king's 'giant guard', a troop of particularly tall soldiers, and the king was more than willing to accept him. When he became aware that Daniel was a head taller than the other soldiers, he declined the giant's offer to join his guard, however, since this colossus would put all the other soldiers to shame. Before Daniel went away, the king ordered his portrait to be painted and hung in one of the galleries of Potsdam. According to tradition, Daniel Cajanus remained in Prussia for some time. One day, a celebrated strong man challenged him to a bizarre duel: they would in turn slap each other's faces until one of them was knocked out cold. Although he was a man of peace, Daniel accepted this challenge. The Prussian won the toss-up and delivered the first, resounding blow. Daniel nearly fell backwards, but did not pass out. Infuriated, he dealt the Prussian such a tremendous box on the ear that the man fell dead to the ground. Since this strange duel was, of course, illegal, Daniel had to flee Prussia, to seek his fortune elsewhere. The reliable later sources on the life and journeys of Daniel Cajanus do not mention any stay in Prussia, but it may be that he himself did not want his exploits there to attract any notice. In 1911, the Finnish antiquary J.R. Aspelin contacted a German colleague to try to find out whether there were any traces of the giant's Prussian career, but none could be found: although portraits of several giant guardsmen were still kept, Cajanus was not among them.

It is certain, however, that Daniel Cajanus spent a considerable period of time at the court of King August II of Poland. This king was a colourful, eccentric character, known as August the Strong, and famous for the great number of his concubines and illegitimate children. During his stay in Poland, Daniel Cajanus was employed as a cornet in the Polish cavalry. He obtained a Polish military uniform and often wore it during his later travels. But King August died in 1733, and his successor did not see the point of having a resident giant lounging about his court. Daniel may have gone on to Germany, since the actor and playwright Theophilus Cibber speaks of him as 'a Fellow of an enormous Height' who came to London from Germany 'to be shewn for a sight'. The Earl of Egmont, who saw Cajanus at Drury Lane on 22 February 1734, described him in his diary as 'the tallest man of all I have ever seen. He is seven feet ten inches and half in height, a German by birth.' Daniel Cajanus may also have been staying in Holland, since he was frequently referred to as 'Mynheer Cajanus' in the London newspapers. The details about his height varied considerably: some advertisements said that he was 7 foot 8 inches tall (this was probably his true height), some that he was 8 foot tall and surpassed the German Maximilian Miller who had exhibited himself in London some years earlier. When Cajanus was in an expansive mood, he even claimed to be 8 foot 8 inches tall; this figure has been quoted in some ill-researched modern books, but has no foundation in fact.

During his visit to Britain in 1734, Daniel Cajanus was later employed as a porter by John, Duke of Montagu, who inhabited Boughton House in Kettering. During this time, two life-sized portraits of the Swedish Giant were painted by the artist Enoch Seeman. These portraits were at Dalkeith Castle, Scotland, in the 1760s, and later belonged to the Dukes of Buccleugh. In 1911, one of them was owned by Admiral Lord Charles Scott. In 1975, it was sold to the National Museum of Helsinki, where this huge portrait of the Swedish Giant has found a fitting home. This portrait depicts the thirty-year-old Daniel Cajanus as a pleasant-looking young man, dressed in his usual Polish uniform, with his cavalry sword at his side, and wearing a turban and a great fur coat. Unlike most other portraits of giants and dwarfs, there is no normal-sized person in it as a contrast, and the only indication that Cajanus is actually a giant is the inscription on a stone tablet in the picture: 'Caianvs, born in Lapland who was in London 1734 his hight is 7 foot and 10 inc. Ae 28. E Seeman pinx. 1734.' The second Seeman portrait, which is very similar to that in Helsinki, was sold at Christie's in 1977 and is still in private ownership.

In 1735, Daniel Cajanus visited Paris, where he astounded everyone when he walked along one of the main avenues, his head towering over those of all the passers-by. For fifteen days he stayed at the Hôtel de la Porte Royale, and exhib-ited himself before large audiences from nine to twelve o'clock in the morning, and from one to seven o'clock in the afternoon. He was even honoured by King Louis XV, the queen and the Dauphin, who met him in a private audience at the court in Versailles. Daniel Cajanus later settled in Amsterdam, where he took up residence at the Blauw Jan, a large inn situ-ated in the Kloveniersburgwal. This remarkable establishment was the meeting place for dealers in exotic animals and natural curiosities from all over Europe. The owner of the Blauw Jan, Evert Metz, encouraged Daniel Cajanus, among other human curiosities – dwarfs, Eskimos, pygmies and conjoined twins – to reside permanently at his inn for exhibition purposes. Daniel stayed at the Blauw Jan from 1735 until 1741. One suspects that he rather enjoyed life at this busy inn, where he could come and go as it pleased him, and eat and drink at the expense of the house. Amsterdam was a pleasant city then as well as today, and Daniel Cajanus gradually began to consider himself a Dutchman. He liked to play chess or draughts in the main hall of the inn, sitting before the great blazing fire. Friend and foe alike acknowledged him as a skilful player. Once, after he had been defeated at draughts by a visiting gentleman, Cajanus slapped his opponent's shoulder so hard that the man screamed out in agony. This story was repeated as evidence that the giant did not know his own strength; one wonders, however, if he was not just a bad loser! Daniel Cajanus was a remarkable sight as he sat on a chair that seemed designed to suit a small child, playing chess before an admiring crowd of spectators. His arms were so long that they almost touched the floor when he was sitting down. He could easily pick up a draughts piece that had fallen off the board without bending forward, as depicted in the drawing by a Dutch artist, engraved in the *Almanak tot Nut van't Algemeen* of 1802. The Dutch doctor Wilhelmus Greve wrote that Daniel Cajanus was a polite, entertaining and well-spoken man, who was very popular among the Blauw Jan habitués. He was a masterly player at draughts. He was good-looking and his body well proportioned, except for his prodigiously long arms. He was well thought of among the Amsterdam burghers and often asked to parties and dinners. When travelling to these festivities, he used a special carriage, from which the front bench had been removed to give him adequate legroom.

Daniel Cajanus had come to Amsterdam a wealthy man, having saved money from his successful tours of England and France. He decided to invest this money by setting himself up as a moneylender. It is recorded that a certain Willem Pelgrom borrowed 3,000 guilders from Cajanus, with an annual interest of 7%. This gentleman made his annual repayments in good order, but the brothers Metz, unscrupulous Haarlem innkeepers, soon refused to pay their half-yearly interest. This was apparently not due to lack of money, but some clauses in the 'fine print' of the lending contract. After a lengthy legal wrangle, Cajanus managed to recover the bulk of his money from these scoundrels, but none of the interest. A certain Anthony van Eck, an Amsterdam merchant who had borrowed 9,000 guilders from Cajanus, went bankrupt shortly after, and the giant could only recover 5,000 guilders from the executors. After these disastrous experiences as a usurer, Daniel Cajanus decided to return to London and once more put himself on show. He was now thirty-eight years old and wanted to provide for his old age. In October 1741, he made a contract with his Dutch friend Roelof Sweris, who arranged to provide him with a showroom in London and to see to it that the Swedish Giant was well advertised. Cajanus was to receive three-fifths of the profits, and Sweris, who had to pay all expenses, the remaining two-fifths. Daniel Cajanus was advertised in the papers in a similar way as in 1734:

> This is to acquaint gentlemen and ladies, that that prodigy of nature, the Living Colossus, or Wonderful Giant of Sweden, is now to be seen, at the Lottery Office, next door to the Green Man, Charing Cross. It is humbly presumed that of all the natural curiosities which have been exhibited to the publick, nothing has appeared for many years so extraordinary in its way as this surprising gentleman. He is near a foot taller than the late famous Saxon, or any person ever yet seen in Europe, large in proportion; and all who have hitherto seen him declare, notwithstanding the prodigious accounts they have heard, that he far exceeds any idea they had fram'd of him.

Daniel Cajanus later rented himself to an English showman for six months for £200, and was taken on a tour to Oxford and then back to London, where he lodged in an apartment facing the Mansion House. A later advertisement in the *Daily Advertiser* tells that Cajanus had been indisposed for five weeks by a violent fever, which had even caused a rumour that he had actually died. Daniel Cajanus had recovered from this disease, however, and was again on show at the sign of the Mansion House and French Horn, between the Poultry and the Royal Exchange, at the usual price of sixpence per person, from nine o'clock in the morning until eight o'clock at night. The advertisement concluded by asserting that it was really the same giant that was on show, since some malicious individuals had evidently started a rumour that Cajanus had died and that his manager had procured a replacement giant to 'let the show go on'!

At the meeting of the Royal Society of London on 21 January 1742, Daniel Cajanus was introduced as an instance of 'gigantic Size of human Body'. Cajanus stood against one of the

pillars at Crane Court and had his height marked on it: he was
7 foot 4¼ inches tall, but the heels of his shoes were about an
inch high. Daniel Cajanus could reach within the architrave
between two pillars, 10 foot above the ground, with the greatest ease. He told the Fellows present that his father was 6½
foot tall and his mother 6 foot 3 inches; his usual daily meal
was about 4½ pounds of meat. Cajanus also told the blatant lie
that he was actually *the brother* of the giant with the same name
who had visited London a few years earlier. This was apparently
something he had planned beforehand, to keep his novelty and
attract also those lovers of curiosities who had already visited
him back in 1734. But several Fellows of the Royal Society had
seen him before, and they objected that the giant's features were
certainly very like those of his presumed brother. The Revd Dr
Pearse, who had also seen Cajanus in 1734, disagreed. He had
observed that although, in 1734, he had been unable to reach
higher than the 'brother's' forehead, he could reach about an
inch higher than the forehead of this man. The President of the
Royal Society of London, the antiquary Martin Folkes, ordered
that Cajanus was to be given a present of 2 guineas. A week
later, as Martin Folkes was reading the minutes concerning 'the
tall Finlander', he added that the painter William Hogarth and
others had informed him that this giant was undoubtedly the
same man who had appeared in London some years earlier, and
not his brother. Folkes told the Earl of Egmont, who had seen
Cajanus in 1734, that the giant had now seemed feeble and
unwilling to stand up for a long time. Another nobleman, the
Earl of Pembroke, had taken the giant's measurements by the
method used to measure men in the army, and found that he
was 7 foot, 4⅞ inches; no mention is made whether Cajanus was
wearing shoes and how tall his heels were.

Later during the Swedish Giant's stay in London, the bookseller Thomas Boreman published his biography, *The History
of Cajanus, the Swedish Giant, from his Birth to the present Time*.
According to Boreman, Daniel had once aspired to marry a
young lady in his native village in Finland, but her parents did

not want a giant for their son-in-law. After this rebuff, he decided
to set out on his voyages. At the time Thomas Boreman knew
him, Daniel's contract with the English showman had run out,
but he stayed on in London to have a look at the town. Boreman
helped to guide him among the sights of the metropolis; in particular, he recommended that the Swedish Giant see the statues
of the legendary giants Gog and Magog in the Guildhall, near
his own bookstall. So, one day, he turned up at the Guildhall
to see these huge statues, twice his own height. According to
Boreman,

> The people began to gather around the strange Giant from all
> parts of the Hall; but he, not caring to be stared at too much,
> strides gently up to the Bookseller's, next to the Giants, looked
> at his books, then turns himself round, and without saying one
> word, takes two or three colossus strides across the Hall, into the
> coach, and away he goes.

Boreman's biography of Cajanus was one of a set of miniature
children's books, and it is today very rare indeed.

In 1745, Daniel Cajanus settled permanently in Haarlem, where
he bought himself a small house in the so-called Proveniershuis.
This was a combined hotel, hospital and old people's home,
where invalids and old soldiers could purchase a small house or
apartment, along with free meals and access to medical attention. To be allowed to stay there for life, Daniel Cajanus paid the
considerable sum of 2,800 guilders. He became a popular public
character in his new home town, and made it his habit to walk
through the streets every day, dressed in his blue Polish uniform,
a periwig and a large, gold-braided hat. After all the years of
being on show, he apparently liked to walk in public, letting
every person see him for free. The Dutch writer Jan Marchant,
who saw Daniel Cajanus in Haarlem, tells us that the giant's head
and shoulders were above the heads of the people thronging
near him, and that he almost resembled an ordinary-sized man
riding on horseback. He could easily light his pipe from one

of the street lanterns. Marchant also mentioned that the giant walked with difficulty. This corroborates the evidence from the Royal Society of London that all was not well with Cajanus' health. Indeed, in June 1746 he drew up a will at the notary's office in Haarlem. He was apparently well aware that his health was failing, and thought it prudent to arrange his affairs. He was particularly worried that his corpse might be indelicately treated after death, and insisted that he wanted to be buried in as secure a fashion as possible. Daniel Cajanus was a Lutheran, and in his will he bequeathed 1,000 guilders to each child of Jacob de Wijs, vicar of the Evangelical Church of Haarlem, and also a legacy to the Lutheran Poorhouse. Whatever remained of the giant's fortune was to be equally divided between his own brothers and sisters; his wretched father, who had once more been defrocked, had died in the 1730s. Three weeks later, however, the giant came stomping back to the notary's office and changed his will completely. He had apparently quarrelled with his Lutheran brethren, and the poorhouse and the children of Jacob de Wijs were left nothing at all. Instead, Daniel Cajanus left his old friend Roelof Sweris, who had accompanied him to London in 1741, a legacy of 1,000 guilders, on condition that he remained living in the Proveniershuis (to act as Cajanus' servant?) and that he repaid all his debts to Cajanus before the giant's demise. Various other friends were given smaller legacies, and Daniel Cajanus again insisted on having a particularly grand funeral in the Groot Sint Bavo Kerk, with a long parade and an ornate carriage to transport his coffin.

Not the least remarkable fact about Daniel Cajanus' later life in Haarlem is that he actually became a published poet. In 1747, he wrote a long valedictory poem to the Prince of Orange, likening himself to the legendary Dutch giant Klaas van Kieten, who had fought for the Counts of Holland, just as Cajanus himself was honouring one of their descendants in verse. Another poem, in the same style, was published the year after. Both Daniel Cajanus' poems contain overblown tirades in the manner of the valedictory ode of the time, but their rhymes are impeccable, and it would take no little talent for any person to compose such poems in a language not his own. Jan Marchant wrote that Cajanus, although a quiet, laconic man by nature, was much more clever than one might suppose. An inventory of Cajanus' effects made in 1749 shows that he was quite well off. His house was no larger than the others in the Proveniershuis square, and its fitted 'cupboard-bed' was so small that the giant could not use it. Instead, he moved his huge bed into one of the rooms upstairs. His furniture was of excellent quality: he had a large, gilt-edged mirror, some giant-sized leather easy chairs, two tables and an elegant cupboard. His wardrobe contained several costly garments, including his blue and red Polish uniform and a red silk coat from Tours. On 27 February 1749, the forty-six-year-old Daniel Cajanus died in the Haarlem Proveniershuis. He must have been ill for some time, since two physicians, two surgeons and an apothecary sent in their bills. His funeral was particularly grand, just as he had wanted. It was compared with that of a statesman or a wealthy noble, except for the obvious fact that the coffin was nearly twice the size of a normal human being. Two horses with black horse-cloths pulled a large ornate hearse; on one side of the coffin was Daniel Cajanus' huge, silver-hilted sword, on the other his enormous gloves. The funeral ceremony was one of the most magnificent ever witnessed in Haarlem. The hearse and the coffin, with its sixty-five pairs of pall bearers, were seen by several thousand spectators.

The Swede C.G. Gjörwell wrote that Daniel Cajanus had died very rich, and that he left legacies of 20,000 Dutch guilders to a Lutheran orphanage and other charities. But when the Dutch antiquary Dr B.C. Sliggers managed to trace Cajanus' will and the inventory made after his death, this statement turned out to be complete fantasy. Daniel Cajanus had many valuable belongings, and quite a treasure of English gold guineas; his estate was valued at 8,000 guilders. But he also had quite a few debts, and when the cost for his lavish funeral had been deducted, it turned out that the giant only just scraped into the black: just 2,000 guilders were finally distributed between his brothers and sisters. A certain Pieter Langendijk wrote that although Daniel Cajanus had earned considerable sums on his tours, he was a bad businessman, and incapable of seeing through the lying scoundrels who applied for loans which they had no intention of repaying. Langendijk suspected that Cajanus had actually feared poverty in his old age when he bought himself into the Proveniershuis. Daniel Cajanus had paid 53 guilders for the privilege of having his grave in a vault inside the Sint Bavo church itself; this was twice the cost for an ordinary tomb. As we know from his will, the main reason for this was that he wanted his body to rest undisturbed. He was probably well aware of the risk that his corpse might be stolen by grave-robbers, and later preserved in a museum of natural curiosities. But in spite of all the Swedish Giant's precautions, his grave did not long remain undisturbed. In the late eighteenth century, it is recorded that Cajanus' vault 'came into the possession of the Hodshon family'. The exact circumstances of this transaction were not explained further. A charitable interpretation is that the giant had as usual been careless in his business transactions, and that he had failed to secure the vault forever, but only for a certain number of years. A more sinister version is that the authorities knew that Cajanus had no descendants in Haarlem that could plead his cause, and that they resold the giant's vault and took away his skeleton. This latter version is supported by the fact that in the early nineteenth century, parts of Cajanus' skeleton turned up at various Leiden museums. Today, the Swedish Giant's pelvis, thighbones, legs and feet are at the Museum of Anatomy and Embryology in Leiden University, along with one of his huge shoes. Three more shoes, and Daniel Cajanus' linen shirt, are at the Teylers Museum in Haarlem.

Giants had been exhibited in London for many years before Daniel Cajanus came to the metropolis. Already in 1620, a certain John Middleton, reputed to be 9 foot 3 inches tall and known as the Childe of Hale, was brought to London by the Sheriff of Lancashire and introduced to King James I.

Clockwise from above:

1 Lazarus Colloredo as a boy; from the 1665 edition of Fortunio Liceti's *De Monstris*.

2 The German handbill about Lazarus Colloredo and his brother, dated Strasbourg, August 1645.

3 The print depicting the Colloredo brothers in 1634, as they set out on their travels.

4 Thomas Bartholin's engraving of the brothers, as reissued as a plate in the *Gentleman's Magazine* of 1777.

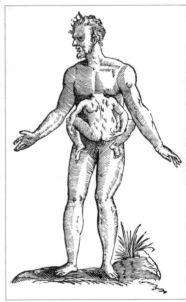

Clockwise from left:

5 A man with a parasitic twin, from Ulysses Aldrovandi's *Monstrorum Historia.*

6 A German print of a dancer with a parasitic twin.

7 The very strange boy seen by James Paris du Plessis in London in 1716.

Barbara Vrslerin ward geboren ihm Iar, 5 6 3 2. den 18. Febru
ary in Augspurg Ihres Alters im 20. Iar. Ist gantz vnd gar
harecht mit schönem gelben haar im angesicht 2 grosse locken
auß beyden ohren gehn. Ihr vatter heyst Balthaser Vrsler
ihr Mutter Anna Vrslerin.

Isaac Brunn delin. et sculpsit se

Clockwise from above:

8 A drawing of Barbara
Urslerin at the harpsichord,
by Isaac Brünn.

9 Another German drawing
of Barbara Urslerin, made in
1653.

10 A portrait of Barbara
Urslerin, engraved by
Gaywood when she was
in London in 1656. This is
probably the best likeness
of her. Note the organ, or
rather harmonium, in the
background.

*Vera Effigies Barbara, vxor Iohannis Michaelis Van Beck, nata Augusta
Vindelicoru in Germania Superiori (vulgo Auspourge) ex parentibus
Balthazaro et Anna Vrsler. Anno Christi. 1629. februar 18:*

A. Gaywood fecit Londini 1656

11 Lavinia Fontana's painting of Tognina Gonzales.

12 An engraving of a group portrait of the Gonzales family, from an article by Dr Bartels in the *Zeitschrift für Ethnologie* of 1879.

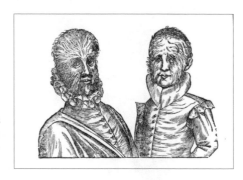

Right and below:

13 Ulysses Aldrovandi's drawings of the Gonzales family, from the 1642 edition of his *Monstrorum Historia*.

14 The later Italian engravings of Horatio and Tognina Gonzales, from an article by Dr Bartels in the *Zeitschrift für Ethnologie* of 1879.

Above: 15 Shwe-Maong, the king's favourite, and his daughter Maphoon, from John Crawfurd's *Journal of an Embassy from the Governor-General of India to the Court of Ava*, Vol. 1.

Left: 16 Maphoon at thirty-one years of age, with her fourteen-month-old younger son on her lap.

Right: 17 Maphoon,
Moung-Phoset and Mah–
Mé in 1872.

Below: 18, 19 Close-
ups of Maphoon and
Moung-Phoset from the
Goss photographs.

Above: 20 A drawing of Julia Pastrana by the German artist Herbert König.

Below left: 21 A Russian drawing of Julia Pastrana.

Below right: 22 A caricature drawing of Julia Pastrana, made in 1859 by the Warsaw artist Kostrzewski.

Clockwise from left:

23 A photograph of Julia Pastrana, taken when she was exhibited in London in 1857.

24 A Russian caricature of Julia Pastrana exhibited together with a very fat man. The individual on the extreme left is probably Mr Lent.

25 Julia Pastrana's mummy photographed during the early 1860s.

26 A very good drawing of Julia Pastrana during life, from a German circus poster dated 1857.

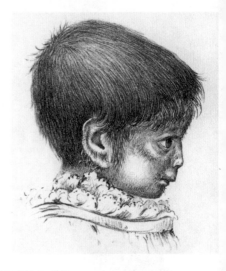

Clockwise from above left:

27 A German advertisement, probably from the 1890s, to see the mummy of 'the most interesting woman in the world', as Julia Pastrana was called.

28 A drawing of Julia Pastrana's mummified son.

29 'Zenora Pastrana', Mr Lent's second bearded wife. She suffered from secondary hirsutism, quite a different condition from that of poor Julia.

Above: 30 A drawing of Adrian and Fedor, from an article in the *Lancet* of 1873.

Below left: 31 Jo-Jo as an adult, a photograph taken in the late 1880s.

Below centre: 32 Fedor, alias Jo-Jo, as a boy.

Below right: 33 One of Krao's exhibition posters.

Above left: 34 An early photograph of Krao with her manager Mr Farini.

Above right: 35 Lionel, the Lion-Faced Boy, from an old photograph.

Below: 36 Lionel, the favourite of women and children. A poster from 1909.

A certaine Relation of the Hog-
faced Gentlewoman called Miftris *Tannakin
Skinker*, who was borne at *Wirkham*
a Neuter Towne betweene the Emperour and the
Hollander, fcituate on the river *Rhyne*.
Who was bewitched in her mothers wombe in the yeare 1618.
and hath lived ever fince unknowne in this kind to any,
but her Parents and a few other neighbours. And
can never recover her true fhape, tell fhe
be married, &c.

*Alfo relating the caufe, as it is fince conceived, how her mother
came fo bewitched.*

London Printed by *J.O.* and are to be fold by *F. Grove,* at his fhop
on *Snow-hil* neare *St. Sepulchers Church.* 1640.

Clockwise from right:

37 The title page to the
original London pamphlet
about Tannakin Skinker,
published in 1640.

38 A fierce-looking pig-faced
lady, from a German print
issued in 1717.

39 A vignette of 'The Long-
nos'd Lass' from a seventeenth-
century ballad.

40 The Pig-faced Lady of Manchester Square plays the piano in this amusing caricature, facing that of the 'Spanish Mule of Madrid'. Note that the sheet music is 'A Swinish Interlude, set to music by Grunt Esq.' and that the portrait on the wall depicts Lord Bacon with a pig's face.

41 A hand-coloured example of George Morland's drawing of the 'Wonderful Mrs Atkinson, born and married in Ireland, fed out of a silver trough, and called to her meals by "Pig-Pig-Pig!"'

THE WONDERFUL Mrs ATKINSON,

Born and Married to a Gentleman in Ireland of that Name, having 20,000 fortune. She is fed out of a Silver Hog Trough and is called to her Meals by Pig-Pig-Pig.

This Wonderful account was told me by George Simpson, who will swear to the truth of it, having heard it on board the Tonorion Gun Boat, from some Irish Sailors who he says cannot tell lies. The above G. Simpson is my Servant, and can tell several curious stories as good as this, all of which he will swear to the truth of.

GEORGE MORLAND.

This Account is verbatim from the hand writing of the late George Morland on the back of the

Clockwise from right:

42 A hand-coloured engraving of a Hog-Faced Gentlewoman, by Fairburn Senior.

43 An 1815 engraving of The Pig-faced Lady of Manchester Square.

44 *Waltzing in Courtship*, another caricature from 1815, depicting the fabulous creature from Manchester Square, this time dancing with a very short admirer, alleged to be Lord Kirkcudbright in some publications, since this nobleman had apparently made inquiries regarding the whereabouts of the wealthy phenomenon.

-FACED LADY, or Manchester-Square.

Clockwise from left:

45 The original handbill about François Trouvillou.

46 Another contemporary drawing of François Trouvillou, from Ulysses Aldrovandi's *Monstrorum Historia* of 1642.

47 Thomas Bartholin's engraving of the horned Dutchwoman Margaretha Mainers, from the 1654 edition of his *Historiarum Anatomicarum Rariorum*, Centuria I-II.

Above left: 48 Mary Davies, the Horned Woman, aged seventy-four. A print issued in 1792, allegedly based on an original painting of her in the British Museum.

Above right: 49 Ann Davis, a woman with smallpox and a pair of horns growing out of her head. A print by Thomas A. Woolnoth, issued in London in 1806.

50 A French drawing of the Widow Dimanche.

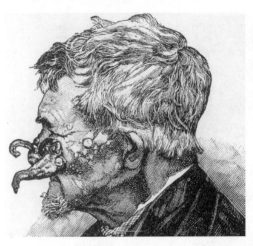

Clockwise from above left:

51 An old sea captain with numerous cutaneous horns growing from the face, from the *Photographic Review of Medicine and Surgery*, 1878.

52 The horn of Elizabeth Lowe.

53 A French wax bust of a horned woman, alleged to be the Widow Dimanche.

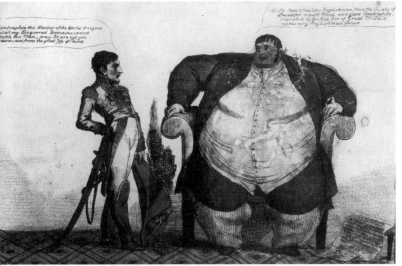

Clockwise from top left: 54 A drawing of Daniel Lambert, engraved in Kirby's *Wonderful Museum* of 1804.

55 An engraving of Daniel Lambert.

56 'Bone and Flesh', a caricature published in 1806.

Top: 57 Daniel Lambert and Napoleon take luncheon in the caricature 'The English Lamb and the French Tiger'.

Above left: 58 Daniel Lambert attacks Napoleon Bonaparte in the caricature 'The Two Wonders of the World'.

Above right: 59 A stone statuette of Daniel Lambert.

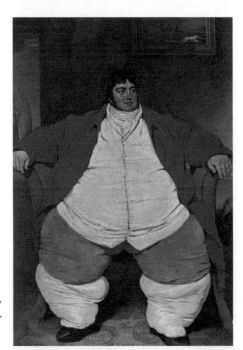

60 A portrait of Daniel Lambert, by his friend Benjamin Marshall, painted in 1806 during his first season in London.

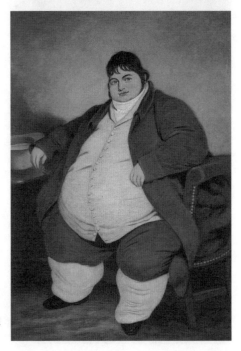

61 Another portrait of Daniel Lambert, owned by the Stamford Town Council.

Clockwise from left

62 Enoch Seeman's portrait of Daniel Cajanus.

63 A Dutch engraving made in 1749 to commemorate Cajanus.

64 Daniel Cajanus plays draughts at the Blauw Jan; a contemporary drawing later published in the *Almanak tot Nut van't Algemeen* of 1802.

65 A watercolour by T.H.
Sheperd of part of the
Hunterian Museum, *c.* 1860.

Right: 66 Henry Blacker, the English
giant, an engraving from Caulfield's
Remarkable Persons.

Below: 67 One of Daniel Cajanus'
enormous shoes, together with one of
ordinary dimensions.

Mᵣ HENRY BLACKER,
(The Irish Giant.)

Top left: 68 An engraving of Bernard Giglio, Henry Blacker's competitor, at the age of nineteen, by Fougeron after Millington.

Top right: 69 The Irish Giant being exhibited.

Above: 70 An etching by John Kay of Charles Byrne and the two gigantic Knipe brothers.

71 John Hunter's portrait by Sir Joshua Reynolds.

72 A drawing of the Irish Giant by Thomas Rowlandson.

73 John Hunter receiving a giant and two dwarfs: an illustration from Jesse Foot's *Life of Hunter*.

Clockwise from top left:

74 A print of Nicolas Ferry standing in the remnants of the pastry he had been 'served' in, before the admiring eyes of King Stanislas.

75 Thérèse Vouvray, the alleged Madame Bébé.

76 A portrait of Nicolas Ferry together with a large dog, by an unknown artist. From an early nineteenth-century engraving in the author's collection.

77 A contemporary engraving of Nicolas Ferry.

78 The statue of Nicolas Ferry
at Drottningholm Castle.

79 The wax statue of Bébé at the Musée
Historique Lorrain, Nancy.

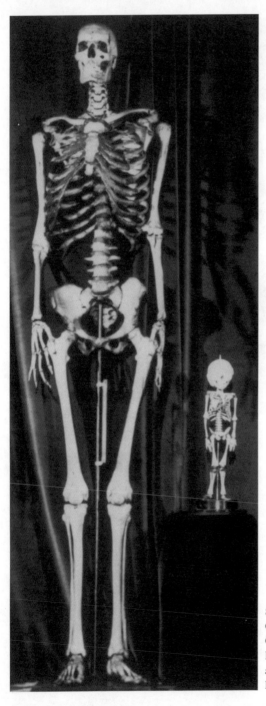

80 The skeletons of
Caroline Crachami and
Charles Byrne, the Sicilian
Fairy and the Irish Giant,
as they can be seen at the
Hunterian Museum.

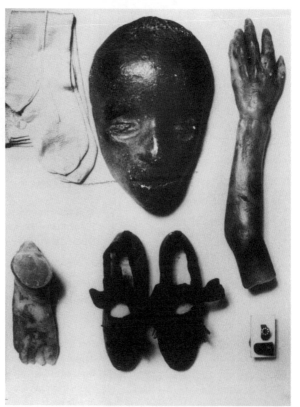

Clockwise from right:

81 The Sicilian Fairy's ring, thimble, shoes and stockings, together with casts of her face, arm and left foot and ankle.

82 The portrait of Caroline Crachami by Alfred Edward Chalon.

83 An engraving of Sir Everard Home, from his *Lectures on Comparative Anatomy* of 1814.

Clockwise from above left:

84 A drawing of two eighteenth-century Biddenden Cakes, reproduced from Dr Ducarel's *Repertory of the Endowments* of 1782.

85 Two eighteenth-century Biddenden Cakes, reproduced from the *Antiquarian Repertory* of 1775.

86 Plaster casts of the three wooden stamps for Biddenden Cakes that were available to George Clinch in 1900, from his article in the *Reliquary* magazine.

87 A broadsheet on the Biddenden Maids and their bequest, published in 1808.

88 A contemporary drawing of the Hungarian Sisters.

89 An advertisement for Millie–Christine being exhibited in London.

Above left: 90 The 'Monster Broadside' describing the Isle Brewers conjoined twins.

Above right: 91 The fine plate depicting the Isle Brewers conjoined twins and their alleged kidnappers Henry Walrond and Sir Edward Phelips.

Below: 92 The original Siamese twins, from an old engraving.

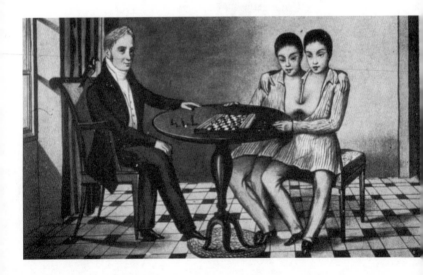

Clockwise from above:

93 Postcard of Josefa and Rosa, and baby.

94 A print of the Blazek sisters performing.

95 The stone portraiture of the 'Fair Maidens of Foscott', from a photograph by Mr Tony Day, churchwarden of Norton St Philip.

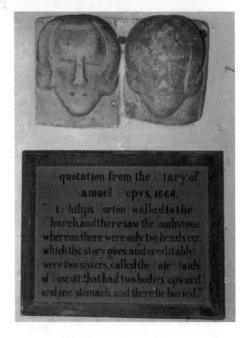

quotation from the ... iary of ... amuel ...epys. 1668. ... t ...hilips ...orton walked to the ...hurch and there saw the ...ombstone whereon there were only two heads cut; which the story goes and creditably were two sisters, called the ...air ...aids of ...oscott, that had two bodies upward, and one stomach, and there lie buried."

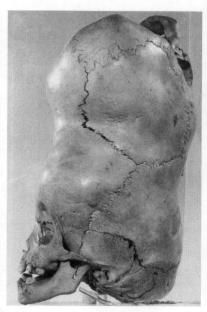

Clockwise from above:

96 The German dicephali born in 1512, from a later re-engraving of the handbill.

97 The double skull of the Two-headed Boy of Bengal, as it can be seen at the Hunterian Museum.

98 The two-headed Turkish Archer, from a print published in 1697.

99 Mr Smith's drawings of the Two-Headed Boy of Bengal, from Everhard Home's article in the *Philosophical Transactions* of 1790.

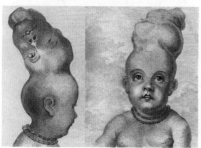

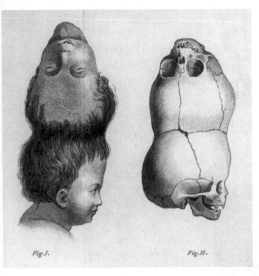

Fig.I.   Fig.II.

Left and below:

100 Mr Dent's drawings of the
Two-headed Boy of Bengal,
from Everard Home's article
in the *Philosophical Transactions*
of 1799.

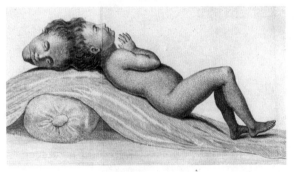

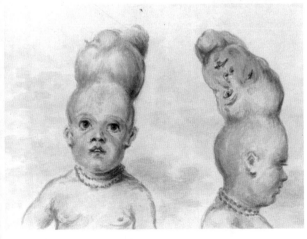

101 A fine coloured
drawing of the
Two-Headed Boy
of Bengal.

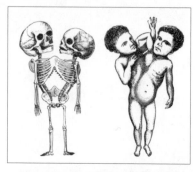

102 Ritta-Christina and her skeleton

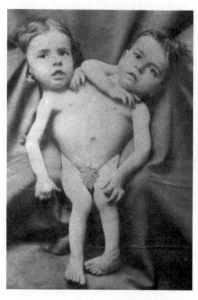

103 A photograph of the Tocci brothers in 1881.

104 The Tocci brothers in 1879, from the article by Dr Grünwald in the *Virchows Archiv*.

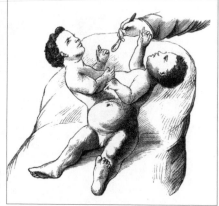

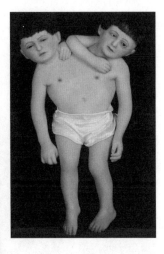

Clockwise from left:

105 A photograph of the twins in Berlin in 1891.

106 A photograph of a wax statue of the Tocci brothers.

107 An 1893 New York cabinet card of the Tocci brothers, signed on the back by both twins.

TOCCI BROTHERS.
GIOVANNI .... GIACOMO.
OBERMILLER & KERN, opp. 5. Str. near 4. Ave. N.

The Surprising
STONE EATER,
With appetite of Farmer he'll feast
On the hardest Stones brought from the East

Clockwise from above left:

108 The Bohemian cat-eating countryman, from a contemporary handbill.

109 Nicholas Wood eating a duck, an illustration from John Taylor's original pamphlet.

110 A portrait of Francis Battalia, from an eighteenth-century engraving.

111 A caricature of George III as the Stone Eater, occasioned by a scandal after the king had received a handsome present (or bribe) of Indian jewels.

Above left: 112 One of Jacques de Falaise's advertisements.

Above right: 113 Jacques Falaise performs.

Below: 114 Louis Claude Delair, alias Mac Norton, from a German advertisement.

Clockwise from above:

115 Louis Claude Delair in action.

116, 117 A cat eater and a stone eater, from the
English caricature 'Fashionable Follies', published in
London in 1788.

118 The freak show line-up of Barnum & Bailey's
Greatest Show on Earth.

Maximilian Miller, the Saxon Giant, had been in London just a few years before Cajanus. Born in Leipzig in 1674, he had toured most of Europe before showing up in London in 1728; he stayed in town until his death in 1734. According to the newspapers, he was 7 foot 8 inches tall just like Cajanus in his prime; this did not prevent the latter from claiming, in his usual manner, to be substantially taller than 'the late famous Saxon'. He may actually have been right, since the aforementioned James Paris du Plessis claimed that Miller was closer to 7 foot 6 inches tall.

After the lucrative career of Daniel Cajanus had shown the amount of money available to a successful human curiosity in London, several other giants were alerted to the excellent prospects for a business-minded giant in the metropolis. Henry Blacker, the English Giant, was born in Cuckfield in Sussex in 1724, and started his career in London show business in 1751. He was admired by William, Duke of Cumberland, who was himself very tall; a popular print showed him together with the giant. Blacker was 7 foot 4 inches tall and thus shorter than both Cajanus and Miller. When he left London in 1752, he was succeeded by Cornelius Macgrath, the Irish Giant, who was nearly 7 foot 10 inches tall. Born in Tipperary in 1736, he was a protégé of the Bishop of Cloyne. It is curious that the newspaper accounts relate that in spite of his great height, Macgrath was not very strong: he was 'clumsily made', quite simple-minded, and crippled by arthritic pains. His hand was the size of a shoulder of mutton. He stayed in London until 1753, when he set out to tour France and most of Europe. He finally went back to Ireland in 1760 and died there; his skeleton can today be seen at Trinity College in Dublin.

In 1755, six years after the death of Daniel Cajanus, another foreign giant appeared in London. The nineteen-year-old Bernard Giglio was born in Riva in the Italian part of the Tirol; he had toured several royal and principal courts before coming to London. Not less than 8 foot tall, he eclipsed all other eighteenth-century giants in London. A handbill announced that, 'An Italian giant is arrived in this city; he is eight feet high, and

every way well-made and proportionable, and nineteen years
of age; his equal has never been seen, nor any come higher
than his armpit. He has had the honour to be seen at several
foreign courts with great applause.' The exhibition was held at
the bottom of the Haymarket, next to the Prince of Orange
coffee house. An illustrated engraving of Bernard Giglio was for
sale at the exhibition; the only surviving example is kept in the
Wellcome picture library. The rather fanciful illustration shows
the huge Bernard Giglio towering over a man dressed as a clown;
his large nose and enormous hands and feet are very much
in evidence. The text is in both English and Italian, and adds
the information that both the giant's parents were of normal
size. Another portrait of the nineteen-year-old Bernard Giglio
was painted by the artist Millington and engraved by Fougeron.
Again, this both elegant and striking image certainly exaggerates
the giant's height in proportion to the other individuals in the
engraving.

In early 1756, Bernard Giglio was again in London, possibly
after having toured the provinces. He lived in a large apartment at the bottom of Pall Mall, near the Haymarket, where
he was exhibited from ten o'clock in the morning until eight
o'clock in the evening. In May the same year, he was exhibited
at the Ship public house in the Poultry; in July, he again toured
Bristol and other provincial cities. In September, the London
newspapers announced that, 'The Italian giant, who has been
beheld with astonishment, as well in England as in most parts of
Europe, will be exhibited during the time of the Southwark fair,
at 6d each person; after which he will immediately set out for
Ireland.' During his prolonged stay in London, there was never
any opposition to Giglio's claim of being 8 foot tall.

Less is known about the Italian Giant's career after he left
London in 1756. In 1763, he was in Vienna, and it is likely
he kept touring Europe throughout the 1760s. In October
1765, he visited Stockholm on his way from St Petersburg to
Copenhagen. He lodged at a Stockholm tavern, where he saw
paying visitors each day. By this time, his reputation was such

that King Adolf Frederick and Queen Lovisa Ulrika of Sweden requested the giant to come to Drottningholm Castle for a private audience. He was solemnly measured by the courtiers, and it was again confirmed that he was 8 foot tall, and thus a good deal taller than Daniel Cajanus in his prime. The queen was particularly taken with the size of the giant's enormous hands, and she ordered that a plaster cast of one was to be made for her private museum. It is still kept in the Royal Museum, although the little finger has been broken off and lost. It remains the most tangible memento of the Italian Giant, about whom nothing more is known after he left Stockholm. Clearly, he either died or followed Cajanus' example and retired permanently from show business.

Probably the most spectacular exhibit in the famous Hunterian Museum, kept in the building of the Royal College of Surgeons at Lincoln's Inn Fields in London, is the skeleton of Charles Byrne, the Irish Giant, another eighteenth-century giant on show in London. This celebrated personage was born in 1761, in Littlebridge, a hamlet near the Derry-Tyrone border in Ireland. Although his mother was, rather unflatteringly, described as 'a stout woman with a strong voice', both his parents were of normal stature, nor was he himself a particularly large infant. The village gossips attributed his great increase in height – already in youth, he 'grew like a cornstalk' – to his conception on the top of a very high haystack. As a child, Charles Byrne was teased by his school-fellows, in spite of his great stature: he suffered from joint pains, his stamina was generally low, and he was constantly dribbling and spitting. When he was in his teens, he was discovered by the Irish showman Joe Vance, who exhibited him at local fairs and markets with considerable success. Later, during a tour to Scotland, the Irish Giant was quite a success in Edinburgh, where he astonished the nightwatchmen by lighting his pipe on one of the street lamps, just as Daniel Cajanus had done fifty years earlier.

In the Old Town, he had great difficulty in getting up and down the narrow stairs, and had to crawl on hands and feet.

In April 1782, Joe Vance took the Irish Giant to London, where he was installed in a disused cane shop next door to Cox's Museum at Spring Gardens. The newspapers spared no superlatives in describing 'the modern Living Colossus', and although it cost as much as half a crown to see 'Mr Byrne, the surprising Irish Giant, who is allowed to be the tallest man in the world', he did not lack interested spectators. In the newspaper advertisements, it was claimed that he was 8 foot 4 inches tall, thus far exceeding both the famous German Maximilian Miller and the Swedish Giant Daniel Cajanus: 'In short, the sight of him is more than the mind can conceive, the tongue express, or pencil delineate, and stands without parallel in this or any other country.' Charles Byrne's mounted skeleton is only 7 foot 7 inches, however, which makes it probable that he was really about 7 foot 10 inches in height, the intervertebral substance taken into account. Just like Daniel Cajanus and many other giants on show, Byrne was exaggerating his height.

Initially, Charles Byrne and his clever manager did quite well in London. A newspaper advertisement from August 1782 claimed that the wonderful Irish Giant, 8 foot 2 inches tall, had been seen by the nobility and gentry, the medical profession, the Royal Society and many other admirers of natural curiosities; all were unanimous that he surpassed any other giant exhibited in public. In reference to Charles Byrne, the summer pantomime at the Haymarket Theatre was entitled *Harlequin Teague, or the Giant's Causeway*. Several contemporary diarists and letter-writers have recorded their visits to the Irish Giant. One of the most perceptive was diarist Sylas Neville, who wrote that: 'Tall men walk considerably under his arm, but he stoops, is not well shaped, his flesh [is] loose, and his appearance far from wholesome. His voice sounds like thunder, and he is an ill-bred beast, though very young – only in his 22nd year.' In a letter dated 15 July 1782, Fanny Burney wrote about an Italian gentleman who had seen the Giant: 'Afterwards speaking of the Irish giant who is now shown in town, he said "He is so large, I am as a baby! I look at him – Oh! I find myself so little as a child! Indeed, my indignation it rises when I see him hold up his hand so high. I am as nothing, and I find myself in the power of a man who fetches from me half-a-crown!'" Late in 1782, the Giant moved to an elegant apartment at the house of Mr Mittenius, confectioner, Charing Cross, and from there to Piccadilly at the sign of the 'Hampshire Hog' where he was seen by ladies and gentlemen for 2 shillings and sixpence, and by children and servants in livery for just one shilling.

After the Giant had been exhibited in London for more than eight months, the fickle public began to crave new attractions. Furthermore, at the rumour of Byrne's financial success, several other giants tried their luck in the metropolis. Charles Byrne was especially annoyed that a gigantic fellow-countryman, Patrick Cotter alias O'Brien, also called himself the Irish Giant. Other competitors were the Gigantic Twin Brothers, who were named Knipe, and also natives of Ireland; they even claimed distant kinship with the Byrne family. In early 1783, Joe Vance lowered the entrance fee to one shilling for all classes of society and moved to a less expensive apartment in Cockspur Street, but to little avail. Charles Byrne wasn't particularly clever, and his health and judgement were further impaired by his habit, since an early age, of drinking large quantities of gin and whisky every day. It was a not infrequent occurrence that the shows were cancelled due to the Giant's drunkenness and lack of punctuality. For a while, he acted as porter at St James' Palace, but he soon tired of this post.

James Graham, a celebrated quack doctor of the time, tried to interest Byrne in quite another project. At his Temple of Health and Hymen in Pall Mall, Graham kept what he called a Celestial Bed, a huge state bed equipped with a variety of electrical apparatus. Graham claimed that no woman could fail to conceive in this marvellous bed, and that sexual ecstasy reached new heights for both sexes. It normally cost £50 per night to spend the night in the Celestial Bed, but to advertise its merits, Graham offered Byrne the use of it for free; it is not known whether the quack's offer included a suitable partner for the night. In any case, the Giant turned his offer down, preferring his usual sustenance from the bottle to such novel sexual thrills.

In mid-April 1783, Charles Byrne went on an extended nightly drinking spree, visiting a public house called the Black Horse, among others. The next morning, the sottish Giant was aghast at finding that his entire savings of £770 in banknotes, which he had been unwise enough to carry with him in his pocket, had been stolen by a pickpocket. Some authors have doubted the veracity of this story, some of them instead crediting a tall tale that the Giant, fearful of being robbed, had hidden his savings in a fireplace. The next morning, a servant lit a fire in that very grate and it consumed the Giant's banknotes! But there is evidence, from an article in the *Gentleman's Magazine* of July 1784, that the Giant's banknotes were really stolen from him. By this time, the larger banknote, for £700, had been traced to a certain Mr Atkinson, who claimed that he had given value for it. The Giant's executors were able to prove, however, that this had happened after notice had been given of the theft, and Atkinson had to pay them £500.

The hard blow of having his entire savings stolen lowered the Giant's spirits considerably, and he sought comfort in new bouts of inebriety. His habitual drunkenness had made him weak and sickly, and in May 1783 he appeared to be a dying man. Already when Charles Byrne was *in extremis*, many London surgeons, who had seen and admired him when he was on exhibition, competed to get hold of his corpse for dissection. A newspaper article stated that, 'the whole tribe of surgeons put in a claim for the poor departed Irish Giant, and surrounded his house just as Greenland harpooners would an enormous whale.' Most eager of them all was the celebrated John Hunter, whom we remember from his pioneering studies of London's horned women. Hunter was building up a large museum of specimens that exists to this day as a memorial to the scientific genius of this pioneering surgeon. Hunter employed a man named Howison to follow Byrne around, in order to be at hand if the invalid giant died.

Charles Byrne was aware of Hunter's schemes against him. Like Daniel Cajanus and most eighteenth-century people, he had a great fear of being dissected. Since Hunter and his colleagues were allied to the gangs of bodysnatchers who prowled the churchyards nightly in search of freshly buried corpses, no grave would be safe for him. The Irish Giant promised some fishermen his last remaining savings if they saw to it that he was buried at sea, where the medical men could not reach his corpse. This confidential deal was 'leaked' to the press, however, and there were several tasteless puns that the body hunters were 'determined to pursue their valuable prey even in the profoundest depth of the aquatic regions; and have therefore provided a pair of diving bells, with which they hope to weigh hulk gigantic from its watery grave.'

When Charles Byrne finally died, another punning journalist wrote that the London medical luminaries were holding more consultations than were ever convened to keep King Henry VIII in existence: the sole purpose of these deliberations was how to get their hands on the Giant's remains. There was talk of undertakers being bribed, and rumours that the Giant's huge coffin had been taken out of London under cover of darkness. One story tells that the fishermen took his body to the Downs, where it was to be sunk in twenty fathoms of water, but that Howison managed to catch up with them. He got the fishermen drunk and bribed them with £500 to be allowed to take charge of the coffin. According to another version, Byrne was properly buried at St Martin's churchyard, but the grave-robbers promptly dug him up and arranged an auction for his remains among the London surgeons. John Hunter was the highest bidder, spending £500 (some sources say £800) to acquire the body. It is certain that the Giant's body was delivered to Hunter's house at Earl's Court, where it was boiled in a great iron kettle and the skeleton prepared for his museum. One of the Giant's boots and one of his slippers and gloves are also there, as well as several drawings of him.

The skeleton of the Irish Giant was one of John Hunter's most prized possessions, and he pondered much on what might be the aetiology of Byrne's abnormal growth. This question was not resolved until 1909, when the famous American neurosurgeon Harvey Cushing, who was the first to propose that acromegaly and gigantism resulted from hypersecretion of the growth hormone from a pituitary adenoma, wrote to the curator of the Hunterian Museum, Sir Arthur Keith, inquiring whether the Irish Giant's cranium might be sawed open for examination. Keith found that the pituitary fossa was greatly enlarged due to the pressure of a pituitary tumour that had grown upward and forward. Nor is there any doubt that Daniel Cajanus and Bernard Giglio also suffered from pituitary gigantism. In this disease, there is a pituitary adenoma producing an excess of growth hormone; if this adenoma is present from an early age, the individual will grow to an enormous height. Such a pituitary tumour is benign and does not metastasise. Some pituitary adenomas may cause hypopituitarism through compression of the remaining functional pituitary tissue by the tumour, or through secondary hypothalamic involvement; whether this was the case in the three giants studied here is difficult to say. Although Boreman's story of the young Daniel Cajanus wooing a village maiden may have been true, the giant showed little interest in the opposite sex during his adult years, something that might well have been due to hypogonadism secondary to hypopituitarism during adolescence. The fact that Daniel Cajanus had what is known as eunuchoid bodily proportions, with prodigiously long arms, supports this notion. Some accounts agree that Charles Byrne also had eunochoid body proportions. It is also of interest that when he declined to use Graham's Celestial Bed, a newspaper claimed that this was on the grounds of being 'a perfect stranger to the rites and mysteries of the Goddess Venus'.

It is of some interest that several of Daniel Cajanus' relatives may also have suffered from pituitary abnormalities. The Swedish writer C.G. Gjörwell courteously stated that his surviving sister Agneta, who came to Haarlem to collect what remained of his estate, 'could by no means be considered as a short-statured woman'. In Tor Carpelan's dictionary of Finnish biography, this same lady is described as 'extremely tall'. Israel Cajanus, the grandson of Daniel's first cousin Gustaf, was well known in Finland for his enormous hands and feet. There is sometimes a hereditary tendency to develop pituitary adenomas of this kind, and although the clinical data are insufficient, it is tempting to suggest that Agneta Cajanus also had pituitary gigantism, and that Israel Cajanus had acromegaly, the condition resulting from a growth hormone-producing pituitary adenoma developing in adult life, when the epiphyseal junctions are closed. Thus the individual can no longer increase in height, but the overproduction of growth hormone leads to soft tissue growth, resulting in enormous hands and feet and a coarsening of the facial features.

Another puzzle surrounding Daniel Cajanus is that of his exact height. In the Sint Bavo church in Haarlem is a pillar indicating the contrasting heights of the two foremost local human curiosities, Daniel Cajanus and the Friesland dwarf Simon Jane Paap. The Swedish Giant is stated to have been 8 foot 4 inches in height, and from such clerical authority, this figure has been widely quoted in both historical and medical works, thereby granting Cajanus a place among the tallest men that ever lived. But as we know, Daniel Cajanus was 7 foot 8 inches tall when he came to London in 1734, and only 7 foot 4 inches in height when he was measured by the Royal Society dignitaries in 1742. Since Cajanus, just like the other eighteenth-century giants on show, was very adept in exaggerating his height, these are the only figures that deserve credence. A study of his skeleton has revealed the reason why Daniel Cajanus shrank in height during the last ten years of his life. In pituitary gigantism, all tissues of the body are affected by the overproduction of growth hormone, including the joint cartilage, which becomes diffusely thickened. This abnormal, thickened cartilage is liable to early degradation, however, leading to a disease similar to osteoarthritis. In Daniel Cajanus' skeleton, it can clearly be seen that the outer condyles of both thigh bones are severely destroyed. This deformation of the joint would lead to the development of extreme bandy-leggedness, and thus a loss in height which would explain why, at the Royal Society, the Revd Dr Pearse was puzzled that Cajanus had actually become a good deal shorter since he saw the giant in 1734. It may well be that Cajanus had actually been 7 foot 7/8 inches tall in 1734, taking into account the deformity of his knees and the degeneration of the intervertebral substance with age; this figure would tally with the most credible accounts of him. That a person with advanced knee joint disease of this kind would be unwilling to stand up for very long is quite understandable; indeed, considering the state of his knee joints, it is remarkable that Cajanus was at all capable of locomotion during his declining years.

As giants come, the three eighteenth-century cases described here were by no means extremes. The tallest man in the world, Robert Pershing Wadlow, was more than 8 foot 11 inches tall, and the most extreme example of pituitary gigantism ever recorded. Wadlow died in 1940, just twenty-two years old, from an infection in one of his enormous feet. Even among eighteenth-century giants on exhibition, Cajanus was no extreme, and his great success was probably as much due to clever marketing – he always claimed to be taller than some other giant recently exhibited, and freely exaggerated his height. Furthermore, all records agree that he was a sociable, amusing character, with an impressive flair for languages. It is only in fairytales that giants are stupid; overproduction of growth hormone does not cause any slowing of the intellect, in spite of its deleterious effect on many other organ systems. It is true that the Irish Giant seems almost to have been an imbecile, but his habit, formed since his early teens, of drinking at least one large bottle of gin or whisky every day, cannot have benefited the development of his intellect. In contrast to this sottish fellow, Daniel Cajanus was a prudent, intelligent man. Although it would have been 'politically correct' to pay lip-service to him as a poor freak condemned to earn his living by exhibiting himself, it would be more realistic to point out that he really made the best of his extreme condition. Rather than to have to fight against poverty in the cold, unpleasant Finnish countryside, Daniel Cajanus saw large parts of Europe, met interesting people, was introduced to the King of France and the President of the Royal Society, and accumulated enough wealth to spend his declining years in relative comfort.

7

THE

King of Poland's
COURT DWARF

AND THE

SICILIAN FAIRY

D rottningholm Castle, an imposing baroque building facing Lake Mälaren just outside central Stockholm, is the permanent residence of the Swedish royal family. In 1990, I visited Drottningholm Castle to see the remains of Queen Lovisa Ulrika's private museum, which I planned to describe in a book on various remarkable seventeenth- and eighteenth-century museums of natural history. As things turned out, this book was never written, but the beautifully designed museum rooms were nevertheless a remarkable sight. In 1803, the museum had been dissolved, and various university institutions and museums helped themselves to the more attractive preparations. Only one of its major original specimens remained: an astonishingly lifelike wax statue of the once-famous court dwarf Nicolas Ferry, alias Bébé, said to have been a present to Queen Lovisa Ulrika of Sweden from King Stanislas Leszynski of Poland. As an act of reverence towards the late queen, the statue was kept at her old museum and not taken away. For 200 years, this statue of the King of Poland's court dwarf has guarded the empty museum rooms like a bizarre sentinel, standing in a niche in the wall.

There is a story that Empress Catherine the Great of Russia once posted a sentry to stand guard over a particularly beautiful garden flower in one of the royal parks. As time went by, the purpose of the posting of this sentry was forgotten, but this does not mean that it was discontinued: many years after the flower had withered, the sentry still stood guarding the flower-bed where it had once grown, since the orders of the Empress could never be questioned. In some strange way, the statue of Nicolas Ferry has suffered a similar fate. The sight of it standing in the near-empty museum inspired me to investigate the life story of Nicolas Ferry, and under what circumstances his statue had been taken to Drottningholm Castle.

Lovisa Ulrika of Sweden founded her private museum around 1750. She was a possessive character, much given to collecting, and a fair proportion of her income was spent on purchases of coins, paintings, minerals and natural history specimens for her museum. According to Carl Linnaeus, who was used as an agent to procure new specimens, her copious purchases of corals, shells and dried insects caused a great boom in the European marketplace for natural curiosities. Queen Lovisa Ulrika housed her museum in three rooms in the newly built north wing of Drottningholm Castle: the cabinet of natural history, the cabinet of minerals and the cabinet of coins. Carl Linnaeus was summoned by the queen to arrange her collection of natural curiosities, since she herself had little knowledge of how to do it. To begin with, Linnaeus accepted this assignment with alacrity, since the queen's collections of shells and dried insects were the finest he had ever seen. The daily social intercourse with the royal family was flattering at first, but Linnaeus soon tired of court life. The king was a stupid, henpecked bore, and the queen haughty, imperious and conceited to a degree remarkable even among eighteenth-century royalty. In a letter to his friend Abraham Bäck, written in 1753, Linnaeus likened himself to a wretched prisoner on the island of Drottningholm, who could not be released without a royal pardon. In a later letter, he wrote that it sent a shiver down his spine every time the name of the royal residence was mentioned!

Queen Lovisa Ulrika kept adding new specimens, some of which had been presented to her as gifts by other royal personages. An Egyptian mummy, an ostrich's egg, a little stick said to have belonged to Julius Caesar, and a cast of the hand of the giant Bernard Giglio were all deposited in her museum. After the succession of her son King Gustaf III in 1771, however, the museum became increasingly neglected, since the young king had no interest at all in his mother's collections. Lovisa Ulrika lived on at Drottningholm Castle, which was her private property, but her son had cut her allowance. Since she kept spending lavishly, she was soon in dire financial straits. In 1777, she had to declare herself bankrupt, and the only way for her to settle her enormous debts was to sell Drottningholm Castle and all its contents, the museum included, to the Crown.

The wax statue of Nicolas Ferry is 3 foot 5 inches tall, including the cocked hat and the sturdy oak fundament; the figure itself is slightly less than 3 feet tall. It is dressed in Nicolas' own clothes, a suit of pale blue silk, with white stockings and cravat. The face was stated to be a wax impression of the famous court dwarf's own. The nose is quite black, since many museum visitors have taken the liberty of pinching it. It is not known exactly when the statue was taken to Drottningholm Castle. The earliest mention of it is in the 1788 castle inventory, and two less detailed inventories made in 1764 and 1777 do not record its presence. There is a tradition, however, that the statue had once belonged to Queen Lovisa Ulrika, and that it had been a gift from King Stanislas Leszynski of Poland, Nicolas Ferry's original patron.

Although this hypothesis cannot be proven with certainty, it is supported by the fact that King Gustaf III took little interest in his mother's museum, and that very few specimens were added after 1771.

ক্ষ

Nicolas Ferry was born on 14 October 1741 in the little village Champenay, situated in the Principality of Salm in France. His mother, who was seven months pregnant according to one account and had gone full term according to another, suddenly and unexpectedly went into labour. Before the midwives and neighbour women could be summoned, she rapidly gave birth. She was horrified to see the diminutive size of the infant: the boy was only 8¼ inches tall and weighed 22 ounces. Despite his minuscule stature, he was well shaped and beautifully proportioned, like a precious little bibelot. When the neighbours finally bustled in, they cried out, 'Un vrai petit Jésus!' According to the village gossips, the pregnant mother of little Nicolas had spent much time praying, in the local church, before a small statue of the infant Jesus in the crib. They supposed that this gazing at the statue had induced a sinister 'maternal impression', and that her unborn son had assumed the same size as this diminutive statue. The boy screamed at a particularly shrill, thin note, which was likened to the squeaking of a mouse. The village know-alls considered this feeble cry, along with his particularly low birth weight, as clear indications that he would not live long. Even the local *curé* seemed to agree, since he decided to postpone the baptismal ceremony.

Nicolas Ferry's mother was determined that he should live, however. Instead of a crib, she put him in a wooden shoe lined with straw. His mouth was too small to allow him to suckle his mother, but it was possible to make him drink small amounts of goat's milk through the use of a diminutive feeding bottle. Later, he suckled the family goat, which was soon well trained enough to come running, on its own accord, whenever it heard the boy crying. The parents of Nicolas, the young farmer Jean Ferry and his wife, thirty-five-year-old Anne Baron, were not very poor people, nor were they particularly wealthy. They were both in excellent health, and would later have two normal children. When he was exactly one month old, little Nicolas was put on a plate covered with hemp, and carried to the Plaine village church, where the *curé*, M. Sebastien Pelletier, baptised him with much ceremony. At the age of three months, Nicolas developed smallpox, and again his life was feared for, but he survived, with two large pockmarks on the forehead as the only marks of his illness. As the years went by, Nicolas grew slowly but steadily, but compared to children of the same age, he developed in a retarded fashion. For several months the goat's milk had been his only sustenance, but later his customary diet was the typical food of the Vosges labouring man: milk, potatoes, vegetables, bread and lard. It took until he was eighteen months old before Nicolas was able to utter some words in the local *patois*; it would be many years before he could express himself fluently. When two years old, he could walk without any support; before that time, he had crawled swiftly on all four limbs to rejoin his foster-mother, the goat. At this time, his first shoes, which were only 1½ inches long, were presented to him by the local shoemaker.

The word spread rapidly about this fantastic dwarf boy, and already when Nicolas was just a few months old, the curious thronged to see him. Although he was never formally put on show, it is not unlikely that his parents were given sums of money by various affluent spectators. In 1746, some noble ladies from the court of King Stanislas of Poland, who was also the Duke of Lorraine and Bar, were passing through the region of Champenay. They visited the Ferry family to see little Nicolas, and were vastly impressed; they later described his appearance before King Stanislas, who was at once particularly interested. King Stanislas Leszynski was married to the daughter of King Louis XV of

France. He had twice been King of Poland, the second time after King Charles XII of Sweden had conquered Poland and made him tributary king; twice he had been dethroned by fierce political opponents and expelled from his kingdom. In the later part of his life, King Stanislas was content to spend his time in affluent idleness in his French duchies. His close relationship with King Louis kept him well supplied with money, which he spent lavishly on his own amusements; his habits were regal and his court opulent. There were noble courtiers, beautiful, high-born ladies and well-mannered servants aplenty; King Stanislas lacked only one thing – a court dwarf.

In July 1746, the king sent one of his court physicians, M. Kast, to Champenay, in order to examine little Nicolas and determine his usefulness as a court dwarf. The now five-year-old boy had become a little more than 2 foot tall, and weighed 10 pounds. His bodily proportions resembled those of an adult, and M. Kast proposed that it was unlikely that he would grow any more. This was an ill-judged speculation, however, since Nicolas later grew nearly another foot. Nicolas Ferry's body was slender, agile and well shaped. His face was handsome except for a large, protruding nose; his eyes were dark brown and the hair a silvery blonde. His voice was thin and shrill, like that of a new-born infant. Nicolas was lively and animated throughout M. Kast's examination; he did not rest for a moment, and when his interest had once been captivated by any object, he could not be distracted from it. M. Kast concluded that even for a five-year-old, Nicolas seemed slow-witted and dull; his memory was weak, and his command of the French language showed much to be desired.

M. Kast described Nicolas Ferry before King Stanislas, who ordered that the boy should be taken to Lunéville without delay, so that the king himself could see him. Jean Ferry was overjoyed when the royal messenger knocked on his door at Champenay to explain his business. Without any delay, he harnessed his donkey-cart, put little Nicolas on the platform normally used for vegetables, covered him up with the tablecloth, and drove off towards the Château de Lunéville. King Stanislas and Queen

Katarina Opalinska were both much impressed by the lively, pretty little boy, and the king suggested to Jean Ferry that Nicolas should reside permanently at his court, and be brought up and educated there. Jean Ferry accepted this offer with alacrity; either because he was pleased that the boy would be provided with a superior education for nothing, or since he had the (misguided) belief that he himself would stand highly in the royal favour. As evidenced by later events, King Stanislas apparently considered that Nicolas was now his own property, purchased just as one buys a puppy or a kitten. Jean Ferry had left home in such a hurry that his wife had been left behind. When she came to Lunéville fifteen days later to say farewell to her beloved son, he did not, at first, seem to recognise her. The courtiers sniggered and gossiped that Nicolas was an imbecile, but when his mother left, a few hours later, the little boy wept bitterly.

Nicolas Ferry's life changed completely when he moved to King Stanislas' court. He was admired by the courtiers and flunkies, treated as an interesting little pet, handed round to be fed bonbons by the ladies, and generally spoilt rotten. On the queen's birthday in 1747, King Stanislas gave Nicolas to her as a present, whether wrapped up in a parcel or not is not known. She gave him the name Bébé (Baby), by which he was to be known for his remaining days, just as a puppy is renamed Fido by its new owner. To be fair, the queen seems to have taken good care of her court dwarf. On her deathbed, later in 1747, she bequeathed him to her cousin, the Princess de Talmont. The princess admired Bébé's pretty looks, and became genuinely fond of him. She proposed to King Stanislas that Bébé should receive a superior education, and the king agreed. Competent teachers of reading, writing, arithmetic, music, dancing and good manners were employed to instruct him. In her spare time, the princess herself attempted to give him lessons, but in spite of all her *esprit*, she was unable to develop any in

Bébé. Her grand scheme of educating the wretched little boy failed miserably, and after some years of bravely struggling, the distinguished pedagogues reported to King Stanislas that Nicolas was almost completely uneducable. Although he had, slowly but steadily, learnt to speak good French, they could not, by any means, induce him to read or write a single word, or to add two figures together. As an illustration of his level of intelligence, they told an anecdote: Bébé had once strayed into a meadow with high grass and weeds; he thought he was lost in a forest and desperately cried out for help. The eminent clergymen charged with explaining the mysteries of the Christian faith to Bébé could only report that the boy was wholly impervious to all kinds of religious thought. He had a certain ear for music: although unable to play any instrument, he liked to beat time on a small drum. He could be taught to dance, but his long-suffering dancing master had to explain every movement many times to his bumbling little protégé, before Bébé was able to reproduce the dancing steps in question. After many years of tuition, Bébé was finally able to perform a dancing show when a troupe of Italian comedians visited Lunéville in 1754.

In a corner of one of the great halls of the Château de Lunéville, King Stanislas ordered a wooden dwarf house erected for his novel acquisition. It was somewhat more luxurious than a dog's kennel, but then Bébé had a much higher standing at court than the king's favourite dogs. The dwarf house had an entrance hall, a bedroom, a drawing room and a dining room, all on a scale to suit Bébé perfectly. The house is reported to have been so small that even a dog could not enter it; this was probably to the benefit of little Nicolas, who was thus safe from being pulled out of his bed by a playful hound the size of a prize bull. Bébé's wardrobe contained a large variety of costly suits and costumes, made at the orders of King Stanislas. The dwarf house also contained a large number of birdcages, and Nicolas was amused by the song and antics of a large number of caged birds: warblers, siskins and goldcrests. There were also two snow-white miniature turtledoves, a gift to Bébé from the Empress of

Russia. When Bébé quarrelled with his royal master, he used to withdraw to his house, where he sat sulking for hours. When King Stanislas sent a footman to knock at the door, Bébé opened a window and haughtily called out 'Vous direz au Roi que je n'y suis pas!' – 'Tell the King that I am not at home!'

King Stanislas was much amused when his court dwarf was up to mischief, and the spoilt, naughty little rascal seldom disappointed him in this respect. The stolid, dignified headwaiter bringing a plate of delicacies to the king's table had to keep a wary eye out for the 'horrid dwarf', who might be lurking under the table, ready to kick his shins or trip him over. The fragile old lady walking in the galleries at Lunéville lived in fear that Bébé should dart in under her long skirts and do her some unspeakable mischief. The scatter-brained, hyperactive court dwarf had the run of the castle, and was perpetually on the move. He darted through the state rooms and corridors, shrieking with his shrill, penetrating voice. The king indulged him in everything, and he was a perpetual nuisance to the elderly, staid and nervous people residing at Lunéville.

Bébé was never punished in any way; even after the worst outrages, the king just gave a merry laugh at the discomfiture of the dwarf's victim. Nicolas was given to terrific temper tantrums, to which he freely gave way whenever he was refused anything: a bonbon, a piece of cake, or a new suit of clothes. He screamed, kicked, and broke vases and china. When reproached, he sullenly walked back to his dwarf house, where he sat sulking for hours. King Stanislas even suffered the mischievous little fellow to jump up onto the gaming table when the king was playing backgammon, and kick the pieces down onto the floor. The king was much worried that Bébé would one day walk out of the castle grounds and then not have sense enough to return the same way, but stray into some forest and be lost forever. Several times, the entire staff of the château had to be commandeered to search for the missing dwarf in the surrounding woodlands. After a long and futile hue and cry, the dirty, exhausted menials trudged back to the castle to face the anxious king, who feared that Bébé had drowned in a pond or that he had been caught and eaten by some wild beast. The next moment, Bébé jumped out from his hiding place with a piercing cry: just as usual, he had hidden deliberately, for the pleasure of seeing the others look for him. There was no risk that Bébé should be punished even for this dire offence; indeed, the king was overjoyed and fed him sweets.

Bébé was always immaculately dressed, according to the fashion of the time. The Princess de Talmont took pride that he should at least look like the perfect little gentleman. His long hair was powdered and arranged by a footman each morning. In spite of his appetite for cakes, chocolate and bonbons, Nicolas did not increase much in girth, but remained lean and agile. He liked to drive about in the garden of the château in a specially built, beautifully decorated little cart, harnessed with four white goats; it must have been a remarkable sight to meet his unique equipage being whipped forth, with enthusiastic yells and screams, on some secluded garden path. Another of Nicolas Ferry's interests was military drill, and he liked to watch the training of the royal guards on the barrack square. The king had a full grenadier's uniform made in Bébé's size, and the court dwarf for once proved a willing pupil: the king could soon amuse his court by drilling Bébé, who stood on a high table, dressed in his uniform and brandishing a miniature rifle.

At one of the court banquets at Lunéville, the dessert was a huge pastry in the shape of a military fortress, decorated with towers, guns and battlements made in sugar and confectionery. It was much admired by the guests, who had already eaten and drunk well during the sumptuous banquet. The king had a surprise in store for them, however. Without warning, Bébé jumped up from the pastry's interior, fired two pistols at the roof, and whirled a sword round threateningly. A young nobleman, the Chevalier de Vintimille, was so frightened that he tipped his chair backwards, shrieking out with fear and alarm, and ran out into the garden.

During the heyday of Nicolas Ferry's reign as the court favourite of King Stanislas, many people were appalled by the bad character of this 'horrid dwarf', who had nevertheless been brought up by cultured, educated people, and indulged in everything. Bébé was choleric, selfish and jealous to a marked degree. Once, when he observed the Princess de Talmont sitting with a little dog on her lap, he ran up to her, snatched the lapdog, and threw it out through the window with the words, 'Pourquoi l'aimez-vous plus que moi?' – 'Why do you love this dog more than me?' He was a petty tyrant, who savoured his privileged position and relished in ordering the court pages, servants and dogsbodies about. Despite his many failings, Bébé remained the great favourite of King Stanislas. His fame had spread like wildfire across Europe, and all the king's guests at Lunéville wanted to meet him. Celebrities like the Duke de Richelieu, Count de Clermont and Prince de Condé were entertained by the king and his faithful Bébé, and a few years later they were visited by Voltaire and Madame du Châtelet.

It was a severe shock to Nicolas when, in 1759, he seemed to have acquired a rival for his royal favour. The Countess Humiecka, one of the ladies-in-waiting at the court of King Stanislas, who knew well the elderly monarch's *penchant* for midgets, had brought a twenty-year-old Polish dwarf named Joseph Boruwlaski to Lunéville. He was just 2 foot 6½ inches tall, and thus more than an inch shorter than Bébé. While poor Nicolas' attempts at conversation quickly palled, Joseph Boruwlaski, whom King Stanislas renamed Joujou in his usual manner, was quick-witted and amusing, with the polite manner of a courtier. When the two court dwarfs were formally introduced, Boruwlaski politely apologised for being the shorter of the two. The confused Bébé merely replied that he himself had been ill, and that he soon would grow up and become tall.

He then retreated to sit sulking in his house. A certain M. Durival wrote in his diary that Bébé 'choked with fury when eclipsed by another little man, and was livid with rage when he saw the king and his court caress and flatter the newcomer, while he himself was ignored.' The king, who had previously showed Bébé much patience, now started to reproach him for his morose stupidity. On one occasion, King Stanislas put a series of questions to his two court dwarfs. Boruwlaski provided witty and apposite replies, but poor Nicolas was as scatterbrained as ever. The king then turned to his old favourite and pointed out the difference between the two: Joujou was merry, amusing and well educated, but Bébé was just 'une petite machine'. Nicolas received this affront in deadly silence, but as soon as the king had left the room, he crept behind his rival, seized hold of him and dragged him across the room towards the open fireplace, where a large bonfire was roaring! Boruwlaski gave a great yell when he felt the clutches of the furious court dwarf. Fortunately, the king heard this outcry and returned just in time to save him. Although Boruwlaski begged for mercy for his rival, the king decided that, for once, Bébé was to receive a sound thrashing, which was immediately administered by some sturdy menials. The wretched court dwarf was so mortified by this novel experience of corporal punishment that he did not speak for several days.

If he had wanted to, Joseph Boruwlaski could easily have usurped Bébé's position at King Stanislas' court. But although the king was rapturous about the new court dwarf he had discovered, Boruwlaski was less impressed by King Stanislas and his court. He was shrewd enough to appreciate that his minuscule stature, coupled with a ready wit, could make his fortune among the many noble and wealthy curiosity-seekers of Europe. He realised that he had to remain his own master, and not settle down as a court dwarf. In late 1795, Boruwlaski left Lunéville for Paris, and to his great relief, Bébé could reclaim his position as the royal favourite. Joseph Boruwlaski later made a brilliant career as an itinerant performer; he was received at most European courts, and made a small fortune. At the age of sixty, he retired from show business, settled in England, and purchased a life annuity, at favourable terms, from a foolish man who did not think that this little fellow could live much longer. Joseph Boruwlaski proved him wrong, however, since he lived to be ninety-eight years old; he survived the money lender, whose relatives had to keep paying the annuity for many years. As befitting a man of his wealth and social position, Joseph Boruwlaski is buried in Durham Cathedral.

Several of the physicians attached to the court of Lunéville were interested in Bébé, and tried to figure out what was the cause of his abnormal growth. A certain Dr Sauveur Morand several times spoke to and examined the court dwarf, while preparing a lecture before the Académie des Sciences. His opinion of Nicolas Ferry's intellect was very low: he wrote that the celebrated court dwarf's mind was generally clouded and confused, and that his capacity did not exceed that of a well-trained dog. A distinguished nobleman, Louis Elizabeth de la Vergie, Count de Tressan, who was Grand Marshal at the Court of King Stanislas, also took an interest in Bébé. The count was actually a member of the Académie des Sciences, and in 1760 he read a paper comparing the accomplishments of Bébé with those of Joseph Boruwlaski. This comparison was of course highly unflattering for poor Nicolas: Count de Tressan wrote that in spite of the king's unceasing attempts to educate him, Bébé remained a complete imbecile. He could not read or write a single letter, and was incapable of doing any useful work.

Count de Tressan continued with the words:

> Bébé can really be brought forward as a better proof for the
> theories of Descartes about the souls of animals, than a monkey
> or a poodle... I must confess that I have never cast an eye on
> Bébé without feeling repugnance and secret horror, inspired by
> this vile caricature of human nature.

Some individual, perhaps the count himself, was unfeeling enough to read these very severe censures out loud to the unfortunate Nicolas, who cried out in horror: 'If this be true, I am nothing – the King will never care for me any more!'

The Princess de Talmont was appalled by the count's actions, and she wrote a pamphlet to avenge her poor Bébé. In this publication, she reproached the cruel count for his invectives against Nicolas, and claimed, with some reason, that far from being like a dumb animal, he was quite capable of reasoning, and by no means an imbecile. Although vain and conceited – 'il connaît le prix de la petitesse de sa figure' – and easily won over by flattery, he was also capable of understanding reproaches and trying to better himself. Nicolas was sincerely attached to the king and princess. Without urging, he distributed alms among the poor country people, often giving them pieces of silver instead of the customary small copper coins. Once, the well-to-do court dwarf gave a piggy bank crammed full of money to his younger brother Louis, who thereby became the wealthiest inhabitant of the village of Champenay.

Until he was sixteen years old, Nicolas Ferry was healthy and agile; he never complained of illness, and his limbs, although small, were strong and supple. But in his later teens, the celebrated court dwarf began to age prematurely. His back gradually became stooped and one shoulder hunched; his legs weakened, and he walked in a weak, tottering manner. The head bent forward and the toothless chin dropped; his already prominent nose became monstrously huge and beak-like as the rest of his face wasted away. Nicolas also lost his cheerful, mischievous personality, and became a dissatisfied, complaining valetudinarian. In 1759, Count de Tressan predicted that Bébé would die of old age before he was thirty years old. In 1760, when Bébé accompanied King Stanislas to Paris, he was seen by the encyclopaedist Diderot, who was much struck by the nineteen-year-old court dwarf's premature ageing: his back was much stooped, and his complexion a sickly grey.

King Stanislas let his court physician, the Swede Kasten Rönnow, examine Nicolas, and several other physicians and surgeons were later consulted. Their diagnosis was that Bébé's premature senility was caused by puberty; this process disrupted the balance of the tissues of his small body: his blood became thin and depleted, and the nerves desiccated. The wicked Count de Tressan added that Bébé's sexual excesses were likely to have accentuated his ageing process further. The vast majority of contemporary chroniclers have disagreed with the insinuating count on this point, but several other sources agree that Bébé did consort freely with the young ladies at King Stanislas' court. It was frequently gossiped at the time that King Stanislas was an elderly libertine, and that the moral tone at his court was deplorably low. There were rumours that the king encouraged Bébé to rush in under the wide crinolines of the ladies, and to make a detailed report of his observations to his delighted royal master. The ladies did not at all appreciate these intimacies, and sometimes – wittingly or unwittingly – the victim put down her pointed heel on the foot of this inquisitive little fellow, who let out a great howl which echoed under the wide skirts, before he crawled out, purple with rage, and limped away to tell the king about the indignity he had suffered.

Another rumour told that, in the late 1750s, Nicolas had proposed to a normal-sized young lady residing in Lunéville, but her parents, who did not want a court dwarf for their son-in-law, refused him in no uncertain terms. In 1761, King Stanislas thought of a novel idea of amusing his court. He had arranged a grandiose dwarf's marriage between Bébé and the equally diminutive Mlle Thérèse Souvray, another native of Lorraine. Although they had never met, both were initially agreeable to spending the remainder of their lives in holy matrimony. Thérèse was delighted to marry the wealthy young court dwarf, and Bébé had seen her pretty portrait and was happy to get a wife after his earlier rebuff. But after viewing her prospective husband, whose ill health is unlikely to have improved his temper and character, Thérèse Souvray asked the king's permission to remain single, which was granted. Nicolas Ferry's reaction to this disastrous course of events is not known, but his flagging spirits can hardly have been revived by the indignity of once more being rejected. There was indeed a rumour that Bébé 'entra dans une violente colère' on being jilted, and that the amorous dwarf rapidly fell into a decline and died, like the heroine of some French novel. This was an after-construction, however, since it is well known that Nicolas had been ill for several years before being rejected. His intended fiancée never married, and at some stage of her career as an actress and performer she actually called herself Mme Bébé, in order to exploit the legendary court dwarf's notoriety. As late as 1819, at the age of seventy-three, she performed in a play titled *Bébé, ou le Nain du Roi Stanislaus*, accompanied by her sister Barbe, who was a little taller than her and an accomplished singer and dancer.

Later in 1761, Nicolas Ferry enjoyed his final triumph as a court dwarf, when Louis XV's two sisters, the Princesses Adelaide and Victoire, visited King Stanislas in Lunéville. As a surprise, Stanislas had arranged a military parade, in which the uniformed 'Capitaine Bébé' led the Grenadiers and the citizen's cavalry past the royal party. The next year, when he was twenty-one years old, Nicolas Ferry fell into a lethargy and became bedridden. He was incontinent and could not even stand up without support. The doctors were again consulted, but they had no worthwhile suggestions at all, except to emphasise the uniqueness of Bébé's case: they were probably already whetting their autopsy knives and corresponding with various scholarly journals likely to publish a paper on the famous dwarf, complete with the post-mortem findings.

To their disappointment, Nicolas rallied after a couple of months and was again able to totter about on his own. A weak, frail, grumbling invalid, he could not even walk 100 steps, and had to be carried upstairs. He always complained of being cold, and could not abide a draughty room; the only thing that would raise his spirits was when the servants carried his stretcher out into the garden on a warm and sunny day. In May 1764, Nicolas caught a cold, which was followed by lengthy fever spells, ague-fits, and excessive weakness. He could not eat or move from his bed; when someone he knew spoke to him, he tried to reply but could not. On 5 June, he seemed a little stronger and was again able to speak; to the astonishment of those present, the ailing court dwarf now displayed more knowledge and reason than he had ever done. Although he had never before appeared to understand religion, he now confessed his sins to one of the court chaplains, partook of the Holy Communion, and received the extreme unction. The day after, the emaciated, exhausted dwarf again seemed on the brink of death, and at eight o'clock in the evening of 8 June he finally died, at the age of twenty-two years and seven months.

When King Stanislas received the news of the death of his favourite, he wept bitterly. At first, he was unwilling to have Bébé autopsied, but Count de Tressan managed to persuade him, with the argument that it would be a great loss to medical science if such a curious *jeu de nature* was not properly anatomised. He also promised the king that he could keep Bébé's mounted skeleton as a souvenir; just as he used to have his favourite dogs stuffed after death.

The autopsy was performed by the court physician, the Swede Kasten Rönnow, assisted by the court surgeon, M. Perret, and the junior surgeon M. Saucerotte. The inquisitive Count de Tressan was present as a spectator. When Nicolas Ferry's corpse was measured, it proved to be 35 inches tall. His inner organs were in good condition, except that there was a small amount of fluid in the pleural cavities, and certain pleural adherences; neither of these findings is of much significance. The curvature of the ribs was greater on one side, due to the scoliosis (curvature of the spine) of the back. Count de Tressan specifically mentioned that the genital parts were normal. The official autopsy report mentions nothing further, but the surgeon Saucerotte published an addition in 1768. He stated that a spongious, reddish tumour was situated between the parietal bones. This tumour pressed directly against the brain. The insides of both parietal bones were covered with a similar substance, and the bony structures in this area seemed brittle and diseased.

After autopsy, Kasten Rönnow boiled Nicolas' skeleton and put the bones in a large box, kept in the Royal Library of Lunéville. Despite Count de Tressan's promise to King Stanislas, it was never mounted. King Stanislas himself followed Bébé to the grave two years later. His way of death was an unusual one. One evening, as the elderly, corpulent monarch stood warming his backside before a roaring fire, his dressing gown suddenly caught alight. A party of servants and courtiers were summoned by the king's cries, but a loyal gendarme, posted outside the bedroom door with strict orders from the king that no one was to enter and disturb his sleep, held them at bayonet point even when thick smoke started to billow from underneath the door! When they finally managed to force their way in, the king was too badly burnt to survive, a victim of his own predilection for court etiquette.

After the death of King Stanislas, Bébé's skeleton was taken to the Cabinet du Roi in Paris, where the celebrated George Louis Buffon personally examined it. He mounted the skeleton and measured all the bones. It was apparent to him that Bébé had been suffering from bilateral genua valga (bandy legs), as had indeed been described already during his lifetime. This was due to early-onset osteoarthritis of the knee joints, affecting the medial compartment of the joints much more than the lateral one. Nicolas had also had a severe, left-convex scoliosis. Poor Bébé did not have a single tooth at the time of his death. Only one alveolar process was observed in the lower jaw, and the upper jaw was in even worse condition. Old Kasten Rönnow had boiled Bébé's skeleton far too long, and thus destroyed all traces of muscles and tendons, which made Buffon's work more difficult. Another odd matter was that two ribs were missing; Buffon suspected that they had either been lost or taken as souvenirs. The latter hypothesis seems quite likely, and is further supported by the fact that several bones from Bébé's hands were also missing; Buffon had to procure suitably sized replacements from the museum's repository of child skeletons. It is by no means unlikely that Count de Tressan and other curiosity-seekers who had known Bébé during his lifetime had taken some of these bones as mementos of the famous court dwarf.

The remains of Nicolas Ferry's body were buried, with much ceremony, in the Église des Minimes at Lunéville. A mausoleum was built over the grave, with an ornate urn, and the inscription:

> *Hic jacet*
> *Nicolaüs Ferry, Lotharingus,*
> *Naturæ ludus,*
> *Staturæ tenuitate mirandus,*
> *Ab Antonio novo dilectus,*
> *In juventute, ætate senex,*
> *Quinque lustra fuerunt ipsi*
> *Sæculum.*
> *Obiit nonà die junii MDCCLXIV.*

This translates:

> Here rests Nicolas Ferry of Lorraine, a jest of nature who was admirable for his small build, and who pleased the novel Anthony. In [the] midst of his youth, he became an old man, and twenty-five years was for him the same as a century. He died on June 9, 1764.

The 'novel Anthony' mentioned in the inscription was of course a flattering reference to King Stanislas himself. The Minimes church was destroyed during the French Revolution, but Nicolas Ferry's mausoleum was saved; it is today exhibited at the Musée du Château de Lunéville. Another, lengthier inscription, adding that not the skeleton, but only the innards, had been put into the grave, was quoted in an engraving at the Cabinet des Estampes.

Throughout his stay in Lunéville, Bébé was a European celebrity. The people who had once seen him did not forget him in a hurry, and he remained famous long after his death. He was frequently mentioned in the contemporary chronicles of court life and society memoirs. Many museums still treasure various mementos of the famous court dwarf. King Stanislas had spared no expense to equip Bébé with splendid clothes and hats, and the dwarf house was kept well stocked with beautiful hand-crafted furniture, porcelain and cutlery. Quite a few of these objects are still kept in museums or in private collections. In 1883, the French antiquary A. Benoît published an inventory of 'les souvenirs de Bébé'. The Musée d'Unterlinden had a hat, a pair of breeches, a costume in blue silk and a short rapier made especially for Bébé. M. Gilliot, a master printer residing in Savenne, had a pair of white socks, a pair of breeches, and two 4-inch shoes. The Benedictine monks at Senones treasured another pair of Nicolas Ferry's shoes. Bébé's drinking goblet was at the Musée d'Amiens, and his easy chair was kept in a private collection.

Bébé's elegant little carriage drawn by four goats reappeared with a noble family in Lunéville, where it was used as a toy by generations of children. When it was in a derelict condition, it was sold to a poor mason, who used it to transport his harvest of vegetables. The architect M. Joly, a historian of the Château de Lunéville, saw it in the 1850s. In spite of its prosaic use, there were still traces of gilding on its ornaments, and the philosophical M. Joly paused to meditate on the change of fortunes for Bébé's 'voiture de gala'; it would have been better if he had given the mason a few francs for this unique vehicle, to save it for posterity.

Today, several of Nicolas Ferry's clothes are kept at the Musée Historique Lorrain in Nancy: his cap, spats and dressing-case, among other objects. A beautiful oil painting of him together with a large dog, and several drawings, are also at this museum. The Musée Municipal at the Château de Lunéville has two other oil paintings of him, and a fourth is in the private collection of a French nobleman. The latter museum also owns a unique life-size porcelain statue of Nicolas Ferry dressed in the uniform of the Polish hussars. It was made in 1746 when he was six years old and had just joined the court of King Stanislas. It has the inscription, 'Portrait.naturel.dvn.enfant.age, de six ans/NP fecit/de.lanee/1746'.

It is apparent that wax statues of Nicolas Ferry were made on several occasions. When Dr Morand held a lecture about him at the Académie des Sciences, he brought with him a life-size wax dummy of Nicolas, dressed in a suit of his clothes. This statue had been made in 1759, when Nicolas was eighteen years old, by M. Jeanet, a surgeon of Lunéville. Some of Bébé's fine coiffure had been cut off to provide it with hair, and its face was carefully moulded to resemble his own. It is not unlikely that another statue was made during Nicolas' lifetime, by a certain Francois Guillot, a specialist moulder of statues, who had his workshop in Nancy. Finally, at least one statue was made after death, probably at the Cabinet du Roi. To get the proportions right, every bone in the skeleton was measured, and the resulting wax statue was 'superbement habillé' in a suit of Nicolas' own clothes.

The statue at Drottningholm Castle is by no means unique: several wax statues of Nicolas Ferry have survived wars and revolutions and are now treasured exhibits in various museums. At the Musée Orfila in Paris is a statue which has been at various Parisian anatomical museums since at least the 1830s. It was a well-known and familiar sight for thousands of medical students. One of them, Dr Liegey, who later read a paper on Bébé before the Société d'Emulation des Vosges, saw it in 1832, 'vêtu à la mode Louis XV', and standing on a window sill. This statue is dressed in a light blue coat with lace cuffs, a long grey waistcoat, red breeches, grey stockings and a black cocked hat. This statue is less detailed than that at Drottningholm Castle: the face is quite unlike that of Nicolas Ferry, and the hair very sparse; the few remaining strands may well be Nicolas' own, however. Furthermore, the proportions of the stocky, ungainly figure do not resemble those of Nicolas Ferry. It is possible that the statue has sunk somewhat; indeed, the stockings are sagging quite badly, which would support this theory. Several authors have identified this statue as the one made in 1759, which Dr Morand took with him to the Académie des Sciences in 1764. It is just below 2 foot tall, which would support this hypothesis, since Bébé grew almost 8 inches during the latter part of his life.

Another statue of Bébé is at the Musée Historique Lorrain in Nancy. Like the others, it is mounted on a wooden fundament and dressed in one of Nicolas' most splendid suits of clothes. The face is stated to be 'moulée rigoreusement authentique' and resembled that of Nicolas more than the Paris statue. Other wax statues of Nicolas Ferry are at the Musée Municipal at the Château de Lunéville, the Hessisches Landesmuseum in Kassel and the Herzog Anton-Ulrich Museum in Braunschweig. The last originally belonged to Duke Anton Ulrich of Braunschweig's private museum, and arrived at Braunschweig before 1806.

THE SICILIAN FAIRY

After the death of John Hunter, his brother-in-law Everard Home moved swiftly forward in the London medical world: he published several influential works on practical surgery and urology, and established a lucrative private practice in London. As a scientist, Home was as versatile as Hunter himself, but he lacked his great teacher's creativity and genius. In 1813, he was made a baronet, and he later became the first President of the Royal College of Surgeons. In April 1824, at the height of his distinguished career, Sir Everard Home went to see 'Caroline Crachami, the Sicilian Fairy', a dwarf who had recently been taken to London for exhibition. The Sicilian Fairy was demonstrated by a certain Dr Gilligan, an Irishman who claimed to be the child's father. The entrance fee was a shilling, but to be allowed to lift her up and examine her more closely, the spectators had to pay double that amount. The lively, animated little girl apparently made a great impression on Home. At the age of nine, she was only 19½ inches in height and 11¼ inches round the waist. She walked without any support, but without much confidence. She was attracted to glittering objects, and liked dressing up in fine clothes; she had a taste for music, and was happy to see some visitor who had previously showed her kindness. Caroline Crachami knew enough English to express herself rather fluently, and gave relevant answers to questions asked her by the audience.

Another, less appealing view of the exhibition is given in the *Memoirs of Charles Mathews* by his wife Anne. When the visitors entered, the Sicilian Fairy sat on a low throne 'in seeming mockery of regal state'. Her voice was very thin and high-pitched, and the showman had to repeat all her utterances for the benefit of the audience; Mrs Mathews noted that he added 'many particulars not mentionable to ears polite' in order to amuse them. The tall Dr Gilligan had dressed up in strange garb in order to look like an Italian, but he could not disguise his thick Irish brogue. Charles Mathews, a long-time habitué of London lowlife, who delighted in various monster shows and whose impressions of Daniel Lambert have been quoted earlier, asked him, upon the mentioning of his alleged place of birth, 'whether it was Palermo in the *County of Cork* where he was born?' The Irishman leered at him in an arch manner and said, 'Och! I see your honour's a deep 'un! Sure, you're right, but don't *peach*!' In order to swear Charles Mathews to secrecy, Gilligan offered to let him take the child up and examine her for nothing, thus saving a shilling, but Mathews declined the rogue's offer with scorn and later freely denounced the man's imposture to his friends.

Sir Everard Home went to see Caroline Crachami several times, and soon became friendly with his unscrupulous colleague Gilligan, who realised that he could make use of the influential baronet's interest in his tiny protégée. They commissioned a tailor to make her a richly embroidered dress, and Sir Everard introduced her to his royal patron, King George IV, at Carlton Palace; it was remarked in the newspapers that the king 'expressed high pleasure at her appearance'. The Fairy's presentation at court heralded a time of greatly improved economic and social circumstances for Dr Gilligan and his alleged daughter. The odd ceremony was reported in many of the newspapers, and as a result of this publicity it became fashionable among the Londoners to visit the exhibition. Soon, the Fairy had as many as 200 paying visitors daily, many of whom became so fond of her that they came several times. In the *Morning Chronicle*, it was reported that 'within the last days, she has been presented at Court by Sir Everard Home, since which period she has eclipsed most of the distinguished fashionables; the morning calls of the Royal Family, the Nobility, the Foreign Ambassadors, and the highest members of the Faculty, and others of rank and fortune, have frequently exceeded two hundred, and the number of presents she has received exceeds all precedents.' Dr Gilligan soon took better lodgings at Duke Street, and also rented a suite of rooms at Bond Street as a new exhibition hall. In the newspapers, his attempt to pose as an Italian was seen through, and it was suspected he had also lied about the place of birth of his alleged daughter, and that 'the phenomenon was really a native of Ireland'.

Dr Gilligan also had an exhibition pamphlet printed, entitled *Memoirs of Miss Crachami, the celebrated Sicilian Dwarf.* It was stated that she was born in Palermo on 15 November 1815, the daughter of Signor Louis Emmanuel Crachami. Like his wife, this gentleman was by profession a theatre musician. He was healthy and of normal stature; of his wife, it was slyly remarked that she 'is justly considered a fine woman.' They had four other children, all of normal stature. At birth, Caroline Crachami had

weighed only one pound, and measured between 7 and 8 inches
in height. Her parents had shown her privately to the Duchess
of Parma and other noble curiosity-seekers, but they did not
consent to having her exhibited for money before the populace.
In the pamphlet, no reason was given for their sudden change
of mind in this respect, nor was it explained why the Fairy had
been taken to England.

One of Caroline Crachami's most fervent admirers was the
newspaperman William Jerdan, who wrote extensive accounts of
this 'wonder of wonders' in his column. In his lifetime he had
never seen anything like her:

> Only imagine a creature about half as large as a new-born infant;
> perfect in all parts and lineaments, uttering words in a strange,
> unearthly voice, understanding what you say and replying to your
> questions; imagine, I say, this figure of about nineteen inches in
> height and five pounds in weight, – and you will have some idea
> of this most extraordinary phenomenon.

Caroline Crachami's large nose and somewhat microcephalous
cranium made her look older than nine years, and her almost
adult bodily proportions added to this impression. Her hands
and feet were slender and graceful, and she moved her arm 'with
all the motions and grace that are found in the same member
of a lovely woman'. Caroline did not like people who wanted
to measure her, or examine her too minutely, and whenever
doctors were mentioned in the conversation, she 'doubles her
filbert of a fist, and manifests her decided displeasure'. In order
to get her measurements, Jerdan invited her to his house and
gave her a ring and a large doll, and treated her to a meal of
biscuits and weak diluted wine, which she relished very much.
Thus favourably disposed, she let him take her measurements: her
height was 19½ inches, the length of her foot 3½ inches, and
the length of her forefinger 1½ inches. Round the head she was
12½ inches, and round the waist 11¼ inches. Caroline Crachami
was animated and observant throughout their conversation, and

expressed many opinions, of like and dislike, of impatience, enjoyment, mirth – the last prevailing.

Some weeks later, the newspapers announced Caroline Crachami's sudden death. For some days, she had coughed and appeared unwell, but this did not dispose her showman to make the exhibition schedule less fatiguing. After she had received more than 200 visitors on 3 June 1824, towards the evening a languor overtook her and she died in the carriage on the way home to the Duke Street lodgings. Sir Everard Home suspected that the cause of death was consumption, since she had suffered from a 'hacking cough'. The Fairy was bitterly grieved by her many admirers in London, and in the newspapers Gilligan was criticised for his callous exploitation of her. The poet Thomas Hood, who had probably seen her during life, gave her a fitting epitaph in his *Ode to the Great Unknown:*

Think of Crachami's miserable span!
No tinier frame the spark could dwell in
Than there it fell in –
But when she felt herself a show, she tried
To shrink from the world's eye, poor dwarf! and died!

A week after the Sicilian Fairy's demise, there was an extraordinary scene in the magistrate's court at Marlborough Street. Her real father, the Italian Louis Emmanuel Crachami, who was employed as a musician at the Theatre Royal in Dublin, approached the magistrate, F.A. Roe, for advice on how to proceed in reclaiming his daughter's dead body. It turned out that he had consulted Dr Gilligan in Dublin about his dwarfish daughter's ill health. The medical man, who was much struck by her extraordinary appearance, had considered the Dublin climate much too cold for her delicate health, and recommended a stay in London. The parents lacked the means to send her there, but Gilligan offered to take her there himself, if he was allowed to exhibit her for money in order to pay their expenses. Thus having secured the hapless child, Gilligan took her on an exhibition tour to Liverpool, Birmingham and Oxford in order to pay the costs for lodgings in London. The parents were kept in ignorance of Gilligan's nefarious proceedings in London, and it was only through the newspapers that they learnt of their child's death. The Fairy's grief-stricken mother wanted to see her child one last time before burial, and Crachami travelled to London to bring her corpse back. He first visited the Bond Street exhibition room, which was just being closed down, and in his quest for the elusive Gilligan he was referred to the Duke Street lodgings. There he was met by the furious landlord, who had been left with a bill for 25 guineas by Gilligan and his entourage. This party had vanished without a trace, leaving behind the costume Caroline Crachami had worn at court, as well as a 'state bed', which had been given her by a wealthy admirer. The landlord said that already during the Fairy's lifetime, Gilligan had bragged that he could earn as much money from her after death; several surgeons had wished to purchase the remains if some misfortune led to her death, and a sum of £500 had been mentioned. This sinister news caused Crachami to appeal to the court in order to prevent his daughter being sold for dissection.

It was not possible for Mr Roe to issue an order to reclaim the corpse, but he recommended that an inquest into the child's death be held by a coroner's jury. In the meantime, Crachami and a friend of his went round to several London anatomists in order to find out whether the body had been offered for sale. At Joshua Brookes' anatomy school, they found out that Gilligan had tried to sell the Fairy's body for 100 guineas, but Brookes had declined to buy it. The landlord suggested that they visit Sir Everard Home's house in Sackville Street, since he remembered that this gentleman had been a frequent visitor at the exhibition. When they arrived, Home, who believed them to be Gilligan's hired hands, told them brusquely that he had no money for them; he would have had these uninvited visitors turned out, had not the distraught Signor Crachami managed to explain that he was really the child's father. Sir Everard told them that Gilligan had visited him on 7 June in order to put the corpse up for sale. Home passed this offer along to the Royal College of Surgeons, and he obviously expected that they would purchase the body for the Hunterian Museum, since it is recorded in the museum's donation book that Home himself took Caroline Crachami's body there in a box the same day. It was agreed that, since Gilligan wished to leave London as soon as possible, he would send a messenger along to collect the money voted to give him by the college.

Louis Emmanuel Crachami was appalled at this final evidence of Gilligan's low villainy. He asked Home if he could see the child's remains for a last look. Sir Everard gave the distraught Italian a cheque for £10 to calm him down, and also a passport to give him entrance to the museum. But the unfortunate father had another shock waiting for him. Home's principal assistant William Clift and his pupils were so eager to examine the body that they had already started, and the dissection was apparently well advanced. With tears flowing, Crachami grasped the dismembered corpse, and it was only with difficulty that his friends could persuade him to leave it. There was much writing in the newspapers about these touching scenes, and the Sicilian Fairy's tragic fate became headline news. The last mention of the scandal in the press was that Signor Crachami left London for Dublin to convey 'the dreadful intelligence' to his wife, and that Gilligan, who had netted 1,500 guineas on the exhibition, was rumoured to have fled to France.

Although the surgeons had promised Crachami that the dissection was not to be taken further, Home ordered that the Sicilian Fairy's skeleton was to be prepared and mounted. He also managed to preserve her pearl ring, thimble and tiny stockings and shoes. Sir Everard Home was not noted for generosity, and it is unlikely that Dr Gilligan ever received any pecuniary reward for his villainous bodysnatching. Home apparently considered that he had purchased the body for the £10 he had given to Crachami, and he donated the skeleton and other objects concerning the Fairy to the museum in his own name. It was set up next to that of the aforementioned Irish Giant, and would easily have fitted into his enormous boot. In a paper published in the Royal Society's *Philosophical Transactions*, Sir Everard Home used Caroline Crachami's case to illustrate the terrible effects of a 'maternal impression'. He stated that in 1815, when Mme Crachami was almost four months gone with child, she was sleeping in a caravan in the baggage of the Duke of Wellington's army in France. In a violent storm, a small monkey, which travelled on the roof of the caravan suddenly bounded in through the window and crept under her skirts to keep warm. Later, she awoke from the pressure of the monkey, and wanted to scratch herself, but came upon the monkey's head. The startled animal bit her fingers and seized hold of her loins, and the poor woman went into fits. It was accepted that she would miscarry, but she went her full time; for a supporter of the ancient doctrine of maternal impressions, it was not difficult to point out the cause of the child's extraordinary appearance.

Sir Everard Home's own description of the Sicilian Fairy's autopsy is regrettably brief, but fortunately William Clift's hand-written autopsy report is still kept in the archives of the Royal College of Surgeons of London. Except for a small portion in the posterior parts of the orbits, there was no fat in any part of the body. The liver was healthy but the bile ducts and gall bladder almost as large as those of an adult. The lungs were almost entirely covered with whitish irregular spots, and very much tuberculated throughout; furthermore, the inguinal and mesenteric glands were numerous and much enlarged. The urinary bladder was extremely extended with urine, but both kidneys seemed healthy. No further examination of these parts was undertaken, and Home only concluded that the monkey's grip upon the loins of the mother had caused this affliction of the bladder already *in utero*.

The description of the Sicilian Fairy was one of Sir Everard Home's last scientific triumphs. He died in 1832, and his later years were embittered by an unsavoury scandal, in which his

long-suffering assistant William Clift reported to the Trustees of
the Hunterian Collection that Home had burnt John Hunter's
invaluable posthumous papers after having plagiarised them in
his own publications for many years. Although these accusations
were probably exaggerated, Home lost the confidence of his
colleagues, and to this day he has been considered the villain of
the Hunterian tradition.

DISCUSSION

The strange life stories of the King of Poland's court dwarf and
the Sicilian Fairy have many parallels. They were both greatly
admired by their contemporaries, and were both introduced to
a king, although, unfortunately for Caroline Crachami, George
IV did not share King Stanislas' *penchant* for keeping a court
dwarf. Nicolas Ferry's existence was by far the preferable. He
had a dwarf house and an endless supply of fine clothes, and
was spoilt and pampered by the court; she had to be content
with the richly embroidered dress she wore when introduced
at court, and her 'state bed', in between being exhibited before
the Londoners in a degrading monster show. Both Nicolas Ferry
and Caroline Crachami were explained as dreadful examples of
'maternal impressions': a teratogenetic dogma that was becoming outdated already in the early nineteenth century. Sir Everard
Home was in fact one of its last scientific supporters, and when
he published Caroline Crachami's case in 1824, he did so to try to
prove the existence of nerves in the placenta, which in this case
had transferred the shock of the mother's perilous encounter
with the monkey to deform the unborn child. Home actually
aided in the exploitation of Caroline Crachami, and the part
he played in her tragic fate is certainly nothing to be proud
of. But the doctors attending Nicolas Ferry were little better
in this respect, and their callous attitude to the ailing, prematurely aged court dwarf does them little credit. The skeletons
of Nicolas Ferry and Caroline Crachami were also treated in
a very similar manner, as both were kept in famous museums

in Paris and London for many years. The Sicilian Fairy has for many years been one of the most spectacular exhibits in the Hunterian Museum: her tiny skeleton, standing between those of the giants Charles Freeman and Charles Byrne, was a familiar sight to generations of English surgeons. Nicolas Ferry's skeleton was moved from the Cabinet du Roi to the Musée d'Histoire Naturelle in Paris, where the wretched dwarf's skeleton was put among the skeletons of animals in the department of zoology; the harsh and unjust censures of the objectionable Count de Tressan were thus confirmed through the irony of fate. Nicolas Ferry's skeleton has now found a more suitable repository at the Musée de l'Homme, where it still is today.

Doctor Morand and Count de Tressan had discussed what kind of obscure disorder had made Bébé into such a remarkable *lusus naturae*. At the time, there was much confusion on how to classify cases of extreme dwarfism. Doctor Morand differentiated between two categories of dwarfs: the deformed and the non-deformed. The former category must have encompassed the chondrodystrophics and those suffering from rickets; Bébé belonged to the latter category, also called 'les véritables nains'. In the nineteenth century, other diagnostic suggestions were put forth, but without much ground being gained. In 1890, the French obstetrician Dr Porak showed Nicolas Ferry's skull to Professor Fournier, a distinguished vene-reologist, and the professor pronounced that the appearance of the parietal bones indicated that Bébé had been a victim of gummous periostitis of the skull, a manifestation of congenital syphilis. Professor Fournier knew well that children with congen-ital syphilis were often of a short stature, and he considered the famous court dwarf as an extreme example. Seven years later, the teratologist L. Manouvrier examined Nicolas Ferry's skull at the Musée de l'Homme. Like Porak and Fournier, he found changes in both parietal bones speaking in favour of what he called an 'ostéo-périostite', but he did not speculate about what disease had originally caused these changes. Among later authors, there have been differing opinions on whether Nicolas Ferry really had

syphilis, and whether this disease could really explain his remarkable growth retardation and premature ageing. The discovery of
the surgeon Saucerotte's autopsy report in an obscure publication
has made it clear that Bébé really had some kind of lesion on
the inside of the skull, just as Porak and Fournier had assumed
from the appearance of the bones. It was not only situated on the
parietal bones, however, but also between them, and this reddish
tumour even pressed against his brain. From the overall clinical
picture, it is extremely unlikely that Nicolas Ferry had congenital
syphilis, however. His parents and siblings were reported to be
strong and in excellent health, and Nicolas himself never showed
any of the typical signs of congenital syphilis (Hutchinson's triad).
It may be, of course, that he caught a venereal contagion at some
later date, but although the gossipy court chronicles have hinted
that he was sexually active, it is unlikely that the frail, sickly dwarf
was capable of any exertions of this kind, at least during the last
five years of his life. The court physicians, who knew him well and
who reported his failings without any concern for the privacy of
their patient, mention nothing about any venereal disease, and at
autopsy his genitals were normal.

In 1911, the British surgeon and teratologist Sir Hastings
Gilford re-examined the cases of both Nicolas Ferry and Caroline
Crachami. He quoted the contemporary French diagnosis of
'syphilis, microcephaly and infantilism, ending in senilism', but
did not agree with it. In particular, he found it impossible to
accept that Nicolas Ferry's remarkable intrauterine and postnatal
growth retardation could be the result of congenital syphilis.
Instead, Gilford compared Nicolas Ferry and Caroline Crachami
with some other cases of 'ateleiosis', a syndrome of symmetrical
dwarfism with 'delay in growth and development', and found
several common characteristics. In particular, Bébé's skeleton
– and the portraits of him during life – showed the same nano-
cephalic profile as several other cases, with a large, beak-like nose
and a feeble, receding chin. In the mid-twentieth century, several
geneticists understood that the old syndrome of 'ateleiosis' was
in fact a heterogeneous group of conditions. In 1960, Professor

H.P.G. Seckel of the University of Chicago was able to propose a new, autosomal recessive syndrome of intrauterine growth retardation, postnatal dwarfism and microcephaly, characterised with a bird-headed profile, a large, beak-like nose, and a receding chin. He considered Nicolas Ferry and Caroline Crachami as two of the earliest and most extreme cases of 'Bird-headed Dwarfism'; their birth weights are the lowest recorded in all time for this syndrome.

In modern clinical genetics, it has become apparent that the old term 'Bird-headed Dwarfism' is an uncouth as well as an imprecise denominator, and also that primordial microcephalic dwarfism (or Seckel syndrome) is quite a heterogeneous condition. Almost all cases have been mentally retarded, often severely so. In contrast, there is no definite evidence that Caroline Crachami was particularly feeble-minded. Both Gilford and Seckel claimed that certain points in Home's description, such as her quickness of sight, attraction to bright objects and pleasure in music and fine clothes, would point towards mental retardation, but since these observations concern a nine-year-old girl, their judgement is a trifle severe. The newspaperman William Jerdan, who appears to have studied her at least as closely as Home, considered her as perfect as a common child of the same age. All accounts of her agree that she was quick-witted and amusing; although Italian was her native tongue, she learnt to speak English with alacrity. William Clift's autopsy report confirms that she suffered from severe tuberculosis, as was correctly diagnosed during life by Sir Everard Home. This might explain some of her bodily infirmities, and also that her mental state might have varied somewhat due to exhaustion. After I had described the case of Caroline Crachami in 1992, it did not take long for some experienced paediatricians to discover similar modern instances. The so-called 'Caroline Crachami syndrome' is today a recognised subgroup within the spectrum of primordial microcephalic dwarfism. Its main characteristics are severe intrauterine growth retardation, absence of osteodysplastic skeletal lesions, scarcity of subcutaneous fat and near-normal intelligence.

In the 1950s, studies by Professor A.E.W. Miles demonstrated that Caroline Crachami's dental age was just three years at the time of her death. In 1998, a group of London scientists reproduced this finding using up-to-date X-ray methodology as well as scanning electron microscopy. Their conclusion was a startling one, however: they claimed that Caroline Crachami had been just three years old at the time of her death, and that there had been a conspiracy to conceal this fact, since a nine-year-old dwarf would be more financially lucrative than a three-year-old one! They leave it unexplained whether Everard Home and William Clift were part of this conspiracy, or whether they were just blithering idiots who could not tell a nine-year-old child from one aged just three. And what about William Jerdan's valuable description of Caroline Crachami's behaviour: if she had been just three years old, her ability to express herself fluently in a foreign language would almost make her into a miniature infant prodigy! The truth would appear to be that in some instances of osteodysplastic primordial dwarfism, dental age is markedly retarded. For example, one late nineteenth-century French case had a dental age of just eight at the age of fourteen, and an American case described in 1995 also had marked delay of dental development.

Nicolas Ferry had many characteristics in common with the typical individual with 'Bird-headed Dwarfism': his microcephaly, mental retardation, large nose, hyperactivity, thin shrill voice and extrovert personality are all recognised features of this condition. In his youth, his facial configuration, with a broad forehead and well-developed mandible, was quite unlike that of a case of Seckel syndrome, however. What particularly differentiates Nicolas Ferry from the vast majority of instances of primordial microcephalic dwarfism is his premature ageing. After the age of eighteen, he developed typical 'bird-headed' features, with a grotesquely large, beak-like nose and a receding chin. In his original monograph, Professor Seckel wrote that 'senile features are virtually unknown in bird-headed dwarfs', but this may, on good grounds, be doubted. Six of Seckel's original fifteen cases died between five and twenty-three years of age. One of them had evidence of cardiomegaly and generalised atherosclerosis. In his teens, an American patient developed, as had Bébé 200 years earlier, alopecia, greying of the remaining hair, a stooped posture, and considerable accentuation of his 'bird-headed' appearance; his growth retardation was much less pronounced than that of the famous eighteenth-century court dwarf, however.

There is a condition called progeria, or the Hutchinson-Gilford syndrome, in which the main symptom is premature ageing. Already in their early teens, the sufferers of this loathsome disease develop a wrinkled, wizened appearance, alopecia, osteoporosis and pronounced arteriosclerosis; they are unlikely to survive after their twenty-fifth birthday, and die as bedridden invalids. Anyone who has seen one of these individuals is unlikely to forget the encounter. In is interesting to note that patients with progeria are often of a short stature, and that individuals with the related Werner syndrome, or *progeria adultorum*, sometimes gradually develop a 'bird-headed' appearance. Considering the case of Nicolas Ferry, and a few others, it seems reasonable to suggest that there is a progeroid variant of osteodysplastic primordial dwarfism, with more or less pronounced intrauterine growth retardation.

During Nicolas Ferry's lifetime, medical men and other observers consistently had a very low opinion of his intelligence and character. He was likened to a trained dog or monkey, and described as highly selfish, jealous, choleric and sensuous. Like the majority of the victims of osteodysplastic primordial dwarfism, Nicolas was definitely mentally retarded. It should be noted, however, that the degree of mental retardation is not related to the size and birth weight of the individual, as evidenced by Caroline Crachami. Her birth weight was only one pound, the lowest ever in the annals of this syndrome. At the age of eight, a time when poor Nicolas could hardly make himself understood in French, Caroline Crachami was able to express herself fluently in a foreign language, and gave witty and apposite replies to questions. Some of the anecdotes about Nicolas Ferry would imply that he was far less mentally retarded than Dr Morand and Count de Tressan had claimed, however. Furthermore, the person who knew him best, the Princess de Talmont, was outraged by the count's accusations. It does not seem unreasonable that the spiteful count, who seems to have loathed the spoilt, scatterbrained, irritating court dwarf, let his detestation cloud whatever scientific judgement he may have possessed. After all, it is rare, even in France, to find a trained dog or monkey expressing itself fluently in French.

Nicolas Ferry's contemporaries were much impressed by his triumphant career at the court of King Stanislas, and he was called the happiest of dwarfs. A local dignitary, the President Hérault, ridiculed Bébé's simple-minded mother, who persisted in having masses said for her son to grow and be tall; was it not his dwarfism that had made his fortune? In fact, King Stanislas probably did Nicolas a great disfavour when he removed the boy from his parents. Voltaire was not the only observer to question the moral tone at Lunéville, and it was certainly a very improper place for an impressionable young child to grow up. Instead of leading a harmonic, rural life with his parents and siblings in Champenay, he was spoilt, overindulged, and treated as an interesting little pet trained to perform a few tricks before distinguished visitors. The ladies at court dressed him in splendid clothes like a little doll, and he had his own doll's house to live in. A popular epigram about King Stanislas said that:

> Voilà les trois jouets d'un roi cher aux Lorrains
> Griffon son chien, son singe et Bébé son nain;

These are the three toys of the king who is dear to the people of Lorrains
Griffon his dog, his monkey and Bébé his dwarf;

The king's dog, monkey and court dwarf were often taken for a walk together in the garden. Although his disease had a genetic origin, environment rather than heredity caused Nicolas Ferry's bad character.

8

THE
Biddenden
MAIDS

On every Easter Monday morning, the village of Biddenden, situated not far from Staplehurst in Kent, is the scene of a curious old custom called the Biddenden Maids' Charity. Through the window of the Old Workhouse, tea, cheese and loaves of bread are given to the local widows and pensioners. Large amounts of Biddenden cakes, baked from flour and water, are distributed among the crowd of tourists and spectators. The cakes bear the effigy of the Biddenden Maids, two female figures whose bodies appear to be joined together at the hips and shoulders. A tradition of obscure and ancient origins tells that these Maids were born in the year 1100 and that they lived joined together for thirty-four years. The Biddenden Maids have been extensively cited in medical literature as one of the earliest genuine cases of conjoined (Siamese) twins upon record, although some antiquaries have considered the tradition to be a mere fable, and others have suggested that the Maids' year of birth was probably closer to 1500.

According to tradition, the Biddenden Maids, Mary and Eliza Chulkhurst, were born to fairly wealthy parents in the

year 1100. Their bodies were joined at the hips and shoulders.
They were naturally close friends, although one source states that
they sometimes disagreed in minor matters, and had 'frequent
quarrels, which sometimes terminated in blows.' In 1134, when
the Maids had lived joined together for thirty-four years, Mary
was suddenly taken ill and died. It was proposed that Eliza should
be separated from her sister's corpse by means of a surgical operation, but she refused with the words, 'As we came together we
will also go together', and herself died six hours later. In their
joint will, the Maids left certain parcels of land in Biddenden,
containing in all about twenty acres, to the churchwardens of
that parish and their successors in perpetuity. The rent from
these fields, henceforth known as the Bread and Cheese Lands,
was to provide an annual dole for the poor. A somewhat suspect
nineteenth-century account tells us that the annual income from
the Maids' parcels of land was 6 guineas at the time of their
death. Every Easter Sunday for many years, the Maids' charity of
bread, cheese and beer was given to the deserving poor. When
Biddenden church was visited by the Archdeacon of Canterbury
on Easter Day 1605, the custom that 'on that day our parson giveth
unto the parishioners bread, cheese, cakes and divers barrels of
beer, brought in there and drawn' was not observed, because it
was usually accompanied by 'much disorder by reason of some
unruly ones, which at such a time we cannot restrain with any
ease.' In 1645, the rector William Horner had brought a lawsuit
before the Committee for Plundered Clergymen to claim that
the Bread and Cheese Lands were glebe land and thus belonged
to the church rather than the villagers. The case caused quite a
controversy between the rector and the churchwardens, but in
1649 the rector was finally non-suited. In 1656, the persistent
clergyman brought another protracted lawsuit in the Court of
the Exchequer for the recovery of these lands, but again without
success, and the Biddenden Easter charity continued as before.
In 1681, another controversial Biddenden rector, Giles Hinton,
reported to the Archbishop of Canterbury that the distribution
was made inside the church 'with much disorder and indecency',

and he suggested that the custom needed 'a regulation by His Grace's Authority.' The charity remained, however, although the distribution of the cakes was removed to the church porch. In the second half of the eighteenth century, the charity was distributed directly after the afternoon service, and the church was filled with a large and hungry congregation. In 1770, the income from the Maids' lands was 20 guineas per annum, and a good deal of bread, cheese and beer was distributed. Those who did not gain an entrance into the crowded church had to be content with the hard Biddenden cakes with the Maids' effigy, which were thrown out among the populace from the church roof; already in the eighteenth century, these cakes were much sought after as curiosities. A broadsheet on the Chulkhurst sisters and their bequest was printed in 1808, and sold outside the church during Easter for twopence. By this time, the income from the Maids' lands had increased to 31 guineas and 11 shillings per annum, and as many as 1,000 Biddenden cakes were baked, as well as 300 quartern loaves and cheese in proportion.

In the 1820s, a 'new and enlarged' account of the Maids was printed, in which it was stated that a gravestone marked with a diagonal line, situated near the rector's pew in Biddenden church, was shown to visitors as the Maids' place of interment. The church floor has since been renewed, and there is no gravestone visible near the rector's pew, but it might be that it is situated beneath the organ, which now stands behind the rector's seat. It is probable that the Chulkhurst sisters were depicted on a stained-glass window in the east wall of the church, which has now been filled in. A poem regarding this was quoted from the old charity documents:

> The moon on the east oriel shone,
> Through slender shafts of shapely stone,
> The silver light, so pale and faint,
> Shewed the twin sisters and many a saint
> Whose images on the glass were dyed;
> Mysterious maidens side by side.

The moon beam kissed the holy pane,
and threw on the pavement a mystic stain.

Thus the grave of the Biddenden Maids cannot be identified with certainty. The oldest parts of the present church of
Biddenden are from the twelfth century; the impressive tower
was added around the year 1400, but an older Saxon church had
been standing on the same spot.

According to the entries for March 1826 in Hone's *Every Day
Book*, Biddenden was at this time completely thronged with
visitors on Easter Sunday, 'attracted from adjacent towns and
villages by the usage, and the wonderful account of its origin.'
The public houses had a busy time, and the day was generally
spent 'in rude festivity'. The increasing fame of the Biddenden
Maids and their charity made the crowds that gathered in the
church on Easter Sunday larger and more unruly; there were
many disturbances during service, and the churchwardens sometimes had to use their long wands as weapons to keep back
the hungry and impatient congregation. As a result of this, the
distribution of the charity was moved to the Biddenden poorhouse and performed immediately after the afternoon service
on Easter Sunday. In 1882, the rector of Biddenden applied to
the Archbishop of Canterbury that the Easter ceremony was still
disorderly as a result of excessive partaking of the beer, and he
wished that it should be discontinued. The Archbishop allowed it
to continue, however, although he deprived the recipients of the
beer. In April 1900, it was stated in a local newspaper that large
crowds of people assembled in the road at the Old Workhouse
on Easter Sunday, and the two police constables who guarded the
approach to the gateway had considerable difficulties in keeping
them back. Altogether 190 loaves and cheese in proportion were
distributed in that year, and the 500 Biddenden cakes baked for
visitors were quite insufficient to meet the demand. The *Times*
also gave attention to this ancient custom, and it was stated that
actual records supported that the distribution of the cakes, on
which the Maids 'were represented as united together, like the

Siamese twins', had taken place as far back as 1740, and very probably long before that date.

In 1907, the Chulkhurst Charity was consolidated with some other local charities, in order to provide the Biddenden pensioners and widows with bread, cheese and tea every Easter and a sum of money at Christmas. In due course, the Bread and Cheese Lands were sold, and today they contain a number of cottages called the Chulkhurst Estate. This has made it possible to extend the charity considerably. For many years, it was a custom to bake special, very large loaves for the Easter festivity, but this was ceased when the Biddenden baker's shop was closed down. The distribution of bread and cheese from the Old Workhouse has been continued as a curiosity, and it is today a popular tourist attraction; every visitor may have a Biddenden cake as a memento of the ceremony. The cakes are so hard as to be almost uneatable, but they are the more enduring as souvenirs. At the Biddenden village green stands a wrought sign of the philanthropic Chulkhurst twins, which was erected in the 1920s.

THE ANTIQUARIAN EVIDENCE

The two best-known early sources on the Biddenden Maids are the 1775 edition of the *Antiquarian Repertory* and Dr Ducarel's *Repertory of the Endowments to the Dioceses of Canterbury and Rochester*, published in 1782. These two early accounts agree that the charity had existed for a very long time and that it had been given by two conjoined twin sisters. According to one version, they were joined together at the shoulders and 'lower part of their bodies' and lived many years, while in the other it is merely stated that they were joined together in their bodies, and that they lived in this state until they were 'betwixt 20 and 30 years old'. The earliest proper account of the Biddenden Maids is an anonymous article in the *Gentleman's Magazine* of 1770. Interestingly, it is stated here that the Maids were conjoined from the waist down to the hips, and thus not joined at two separate anatomical sites; they lived in this way until they were considerably advanced in years. It is specifically stated that they were not known by any particular name. In spite of the high antiquity of the tradition, the writer of the article did not doubt its authenticity: 'An enquiry in the parish itself will procure abundant testimony, that the reality of this prodigy has always been honoured with the highest credit.' None of these three independent eighteenth-century accounts of the Maids mentioned two veritable cornerstones in their legend: the name of Chulkhurst and their alleged year of birth, 1100; these details were added in the broadsheet that appeared in the 1790s.

While these three early accounts of the Biddenden Maids took their existence for granted, the antiquary Edward Hasted declared the tradition to be nothing but an old fable, in his *History of Kent*. This monumental historical work, which had cost its author more than forty years of labour, was published in four folio volumes between 1778 and 1799. Edward Hasted stated that the legend of the Biddenden Maids was merely 'a vulgar tradition' and that the charity had in reality been initiated by two maidens by the name of Preston; the picture of the women on the cakes was the likeness of two poor widows, the most likely recipients of the Biddenden charity. He also claimed that the print of the women on the cakes had only occurred during the last fifty years (he was writing in the 1780s). Edward Hasted was an acknowledged expert on topography and genealogy, but although his conclusions about the Biddenden Maids have been largely accepted by later British antiquaries, it might be doubted whether he had appreciated the ethnological aspects of the problem. Hasted's contemporary, Sir Egerton Brydges, described him in his autobiography as 'a little, mean-looking man, with a long face and a high nose; quick in his movements and sharp in his manner. He had no imagination or sentiment, nor any extraordinary quality of mind, unless memory.' Although this severe judgement of the old antiquary is probably exaggerated, some later critics have also had a low opinion of the social and biographical parts of Hasted's *History of Kent*.

Edward Hasted's harsh judgement of the Biddenden Maids tradition was uncritically accepted in several nineteenth-century British ethnological and archaeological works, and during this time there was little new information on the Chulkhurst sisters and their curious bequest. The Maids were sometimes mentioned in articles concerning the celebrated Siamese twins: a note about the Maids was added after Sir James Simpson's lecture on Siamese twins had been published in the *British Medical Journal* of 1869. The Maids were several times mentioned in the pages of the *Notes and Queries* magazine, particularly after the original Siamese twins, Chang and Eng, had toured Europe and showed that such a condition was certainly not incompatible with life for a considerable period of time. In a note from 1866, the editors of this journal doubted Hasted's explanation of the print of the conjoined twin sisters and the name Chulkhurst on the Biddenden cakes, and considered that the mystery of the Maids was yet unsolved, and that it was well worth the attention of some of the Kentish antiquaries to investigate it.

This challenge remained unanswered for many years, but in 1900 the antiquary George Clinch published a thorough paper on the Maids, in which a good deal of new information was given. He had obtained plaster impressions of the moulds for the Biddenden cakes, and examined them closely, attempting to determine the custom's antiquity. His photographs of the three cake moulds all depict the Biddenden Maids as conjoined twins. On the broadsheet, the Biddenden Maids are depicted as handsome in feature and elegantly dressed in the costume of the time of Mary I, but their picture on the oldest cake mould is primitive and bizarre. The eyes, faces and breasts are represented only by protrusions, and the wear and tear of the old mould in the baker's shop could only partially be blamed for the snout-like expression of the faces. There are several other odd details, such as the arrangement of the hair, the presence of naked branches of trees on either side of the Maids, and a star-like object between their waists. The second type of cake differs from the first in that the design of the faces is flatter and more detailed, and that the dress is more ornamental. The headdress is new to this mould, as are the large earrings. This mould was used for Biddenden cakes in the 1820s and also in the 1860s; it is most probable that it was also used in 1875 and spoken of as boxwood dies cut in 1814. The third mould is the most detailed and ornamental, and certainly the latest; the semicircular top has the picture of a sun, and the tree branches from the first mould recur. The costume is not unlike that of the second mould. Another writer, the teratologist J. W. Ballantyne, speaks of two moulds for Biddenden cakes being used in 1895, one being the older (probably 150 years old), while the other was made much more recently. It is likely that these were the first and third moulds, respectively, of those photographed by Clinch. Today, only one cake mould is used, and this is of much later date. According to the trustees of the Chulkhurst charity, none of the older moulds have been kept for posterity.

From his examination of the lettering and costume of the moulds, George Clinch considered them to be from the sixteenth century. An expert in such matters, Mr Mill Stephenson F.S.A., suggested that the Maids' clothing was from the latter part of the sixteenth century. However, there are strong arguments that none of the moulds depicted by Clinch were actually in use before the 1780s. Specimens of Biddenden cakes from the 1770s were reproduced by Dr Ducarel and by the writer in the *Antiquarian Repertory*; they differ markedly from those described by Clinch, which were probably nineteenth-century specimens. None of the three cakes from the 1770s record the names of the Maids, nor their year of birth or age at the time of their death. Clinch blames the carelessness of the eighteenth-century engravers for this inconsistency, but this seems less likely. It is reasonable to suggest that there were in fact several older moulds, used during the eighteenth century: it was reported in the *Antiquarian Repertory* that the cakes were 'of different fineness and forms', and drawings of two different cakes were reproduced. The pictures of the women on the Biddenden cakes from the 1770s have many details in common with those of the later cake moulds, especially the oldest of these. The three eighteenth-century accounts of the Maids previously quoted do not mention their names, and it is even explicitly stated that 'the Maids of Biddenden are not known by any particular name'. Had the cake moulds photographed by Clinch been in use during this period, there would have been no difficulty in determining their proper names as well as their alleged year of birth. Clinch's arguments about the Maids' clothing may certainly be correct, since the effigy was obviously copied from the older moulds. In the *Antiquarian Repertory* of 1775, it was stated that the sisters had lived 'as tradition says, two hundred and fifty years ago', and Clinch considered this estimate more trustworthy than the popular belief that they had been born in 1100; their year of birth would thus have been in the beginning of the sixteenth century. Furthermore, Clinch's examination of the oldest cake mould led him to believe that the second numeral from the left in the date was really a slightly curved five, and that the Maids were thus born in 1500. However, I am unable to detect any difference at all between the two first numerals in the date of this, or any other, of the Biddenden cake moulds.

Several antiquaries commented on Clinch's article, usually to defend Hasted's arguments; in the *Notes and Queries* magazine it was even stated that 'the whole story is discredited by competent antiquaries'. The antiquary Arthur Hussey had examined the index of wills at the Canterbury Probates Office, and found none with the name of Chulkhurst. Among the historical and ethnological writers of today, opinions on the Biddenden Maids are divided: some agree with Hasted that the old tradition is entirely fabulous, while others favour the version that they lived in the sixteenth century. In the medical literature, however, the legend of the Biddenden Maids is uncritically accepted, including their year of birth, 1100.

THE MEDICAL EVIDENCE

In all time, the phenomenon of conjoined twinning has fascinated both laymen and the medical profession, and the literature on this subject reaches back far into time. Normal twins are either dizygotic (70%) or monozygotic. Dizygotic twins are the result of the fertilisation of two separate ova; monozygotic (identical) twins are the result of splitting of the fertilised ovum at an early stage of its development. In the majority of monozygotic twins (97%) this splitting of the ovum happens at what is known as the morula or blastocyst stages, before the development of an amniotic cavity; the twins will thus have one amniotic membrane each. If the splitting happens at a later stage, the twins will share one amniotic membrane. If the splitting is only partial, which happens in about 10% of twins that share their amniotic membrane, the twins will be conjoined. Conjoined twins are thus always monozygotic, always of the same sex, share one placenta and one amniotic membrane, and have identical chromosomal patterns. The incidence of conjoined twinning is approximately one in 100,000 deliveries, but approximately 60% of these twins are stillborn.

Conjoined twins are classified by the site of connection. The most common type is thoracopagus twins, which are joined at the chest, followed by omphalopagus (or xiphopagus) twins, which are joined at the upper abdomen. Other sites of connection include the sacrum (ischiopagus), the pelvis (pygopagus) and the skull (craniopagus). A major difficulty in accepting the tradition of the Biddenden Maids as entirely authentic is the nature of their malformation: in the available cakes and drawings, they are depicted as being conjoined both at the shoulders and at the hips. It is extremely rare for Siamese twins to have two separate parts of conjunction. In those few instances, two quite closely related points of fusion have been involved, such as the thorax and abdomen or lower abdomen and peritoneum. Although Professor Ian Aird, a well-known English expert on conjoined twins, did not consider such a double conjunction to be impossible, with the motivation that separate blastomeres might fuse at two different points, or that twins fused primarily at one point might obtain a secondary fusion later, very few modern teratologists would accept the possibility of a fusion at the hips and shoulders, particularly in a pair of viable twins.

In 1895, the surgeon J.W. Ballantyne was the first to consider the Biddenden Maids from a teratological point of view. He suggested that they were in fact only conjoined at the hips and thus belonged to the teratological type pygopagus. Such conjoined twins each have two arms and legs, and it has often been noted that in order to walk without difficulty, they put their arms around each other's shoulders; this might have led to the Biddenden Maids being depicted in the way described earlier. The German teratologists Ernst Schwalbe and Hans Hübner agreed with Ballantyne's hypothesis, as did the French surgeon Marcel Baudouin. The teratological type pygopagus, where the twins are joined at the sacrum, accounts for about 8% of conjoined twins. The twins have more or less complete fusion of the rectum and other perineal structures, but the spinal cords are usually separate. The first case of pygopagi upon record, living twins born in Rome in 1493, was described by Conradus Lycosthenes in his *Chronicon Prodigorum et Ostentorum*. The first attempt at separating such twins was made in 1700 by the use of caustic, resulting in the death of both twins. The first successful surgical separation of pygopagus twins was performed in 1950, and in later years several pairs of such twins have been separated. The success of the operation depends very much on the extent of the conjunction between the bodies and the number of shared organs, as well as the occurrence of additional malformations of the heart and lungs.

A fair proportion of the pygopagus twins are perfectly viable at birth, and several of the historical cases have reached maturity. The Hungarian Sisters, Helen and Judith, were a celebrated pair of eighteenth-century pygopagus twins; they travelled extensively through Europe and were examined by many eminent anatomists and naturalists. In 1708, at the age of seven, they were brought to England and publicly shown in London. James Paris du Plessis, the writer on monstrosities whose thoughts on pig-faced ladies have been quoted earlier, had occasion to see them, as evidenced by his manuscript *History of Prodigies* in the British Library:

They were brisk, merry, and well-bred; they could read, write, and sing very prettily: they could speak three different languages, as Hungarian, Low Dutch, and French, and were learning English. They were very handsome, very well shaped in all parts, and had beautiful faces. Helen was born three hours before her sister Judith. They loved each other very tenderly.

Other sources agree that Helen and Judith were both intelligent and beautiful, and that their extensive tours of Europe during their most impressionable age had made them very accomplished linguists. In later life, the Hungarian Sisters entered a convent, and died there in 1723 aged twenty-two. Among the theologians, there was a debate about whether their souls were united beyond death, but the question was never resolved.

Millie and Christine, pygopagus conjoined twin girls born in Columbus County, North Carolina, in 1851, had a tempestuous early life. Their parents were black slaves, and they were repeatedly sold, traded and even kidnapped by unscrupulous showmen, who appreciated their value as natural curiosities. They were later taken care of by the wife of one of their showmen, a certain Mrs Joseph Smith, who became their guardian. They became very proficient performers, and danced, jumped and skipped rope during the shows. Christine could lift Millie completely off the floor, and walked or ran carrying her with complete ease, without any pain or strain at their junction. This is likely to be because they had fused pelvises, and thus a rigid bony barrier between them. Their voices were excellent – one a soprano, the other a contralto – and their artist's name, 'The Two-Headed Nightingale', took little coining. All accounts describe them as cheerful, pious and intelligent: they could speak seven languages fluently. They had no desire to be parted by surgical means, saying that they hoped to leave this world as they came into it, together. Millie and Christine were on tour for the larger part of their adult lives, and travelled to Europe several times. They were particular favourites of Queen Victoria, who received them in audience whenever they came to England. In the early 1900s, they retired from show business and bought a large house in North Carolina, which they filled with the souvenirs of all their tours. Millie became ill with tuberculosis, however, and died on 9 October 1912; Christine followed her eight hours later.

The pygopagus twins Rosa and Josefa Blazek were born in rural Bohemia in 1878. Their parents were much astonished by this 'monstrous' birth, and consulted the local witch, who recommended that the children should be kept without food for eight days. The twins survived this cruel treatment, however, and after this impressive demonstration of resilience, even the witch agreed that they should be kept alive. Several showmen applied to Rosa and Josefa's parents to get permission to exhibit them, but the parents refused until the twins were thirteen years old. Then, a local showman took them to Paris, where they were examined by Dr Marcel Baudouin. He thought them lively, intelligent little girls, and contrasted them to the morose stupidity of their parents, who were also present. Rosa and Josefa went on to make a career for themselves, of course preferring life in gay Paris to the drab existence in the cabin of their rustic parents in the Bohemian backwoods. They were called 'Le Pygopage du Théâtre de l'âge Gaité', and were a well-known attraction at the Paris stage of the 1890s; they amused the audience with singing and playing violin duets. Later, they passed out of public notice until they consulted the surgical clinic at the Prague General Hospital in 1910, after Rosa had noticed a large and rapidly growing abdominal swelling. She was asked whether she might be pregnant, but denied it vehemently; her sister, who was certainly in a position to know, supported her denial. But before the medical investigation was brought any further, Rosa was delivered of a healthy son. Later, the two inseparable sisters were rumoured to have married the same man. In 1922, they moved to the United States in the company of their brother; they died there later the same year at the age of forty-three.

In the light of these three case histories, it is certainly not unlikely that the Biddenden Maids may have lived as long as thirty-four years. Nor it is impossible that one sister survived the other for six hours. At the deathbed of the original Siamese twins, Chang survived Eng for at least two hours, despite the fact that their livers were connected, and in a French case, one conjoined twin survived the other for more than ten hours. The German teratologist Hans Hübner quotes several similar cases, including that of a pair of omphalopagus twins where one individual survived the other for seven hours.

EARLY BRITISH CASES OF CONJOINED TWINS

It was considered of interest to examine some of the old standard works of teratology, as well as some English historical chronicles, in order to look for early references to the Biddenden Maids and other live-born British conjoined twins. Due to Clinch's argument about the Maids' time of birth, both the twelfth century and the fifteenth and sixteenth centuries were taken into account. It turned out that the Maids were not mentioned in any of the major teratological works of the sixteenth and seventeenth centuries, such as those by Aldrovandi, Liceti, Paré, Schenckius and others. Nor were they noticed in the *Philosophical Transactions* or any other British collection of teratological descriptions. This is an argument against the opinion that they lived in the sixteenth or seventeenth century, since most other remarkable conjoined twins who reached maturity were noted in the popular and scientific works of this period. For example, both the Scottish Brothers, who had only one pair of legs but two perfect bodies from the waist upwards, and Lazarus Colloredo, who had an imperfect parasitic twin, Joannes Baptista, hanging from his epigastrium, aroused much interest among men of learning. There were also several notable early English cases. In 1552, ischiopagus conjoined twin girls were born in a village near Oxford; they lived for eighteen days, and were much admired by the country people. The births of stillborn conjoined twins at Plymouth in 1670 and at Petworth in 1677 were both recorded in the *Philosophical Transactions.* Conjoined twins who lived for thirty-four years would have been quite a sensation, and it is reasonable to presume that if the Biddenden Maids had lived in the sixteenth or seventeenth century, they would certainly have been mentioned in the annals of teratology.

The next case of living conjoined twins in Britain attracted even more attention, and is noteworthy in its own right. On 19 May 1680, a strange happening occurred in the village of Isle Brewers in Somerset. A poor village woman was uncommonly big with child, and the old women predicted that she was going to bear twins. After a tedious childbirth, she was delivered of conjoined twin girls. The spectators were of course mightily impressed with this singular event:

> The groaning Mother was disburthened of the Monstrous Birth, whose frightful Apparition so amazed the several Assistants and Spectators, that starting back all pale, they knew not what to think, but long time stood doubtful in their wonder, e're they durst approach, supposing it more dreadful than it was, but after a more curious View, they found it was a humain Creature, and bore the Stamp (though in an unusual Form) of woman, so that taking heart, they annimated each other so far, as to take it in their Arms, whilst in a double voice it cried aloud.

When the midwife and the villagers dared examine the twins more closely, they saw that they were joined back to back from the nipples down to the navel. The children were lively and seemed to be in perfect health. It was considered remarkable that 'when the Infant or Infants, which you please, cry, their Voices or Cries are of the selfsame note, though 'tis seldome that both heads cry together.' On 29 May, when they were ten days old, the twins were taken to be christened by the Revd Andrew Paschall. The conjoined twins were named Priscilla and Aquila; probably the parents considered these uncommon names suitable for such extraordinary children.

Later in 1680, a gentleman in Taunton wrote a short pamphlet about the Isle Brewers conjoined twins, illustrated by a coarse

drawing of the twins. It was clear to him that the conjoined
twins were two separate beings, and he even dared express the
theologically hazardous opinion that they also possessed two
immortal souls. The twins' bodies were conjoined at the backs,
and the ribs, breast-bones and bellies appeared to be distinct. The
twins had no further malformations: it amazed the pamphlet
writer that their tiny hands were perfection itself, 'having in all
sixteen Fingers and four Thumbs'. Their heads were of normal
size and form and they had 'two Female Faces, beautiful, fair,
and of pleasant Aspect; in which were plainly imprinted all the
smiling Graces of well-promising Virgins'. The pamphlet writer
found it unlikely that the conjoined twins were a punishment
for the sins of their parents, or a portent for the local people to
fear God: he seems to have regarded the twins more as a natural curiosity, and exclaimed: 'This is the Lord's doing, and it is
marvellous in our Eyes!' Hundreds of people visited Isle Brewers
daily 'to see the monstrous work of Nature, and admire so great
a piece of curiosity'. A plate in red pitcher clay was made to
commemorate the birth of Priscilla and Aquila; in the centre is
the likeness of the twins, with their date of birth across the middle
of the bodies. After the publication of the pamphlet about them,
the fame of the conjoined twins spread further. In 1681, the
aforementioned Andrew Paschall wrote a short description of
them for the Royal Society's *Philosophical Collections*. According
to Paschall, the twins' bodies were joined from the navel up to
a point just beneath the nipples. When the children were laid
supine, they seemed to have but one body where joined, but
when they were turned over, there was a deep furrow between
their bodies. Andrew Paschall was fascinated to see that one of
the twins could sleep calmly while the other cried. He concluded that Priscilla and Aquila appeared to be in perfect health:
'they Suck and Cry heartily, Exonerate apart freely, and are likely
to live, if the Multitudes that come to see them (sometimes 500
in a day) do not occasion the shortening of their Lives.'

In the 1680s, it was not uncommon that country squires
arranged cruel persecutions of the members of the Society

of Friends, or Quakers, within their jurisdiction. In Somerset, one of the worst of these harriers of the Quakers was Henry Walrond Esq., of Walrond's Hall near Isle Brewers. The Walrond family had been Lords of the Manor of Isle Brewers for many years. Walrond's daughter had married a local gentleman named Laurence Broom, and several of Broom's relations took up permanent residence at Walrond's Hall. Henry Walrond was struck by penury in the early 1680s, possibly because his extravagant friends, the Broom brothers, devoured a good deal of his income. To repair his financial difficulties, Walrond took the extraordinary step of abducting the conjoined twins from their mother, in order to have them exhibited for money. Sir Edward Phelips of Montacute, another enemy of the Society of Friends, was alleged to be Walrond's accomplice in this scheme. It is impossible to explain how these two worthies could have thought up such a bizarre plan to make money. It may be that they were impressed by the many spectators who wanted to see Priscilla and Aquila as a curiosity, and decided to turn this to their own advantage. The twins' mother might have been a Quaker, and by threats of reprisals, Walrond and Phelips could have taken the twins away from the wretched woman and placed them with some travelling exhibitor of monstrosities. It is unclear exactly when the conjoined twins were abducted, and how long they were exhibited before their death. Priscilla and Aquila were clearly alive in 1681, and there is some evidence that they may have died in 1683. Popular sentiment near Isle Brewers was of course very much against Walrond and Phelips, and in order to expose and shame them, a large plate in Lambeth Delft was made. It was glazed in an unusual shade of pale green, and depicts two well-dressed gentlemen, with epaulettes, sashes, wigs and swords. They support a likeness of the conjoined twins, whose names are given on each side. The inscription round the border says: 'BEHOVLD : TO : PARSONS : THAT : ARE : RECONSILD : TO : ROB : THE : PARENTS : AND : TO : KEEP : THE : CHILD.' At the feet of the two men are the words 'HEARE : IS : GAIN <> O'THE : BROOM'; evidently a punning allusion to the family of parasites who were Walrond's assistants.

From the available descriptions of them, it is evident that the Isle Brewers conjoined twins belonged to the type omphalopagus, in which the twins are joined from the lower part of the sternum down to the navel. Such omphalopagus (or xiphopagus) twins are often capable of prolonged extrauterine life. The extent of shared tissues varies a good deal: it has been shown that 52% of these twins have a common liver, and 17% also have a common diaphragm. A small group (12%) have only skin structures as a connecting, fibrous band, and are of course much easier to separate surgically. Already in 1689, the German practitioner Dr König operated on such a pair of omphalopagus twins by tightening ligatures around the connecting band of tissues, with complete success. Both twins lived, without any disfigurement. The original Siamese twins, Chang and Eng, also belonged to the omphalopagus group, but their conjunction was more extensive. They were born in 1811 and lived united for sixty-three years. It was often debated whether they could be separated, but when they were younger, the twins themselves were unwilling to submit to such an operation. When the Siamese twins grew older, they became afraid that if one died, the other would be tied to a corpse, and during a journey to London and Edinburgh they consulted several eminent surgeons. The verdict of Sir William Ferguson, among others, was that it was inadvisable to attempt a surgical separation. At autopsy, it was seen that the Siamese twins' liver and several major vessels were shared, and although they could have been separated with ease if they had lived today, an attempt at operation with nineteenth-century techniques would probably have been fatal. Today, surgical separation of omphalopagus twins is performed with excellent results. From the descriptions and illustrations of them, it is likely that the conjunction of Priscilla and Aquila was relatively extensive, and they are likely to have had a common liver. Nevertheless, they appeared to be in good health during their short life, which rules out the coexistence of additional malformations of the heart and

intestinal tract. With modern techniques, it is very likely that the
Isle Brewers omphalopagus twins could have been separated, but
with the surgical knowledge of the time, such an attempt was
of course not even considered.

EVIDENCE FROM HISTORICAL AND TERATOLOGICAL CHRONICLES

Due to the mystery and fascination of congenital malformations,
the annals of teratology stretch back far into the Dark Ages. The
'monsters' and strange births were considered as portents of war
and misery, or frightening signs of divine displeasure. Although
the old prodigy books and chronicles of strange events are unreliable sources, it was considered of interest to examine some of
the old English historical chronicles, in order to look for early
references to the Biddenden Maids. It turned out that there is a
remarkable accumulation of reports of English conjoined twins
at the beginning of the twelfth century. Ballantyne observed
that Lycosthenes, in his *Chronicon Prodigorum et Ostentorum* of
1557, had stated that there were conjoined twin brothers born
in England in 1112, and that their bodies were joined at the
hips and 'ad superiores partes', as in the popular descriptions of
the Biddenden Maids. Even more interesting is that a medieval
historical chronicle, the *Chronicon Scotorum*, tells us that in 1099
a woman gave birth to 'two children together, in this year, and
they had but one body from the breast to the navel, and they
were two girls'. In the Irish chronicle *Annals of the Four Masters*
is an almost identical description, although the conjoined twin
girls are stated to have been born in 1103; in the *Annals of
Clonmacnoise* their year of birth is given as 1100. These ancient
descriptions are unreliable in details and probably dependent
on each other, but in spite of this they add some credibility to
the old tradition that the Biddenden Maids were really born in
1100. It should be added that in this year there was a strange
happening that excited popular imagination: King William Rufus
was found dead in the New Forest with an arrow, from either a

hunter or an assassin, in his breast. Several prodigies were said to have preceded the death of this sinful and extravagant monarch, and at Pentecost blood was seen to gush up from the earth like a fountain. Conjoined twins born this year might well be regarded as another strange prodigy foreboding the king's death, and thus be much noticed both in the chronicles and in folk tradition.

Another unexpected source on the Biddenden Maids was pointed out in 1869 by a certain Mr R.H. Cresswell, in a letter to the Revd James Boys, rector of Biddenden; this letter is now kept by the Biddenden Local History Society. Mr Cresswell had read an obscure 3,000-line medieval poem entitled *De contemptu mundi*, written in the first half of the twelfth century by Saint Bernard of Morlaix, an English monk in the monastery of Cluny. One section, given here in free translation, dealt with a strange birth in England at this time, which the pious monk considered a portent of the Day of Judgement:

> Two twin women in the English countryside
> Having, between them, only one set of legs,
> But wondrous to tell, both of them had
> a trunk, two breasts, two arms to themselves.
> If you wish to believe what I say and write,
> that when one of these united women, or sisters even,
> who had spent their lives sitting next to each others,
> was finally released by death from her bondage,
> the other followed her shortly after.

The rector believed that this poem proved without doubt the existence of the Biddenden Maids, but this was a somewhat hasty conclusion. Although the sex and geographical location agree with the legend of the Maids, the nature of the malformation in question does not agree with the early descriptions of them.

In many books and articles on conjoined twins, the Biddenden Maids are stated to be the earliest case of such a malformation in the history of mankind. However, this is quite untrue, and there are several earlier examples. The first of these cases is from Constantinople of the tenth century: conjoined twin boys from Armenia were taken to this city in 945 to be exhibited for money. They were both fully developed, with all members complete; their bodies were connected from the umbilicus to the lower part of the abdomen. They were for a long time residents of Constantinople, and were admired by many until the superstitious townspeople had them expelled for being a bad omen. They returned during the reign of Constantine VII; when one of them died, skilled doctors were audacious enough to attempt a surgical separation, but the surviving twin died after three days.

CONCLUDING REMARKS

The legend of the Biddenden Maids has many elements of truth. Several events in the Maids' story, such as their living joined together for a considerable time, their refusal to be separated and one of them living for some hours after the other had died, are likely to have had a great impact on popular imagination. The old tradition is teratologically quite possible, providing that the hypothesis of Ballantyne, that the Maids were pygopagus conjoined twins, is accepted; this interpretation has support from the earliest description of the Maids, and it is possible that the idea that they were joined in two places derives from a later misinterpretation of the figures on the Biddenden cake. The historian Edward Hasted's attempt to discredit the old legend seems less convincing, and some of his statements have been proven wrong. The antiquary Robert Chambers supported Hasted's arguments and presumed that the ignorant villagers had invented the story of the conjoined twin sisters, after the real origin of the charity had been forgotten. However, it is impossible to find a reasonable motive for the eighteenth-century Biddenden villagers to make up such a story, and it would certainly have been beyond their capacity to make it teratologically correct.

The Biddenden Easter charity can be traced back into the first years of the seventeenth century, and the mid-seventeenth-century legal documents from Parson Horner's unsuccessful lawsuit about the Bread and Cheese Lands stated that it had existed for many years. Furthermore, the depositions of witnesses among these documents inform us that these lands had originally been given by 'two Maidens that grew together in their bodies'. This important finding proves that already in the 1650s, tradition stated that the Biddenden Maids were conjoined twins. Edward Hasted's unsupported claim to the contrary can thus be disproved with certainty. It is remarkable that these depositions of witnesses do not contain the names of the benefactors, neither Chulkhurst nor Preston; because the twin sisters' names were stated to be unknown also in the reliable eighteenth-century accounts of the tradition, the names Mary and Eliza Chulkhurst must be suspected to be a later invention. It should be noted, though, that the International Genealogical Index reveals that a family with the uncommon name of Chulkhurst lived in Biddenden in the seventeenth and eighteenth centuries, and that no family named Preston was native to this district at the time.

Of the two earlier writers on the Biddenden Maids, the surgeon J.W. Ballantyne favoured the traditional version of the legend that they were born in 1100. The antiquary George Clinch suggested that they had in fact lived in the fifteenth or sixteenth century, but his arguments concerning the cake moulds do not stand up to a critical examination. Furthermore, it would seem odd that the only pair of British conjoined twins to reach maturity would have gone totally unnoticed in the popular and scientific literature, if they had lived at this time of great interest in the study of congenital malformations. Instead, there is a remarkable accumulation of old records concerning the birth of conjoined twins in the early twelfth century; the old legend that the Maids were born in 1100 cannot be dismissed.

9

The Tocci Brothers
AND OTHER
DICEPHALI

On 12 June 1668, Samuel Pepys visited the village of Norton St Philip in Somerset, not far from Bath. He decided to walk to the church, hoping to see the very ancient tomb of a knight templar. In the church, he also saw an old tombstone on which there was only two heads, and no other text or ornament, and made enquiries about its meaning. He was told, in a manner he described as fully credible, that there lay buried 'the Fair Maidens of Foscott, who had two bodies upwards, and one belly.' More than 100 years later, the Revd John Collinson wrote a brief description of Norton St Philip and its church in his *History of Somersetshire*. The much mutilated stone portraitures of the united twin sisters were on a tombstone in the floor of the nave of the church. They were called 'the Fair Maidens of Foscott' in local tradition. Foscott had once been a neighbouring village, but it was depopulated already in Collinson's time. According to tradition, the twins had been born with conjoined bodies, but nevertheless grew to mature years. Collinson wrote that when one of them died, 'the survivor was compelled to drag about her lifeless companion till death released her of the horrid burden'. It is clear from Collinson's account that the Fair Maidens of Foscott must have lived a long time before he came to Norton St Philip: not only was the village of Foscott, their place of birth, depopulated, but the stone portraiture of them on the tombstone in the nave of the church was severely mutilated through many years of wear and tear.

In the 1890s, the writer James John Hissey visited Norton St Philip, which he described as a thoroughly old-world place, looking the same as it had done many generations ago. The church, although ancient, did not appear to him very note-worthy architecturally, but a local garrulous old woman he met in the street pointed it out as very curious and promised to fetch a book on the history of the building. She returned with an old and much-thumbed book in her hands, and recommended Hissey to see 'the heads of the two ladies' on the top of the cupboard under the tower. When they reached the cupboard in question, however, nothing was there, and the old lady declared herself astonished, since the heads of the ladies had been there as long as she could remember. When the puzzled Hissey asked for further particulars about these mysterious 'ladies', the woman brought out her book, in which there was a chapter (or perhaps rather a bound-in pamphlet), amounting to about twenty pages of small print, giving 'A true account of the twin maidens of Foscote'. It transpired that the tombstone of the twin maidens, with their heads carved in stone and with hair down their sides, had once been in the floor of the chancel of the church, beneath which they were buried. They had two heads and only one body.

Posterity would have been better served if Hissey, instead of regaling his readers with another ten pages of vapid travelogue in his *Through Ten English Counties*, had made a proper reprint, or at least an abstract, of this curious old pamphlet. Not a single copy of it seems to be extant today, neither in the British Library nor in any local collection. It is particularly unfortunate that the exact age of the monument, and thus the twin sisters' date of death, is unknown, but from Pepys' description, it is likely to have been before the early seventeenth century. The remains of the tombstone, with the mutilated portraits of the heads of the twin sisters, have now been mounted on the wall of the entrance hall of the Norton St Philip church, where I saw it in 1997.

If the brief descriptions of the Fair Maidens of Foscott are trustworthy, they are one of the earliest examples of live-born conjoined twins belonging to the group 'dicephalus'. These twins have only one pelvic girdle and only one pair of legs, but a variable degree of duplication of the upper body. In the subcategory of dicephalus twins known as dicephalus tetrabrachius, the bodies divide above the waist: there are two torsos, four complete arms, and two heads. These dicephalus twins are the most likely to be viable, as evidenced by both historical and modern instances; it is not unlikely that the Fair Maidens of Foscott, with their 'two bodies upwards, but just one belly' belonged to this group. In another subcategory, known as dicephalus tribrachius, there is just one torso, with one arm to each side, and a third, sometimes atrophied, arm between the two heads. Finally, in the most extreme subcategory dicephalus dibrachius, there is one torso, two arms, and two heads and necks situated next to each other.

The perpetual wonder and fascination of conjoined twins has ensured that they are often mentioned in ancient chronicles; the dicephali, with two heads and just one lower body, were considered the most remarkable of all these prodigies of nature. Higden's *Polychronicon* and Capgrave's *Chronicle of England* agree that in AD 375, a two-headed boy was born in the castle of Emaus. Higden wrote that this boy was 'divided from the navelle upwarde, havenge 2 brestes and 2 hedes, with wittes dividede, in so moche that the oon slepynge or eitenge, that other did not eyte neither did slepe.' The twins died when two years old. Roger of Wendover's *Flowers of History* mention another pair of medieval dicephali reaching adulthood, this time in Gascony, France. A woman in these parts had two heads, four arms, and everything double down to the navel, but two legs and feet. When one twin laughed, ate and talked, the other wept, fasted and kept silence. What they ate with two mouths was expelled through a single orifice. According to Higden's chronicle, they both died within the space of two days, but Roger of Wendover added some lurid details, presumably of his own invention. One of the twins died, and the other had to carry the dead carcass on her back for nearly three years, until she herself died from the oppression and stench of the corpse.

By far the most fascinating of these early instances of dicephalus conjoined twins are the famous Scottish Brothers, who were born near Glasgow in 1490. Like the twins described earlier, these brothers were two complete indi- viduals above the waist, with two heads and four arms, but only one set of lower extremities; they belonged to the type dicephalus tetrabrachius. According to the historian George Buchanan, the Scottish Brothers were taken to the court of King James IV of Scotland at an early age. Just as Henri II of France wanted to study hairy little Petrus Gonzales as a curios- ity, King James ordered that these unique children were to be carefully brought up and educated. They had a particular talent for music, and learned to sing and to accompany themselves on various instruments of music. Another Scottish historian, Robert Lindsay of Pitscottie, who had probably heard them perform, wrote that they 'became very ingenious and cunning in the Art of Musick; whereby they could sing and play two Parts, the one the Treble, and the other the Tenor; which was very dulcet and melodious to hear.' The Scottish Brothers were also very profi- cient linguists, and the king took care to educate them: by the time they were twenty years old, one or both of the twins could speak English, Irish, Latin, French, Italian, Spanish, Dutch and Danish. They could stand up, and even walk, and used all four upper extremities with dexterity. It was observed that they often differed in opinion, and sometimes quarrelled; the inseparable brothers were also prone to chide others for various 'disorders in their behaviour and actions'. George Buchanan wrote that 'in their various inclinations the two bodies appeared to dis-agree between themselves, sometimes disputing, each preferring different objects, and sometimes consulting for the common pleasure of both.'

The Scottish Brothers died in 1518, during the regency of John, Duke of Albany; they were then twenty-eight years old. The majority of chroniclers did not notice anything remark-able about their death. George Buchanan, who was himself twelve years old when the Scottish Brothers died, pointed out that at the time he was writing his history, there were many people of undoubted veracity still alive, who could vouch that his description of them contained no exaggerations. Lindsay of Pitscottie added some details that were probably the remnants of a medieval popular legend about conjoined twins. One of the Scottish Brothers died long before the other, Lindsay asserted, and when the living twin was requested to sing and be merry by the courtiers, he replied:

> How can I be merry, that have my true Marrow as a dead Carrion about my Back, which was wont to sing and play with me. When I was sad he would give me Comfort, and I would do the same to him: But now I have nothing but Dolour of Bearing so heavy a Burden, dead, cold, and unsavoury, on my Back, which taketh all earthly Pleasure from me in this present Life: Therefore I pray to Almighty God, to deliver me out of this present Life, that we may be laid and dissolved in the Earth, wherefrom we came.

This fanciful addition, which is of course medically quite impos-sible, still does not undermine the veracity of the main part of the story of the Scottish Brothers.

The *De Monstrorum Naturae* of Fortunio Liceti, a valuable early chronicle of strange births published in 1665, does not mention either the Fair Maidens of Foscott or the Scottish Brothers, but this is probably due to Liceti's lack of knowledge about British sources. He knew much more about the European annals of monstrous births. In Florence, there was at this time an ancient monument, rather like that in the church of Norton St Philip, depicting a pair of conjoined twins born in 1316. It was an effigy placed in a stairway of the Ad Scala hospital in Florence, with an epigram from Fransisco Petrarca's *De Rebus Memorandis*. The twins were named Peter and Paul, and they lived thirty days. Liceti's illustration depicts them with two heads, four arms and two torsos, but just one pair of legs. The German naturalist Johannes Schenck von Gräfenberg tells us that when he was just seven years old, his father showed him a picture of the monument to Peter and Paul, which had been sent him by a burgher in Florence. The boy was told to contemplate this hideous monster, and to promise one day to show the picture to his own children. In Professor Luigi Gedda's *Twins in History and Science*, a picture of what may well be the original monument is reproduced from a bas-relief in the San Marco Museum: if that is the case, Liceti was wrong, since the twins are depicted with three legs; they are thus an example of ischiopagus tripus conjoined twins rather than dicephali.

Fortunio Liceti also depicts the dicephalus twins born in Esslingen in Schwaben, in the year 1512. They were named Elsbeth and Elisabethen in a broadsheet issued in the same year; it is illustrated with a crude portrait of the twins, and the arms of the families involved. According to a German historical chronicle, Schedel's *Weltchronik*, 'this horrible monster' died just an hour after birth. None less than Albrecht Dürer has left a compelling, if somewhat fanciful, drawing of these twins. Some art historians have claimed that Dürer never even saw the twins, and that his drawing was inspired by the aforementioned broadsheet. As in the broadsheet, he depicts them standing up, which is manifestly impossible. The anatomy and proportions of the twins are perfectly illustrated, however, and Dürer's drawing was to remain the best illustration of dicephalus twins for many years to come. Five years later, in 1517, another pair of dicephali was born not far away, in Landshut an der Donau in Bavaria. The right twin died just half an hour after birth, and the other soon also died, but the mother survived. The twins were dissected by

At autopsy, it was noted that Tarrare's habit of swallowing huge chunks of meat, apples and buns whole had caused a considerable widening of the gullet and stomach. The cause of his death is likely to have been intestinal tuberculosis, resulting in intestinal perforation and peritonitis.

The similarity among these three cases would tempt one to suggest that they suffered from a similar abnormality in the cerebral centres regulating the appetite and intake of food. It is known that appetite is primarily regulated by two hypothalamic centres in the brain: a 'satiety centre' in the ventromedial nucleus and a 'feeding centre' in the lateral part of the hypothalamus. In experiments with animals whose satiety centres have been destroyed, they eat copiously, but only until they reach a certain body weight. It is notable, however, that animals with an injury in another region of the brain, the amygdaloid nuclei, develop a veritable omniphagia, eating even adulterated and tainted food. No case even moderately resembling Domery, Tarrare or Langulet has been published in the annals of modern medicine, however, and it is thus impossible to determine their correct diagnosis.

Several other historical polyphagi, like Jacques de Falaise and Bijoux, showed distinct signs of mental illness even according to the criteria of their contemporaries. Others, like Thomas Eclin, were simple-minded fools, who were forced to perform their disgusting and dangerous feats before the cruel populace. 'Human ostriches' have performed at nineteenth- and twentieth-century circuses, swallowing corks, glass, lemons and paraffin. One of the most famous was English Jack, the Live Frog Eater, who was depicted in a poster, standing beside an aquarium containing his hapless partners. The Great Waldo, active in the American sideshow, had a similar act: he swallowed live rats and mice and then regurgitated them. A step down the social ladder were the unskilled street performers who swallowed swords, stones, coal, live animals – indeed, anything that would attract an audience. A speciality of the American sideshow well into modern times was 'the Geek', a purported wild man who bit the heads off live rats and chickens to drink their blood. The traditional Geek was a rundown alcoholic: using a bottle of cheap whisky as a lure, the impresario could be persuaded to perform the most degrading feats. It might be a relief for animal lovers to find out that some humanitarian Geeks of the 1990s have started to use rubber chickens in their shows.

An artist with much more talent and panache was the Frenchman Louis Claude Delair, who performed as Mac Norton, the Human Aquarium. This stocky, tail-coated gentleman never changed his one act, but it was singular enough for him to make a comfortable living out of it. After rapidly drinking a large amount of water, Delair swallowed a number of goldfish and frogs. To the astonishment of the audience, he then vomited them, one by one, until they had all been transferred from their human aquarium within his stomach, to their usual glass bowl. Delair bragged that during his forty-year career in show business, he had never lost a single pet. At his final show, held in 1949 four years before his death, Delair resurrected his partners, six fish and twelve green frogs, from their human aquarium; when the trick was done, he took his bow before the audience, calling out 'All alive and kicking!'

SOURCES

I THE TWO INSEPARABLE BROTHERS AND A PREFACE

For specific sources on Lazarus-Joannes Baptista Colloredo, see the books and articles by Th. Bartholin, *Historiarum Anatomicarum Rariorum, Centuria I-II* (Amsterdam 1654, 117); F. Liceti, *De Monstris* (Amsterdam 1665, 114, 117, 346); P. Zacchias, *Questionum Medico-Legalium*, Vol. 2 (Frankfurt am Main 1688, 601); H. Sauval, *Histoire et Antiquités de la Ville de Paris*, Vol. 2 (Paris 1724, 564-65); J. Greene (*Gentleman's Magazine* 47 [1777], 482-83); J. Spalding, *Memorialls of the Trubles in Scotland and in England*, Vol. 2 (Aberdeen 1850, 125-26). A valuable secondary source is the work of H.E. Rollins, (*Modern Philology* 16 [1919], 113-38 and *The Pack of Autolycus* [Cambridge MA 1926, 7-14]).

To write a complete bibliography on the history of teratology is a difficult task, but I have here listed some of the outstanding sources from the last 150 years. The German teratologists were the leaders in their field in the late nineteenth century, and books like Friedrich Ahlfeld's *Die Missbildungen des Menschen* (Leipzig 1880) and Ernst Schwalbe's *Die Morphologie der Missbildungen* (Jena 1906) still command respect. Another work in the same tradition is the long article by Hans Hübner (*Ergebnisse der Allgemeine Pathologie und Pathologische Anatomie* 15(2) [1911], 1-348). The modern German sources are equally valuable, although often overlooked by foreign writers. Eugen Holländer's *Wunder, Wundergeburt und Wundergestalt* (Jena 1922) is a classic: well written, with many curious illustrations, and abounding in valuable source material, but somewhat lacking in its scholarly apparatus. This has been put right by later writers, like M. Zoller, *Untersuchungen zu teratologisch-historischen Aussagen kulturhistorischer Dokumente* (Thesis, University of Rostock 1976) and A. Ewinkel, *De Monstris* (Tübingen 1995). Hans Scheugl's *Showfreaks & Monsters* (Köln 1975) is lacking in historical sophistication, but it is based on the great collection of Felix Adanos, which means that much new material is presented. Two other worthy German sources are A. Sondereggger, *Missgeburten und Wundergestalten* (Zürich 1927) and J. Kunze & I. Nippert, *Genetik und Kunst* (Berlin 1986). The French sources begin with Isidore Geoffroy Saint-Hilaire's classic *Histoire Générale et Particulière des Anomalies de l'Organisation* (Paris 1836). Later sources include E. Martin, *Histoire des Monstres* (Paris 1880) and L. Guinard, *Précis de Tératologie* (Paris 1893). The more recent French literature is less worthy: M. Monestier, *Human Oddities* (Secaucus NJ 1987) has been (badly) translated into American, but although this book contains some interesting facts and curious illustrations, it perpetuates many old errors and creates some new ones. An interesting Dutch book is *De Tentoongestelde Mens* by B.C. Sliggers & A.A. Wertheim (Eds) (Haarlem 1993). As for English-language sources, G.M. Gould & W.L. Pyle's *Anomalies and Curiosities of Medicine* (Philadelphia 1897) is a classic account. A curiously overlooked source is the very thoroughly researched *Diploteratology* by G.J. Fisher, originally published in the *Transactions of the Medical Society of the State of New York* of 1865–1868. C.J.S. Thompson's *The Mystery and Lore of Monsters* (London 1930) is somewhat dependent on Gould and Pyle, but adds much valuable material based on this author's research in the British Library and in the Archives of the Royal College of Surgeons of London; unfortunately, it is not annotated and lacks a comprehensive list of sources. B. Humphries, *Bizarre* (London 1965) is a confused account with many errors, and M. Howard, *Victorian Grotesque* (London 1977) depends much on Gould and Pyle. Two more valuable sources are Frederick Drimmer's *Very Special People* (New York 1973) and *Born Different* (New York 1988), which are largely based on original research. A curious 'picture supplement' to the former book is M. Rusid, *Sideshow* (New York 1975). Another worthwhile book, although unreliable in details, is D.P. Mannix, *Freaks: We who are not as Others* (New York 1999). In a similar vein is James Taylor's curious *Shocked and Amazed*, of which I possess Vol. 3-6 (Baltimore 1996–2002). The scholarly articles by J.F.D. Shrewsbury (*Journal of Obstetrics and Gynaecology of the British Empire* 56 [1949], 67-87 and 60 [1953], 417-20), K. Park & L.M. Daston (*Past and Present* 92 [1981], 20-54) and P.K. Wilson (*Annals of Science* 49 [1992], 63-85 and *Literature & Medicine* 21 [2002], 1-25) deserve particular mention. The brilliant *The Shows of London* by Professor Richard Altick (Cambridge MA 1978) is an encyclopaedic source on all kinds of exhibitions in the metropolis. Among the recent books on the American sideshow are R. Bodgan, *Freak Show* (Chicago 1988), R.G. Thomson (Ed), *Freakery* (New York 1996) and R. Adams, *Sideshow USA: Freaks and the American Cultural Imagination* (Chicago 2001).

2 THE HAIRY MAID AT THE HARPSICHORD

General reviews of older cases of hypertrichosis include the valuable papers by M. Bartels (*Zeitschrift für Ethnologie* 8 [1876], 110-29; 11 [1879], 145-94; 13 [1881], 213-33); A.F. Le Double & F. Houssay, *Les Velus* (Paris 1912); F. Drimmer, *Very Special People* (New York 1973, 141-47, 311-19); and the papers by A. Ecker (*Globus* 33 [1878] 177-87, 221-24); J. Boullet (*Aesculape* 44 [1961], 3-39); W.R. Felgenhauer (*Journal de Genetique Humaine* 17 [1969], 1-44); and T.K. Nowakowski & A. Scholz (*Der Hautarzt* 28 [1977], 593-99).

Barbara Urslerin was described by Th. Bartholin (*Historiarum Anatomicarum Rariorum, Centuria* 1, Hist 42, 1654); H. Jacobsen (*Acta Medica et Philosophica Hafnensis* 1 [1671-72] 274-75); G. Seger (*Miscellania Curiosa* Dec 1 Ann 9 [1680], 246); J.H. Degner (*Miscellania Curiosa* 6 [1742], 35-42); W. Stricker (Virchows *Archiv* 71 [1877], 111-13); V.A. Ecker (*Archiv für Anthropologie* 11 [1879], 176-78); and E. Brackenhoffer, *Voyage de Paris en Italie* (Paris 1927, 70).

The Gonzales family were further described by C. Th. von Siebold (*Archiv für Anthropologie* 10 [1878], 253-60); F. Kenner (*Jahrbuch der Kunsthistorischen Sammlungen* der *Allerhöchsten Kaiserhauses* 15 [1894], 250-53); J.G. Ravin & G.P. Hodge (*Journal of the American Medical Association* 207 [1969], 533-35); A. Zanca (*Physis* 25 [1983], 41-66); R. Zapperi (*Annales Économies, Sociétés, Civilisations* 40 [1985], 307-27); L. Hendrix (*Word & Image* 11 [1995], 373-90); and C. Hertel (*Journal of the History of Collections* 13 [2001], 1-22).

Concerning Julia Pastrana, the articles by A.E.W. Miles (*Proceedings of the Royal Society of Medicine* 67 [1974], 160-64) and J. Bondeson & A.E.W. Miles (*American Journal of Medical Genetics* 47 [1993], 198-212) contain a complete bibliography of the relevant literature. The recent reports of very similar cases are those by E. Guevara-Sanguines *et al.* (*Pediatric Dermatology* 19 [2002], 114-18) and S. Canun *et al.* (*American Journal of Medical Genetics* 116A [2003], 278-83)

The earliest accounts of the Hairy Burmese are in the books by J. Crawfurd, Journal of an Embassy from the Governor-General of India to the Court of Ava, in the year 1827, Vol. 1 (London 1834, 318) and H. Yule, A Narrative of the Mission sent by the Governor-General of India to the court of Ava in 1855 (London 1858, 193-95). Later articles include those by H. Beigel (Virchows Archiv 44 [1868], 418-27); Anon. (La Nature 3 [1875], 121-23); M.E.T. Hamy (Bulletin de la Société d'Anthropologie de Paris (Sér. 2) 10 [1875], 78-79); J.J. Weir (Nature 34 [1886], 223-24); M. Guyot-Daubès (La Nature 15 [1887], 41-43, 86-87). The paper by J. Bondeson & A.E.W. Miles (Journal of the Royal Society of Medicine 89 [1996], 403-8) has a complete list of references.

Adrian and Fedor Jeftichejev were described by R. Virchow (*Berliner Klinische Wochenschrift* 10 [1873], 337-39); C. Royer (*Bulletin de la Société d'Anthropologie de Paris* (Sér. 2) 8 [1873], 719-25); E.R. Perrin (*Bulletin de la Société d'Anthropologie de Paris* (Sér. 2) 8 [1873], 741-50); C.S. Tomes & O. Coles (*British Medical Journal* i [1874], 413); Anon. (*Popular Science Monthly* 4 [1874], 448-51); M. Bartels (*Zeitschrift für Ethnologie* 16 [1884], 106-13); and J. Parreidt (*Deutsche Monatschrift für Zahnheilkunde* 4 [1886], 41-54). D. Snigurowicz (*Canadian Journal of History* 34 [1999], 51-82) adds some interesting details about them and other hairy individuals exhibited in Paris.

On Krao, see the articles by A.H. Keane (*Nature* 27 [1883], 245-46); A.B. Meyer (*Zeitschrift für Ethnologie* 17 [1885], 241-66); Dr Fauvelle (*Bulletin de la Société d'Anthropologie de Paris* (Sér. 3) 9 [1886], 439-48); and Hr. Maas (*Zeitschrift für Ethnologie* 25 [1893], 624-25). On 'Lionel', see the articles by F. von Luschan (*Zeitschrift für Ethnologie* 39 [1907], 425-29); P. Sarasin (*Zoologische Jahrbücher* Suppl. 15 Vol. 2 [1912], 289-328); and P. Mense (*Beiträge zur Pathologische Anatomie und zur Allgemeine Pathologie* 68 [1921], 486-95). Percilla's biography is told by James Taylor (*Shocked and Amazed* 6 [2002], 8-21).

The modern scientific discussion of congenital hypertrichosis has been contributed to by M.A. Macias-Flores *et al.* (*Human Genetics* 66 [1984], 66-70); F.A.M. Burmeister *et al.* (*Clinical Genetics* 44 [1993], 121-28); L.E. Figuera *et al.* (*Nature Genetics* 10 [1995], 202-7); and R. Balducci *et al.* (*Clinical Genetics* 53 [1998], 466-68).

3 SOME WORDS ABOUT HOG-FACED GENTLEWOMEN

The oldest sources are the pamphlet *A Certaine Relation of the Hog-Faced Gentlewoman* (London 1640) in the British Library, and the poems in H.E. Rollins,

A Pepysian Garland (Cambridge 1922, 449-454). James Paris du Plessis' account is in his *History of Prodigies*, kept in the British Library Department of Manuscripts (Sloane MSS 5246). The Grenville volume on Hog-Faced Gentlewomen is in the British Library (G. 2188). The original 1815 newspaper articles were in the *Times* (16/2 3d and 17/2 3b) and the *Morning Chronicle* (17/2 3b). Other sources include T. Prest's *Magazine of Curiosity and Wonder* (1(22) [1836], 168-69); anonymous articles in *Chambers' Edinburgh Journal* (14 [1850], 106-7); the *Notes and Queries* (2s. 11 [1861], 266, 496-97) and the *Dublin Medical Press* (51 [1864], 313); H. Wilson & J. Caulfield's *The Book of Wonderful Characters* (London 1869, xi-xix); J. Ashton, *Humour, Wit, and Satire of the Seventeenth Century* (London 1883, 49-55); R. Chambers, *The Book of Days*, Vol. 2 (London 1888, 255-57); and J. Ashton, *Social England under the Regency*, Vol. 1 (London 1890, 377-84). The Dutch sources are the articles by G.J. Boekenoogen (Volkskunde 16 [1904], 1-17 and 20 [1908], 1-8), and A. de Cock, *Volksage, Volksgeloof en Volksgebruik* (Amsterdam 1918, 19-20). Modern sources include T.P.C. Kirkpatrick, *The History of Doctor Steevens' Hospital* (Dublin 1924, 112-13); A.C. Posner & M.A. Beer (*American Journal of Obstetrics and Gynaecology* 63 [1952], 1157-61); F.C. Sillar & R.M. Meyler, *The Symbolic Pig* (London 1961, 35-36); R. Jay, *Learned Pigs and Fireproof Women* (London 1987, 27-36); and D. Coakley, *Doctor Steevens' Hospital* (Dublin 1992).

4 HORNED HUMANS

Thomas Bartholin wrote widely about horned humans in his *Historiarum Anatomicarum Rariorum* (*Centuria* 1, Hist. 78, 128-129; *Centuria* 5, Hist. 27, 44-46) and his *Epistolae Medicinales*; see also his correspondence with Olaus Wormius in *Breve til og fra Ole Worm*, Vol. 1 (Copenhagen 1965, 338, 356, 452, 460). By far the best older reviews of horned humans are the thesis-books *Des Cornes* by A. Dauxais (Paris 1820) and *Ueber Keratose* by H. Liebert (Breslau 1864). Older medical articles on horned humans include those by W.C. Worthington (Lancet i [1836], 143-44), E. Wilson (*Medico-Chirurgical Transactions* 27 [1844], 52-69) and W. Giese (*Magazin für die Gesammte Heilkunde* 66 [1848], 474-84). Paul Rodriguez was described in the *Medical Repository* (New York) (NS 5 [1820], 88-90), Mother Horn in the *American Journal of the Medical Sciences* (New York) (NS 21 [1851], 50-51), and the horned Indian boy by J.M. Richardson in the *Indian Medical Gazette* (70 [1935], 159). Mary Davies and her horn were described in Kirby's *Wonderful and Eccentric Museum* (6 [1820], 164-67), in the *Notes and Queries* (159 [1930], 159, 171, 212-213, 249, 282), and by A. MacGregor (*The Ashmolean* 3 [1983], 10-11). Later articles include those by H.L. Nietert & E.A. Babler (*Annals of Surgery* 43 [1906], 907-11); M. Joseph (*Archiv für Dermatologie und Syphilologie* 100 [1910], 343-54); J. Avalon (*Aesculape* 41 [1958], 3-9); B. Lennox & B.R. Sayed (*Journal of Pathology and Bacteriology* 88 [1964], 575-79); R.C.H. Yu *et al.* (*British Journal of Dermatology* 124 [1991], 449-52); and T. Korkut *et al.* (*Annals of Plastic Surgery* 39 [1997], 654-55). The article by J. Bondeson (*American Journal of Dermatopathology* 23 [2001], 362-69) reviews medical aspects of historical cases, and the valuable article by M. Michal *et al.* (*American Journal of Surgical Pathology* 26 [2002], 789-94) adds some curious modern instances of horned people. Later popular and/or literary articles include those by J.O. Wood (*Huntington Library Quarterly* 29

[1966], 295-300 and *Isis* 58 [1967], 239-40); C.L. Regan (*English Language Notes* 5 [1967], 34-39 and *American Notes and Queries* 12 [1974], 133-34); P. Sieveking (*Fortean Times* 43 [1985], 36-40); J.P. Runden (*Melville Society Extracts* 71 [1987], 9-11); and R. Mellinkoff (*Journal of Jewish Art* 12 [1987], 184-98). Dr Arthur MacGregor, of the Ashmolean Museum, Oxford, and Professor M.H. Kaufman, of the Department of Biomedical Science, University of Edinburgh, are thanked for valuable help.

5 DANIEL LAMBERT, THE HUMAN COLOSSUS

Contemporary newspaper accounts of Daniel Lambert include those in the *Leicester Journal* (4/4, 11/7, 19/9, 5/12 1806; 2/10, 9/10 1807; 23/6, 30/6 1809; 13/9 1811), the *Times* (9/4 3a, 12/4 3a 1806; 17/10 3a 1808; 26/6 4b 1809) and the *Morning Post* (14/4 3d 1806). Other contemporary accounts were in the *Medical and Physical Journal* (15 [1806], 582-83), the *Gentleman's Magazine* (79 [1809], 219-20, 681-83; 80 [1810], 153-54; 88 [1818], 207), and in a short-lived magazine called the *Beau Monde and Monthly Register* (1(4) [1809], 375-377). Also in Kirby's *Wonderful Museum*, Vol. 2 (London 1804, 408-10); Granger's *Wonderful Museum and Magazine Extraordinary*, Vol. 6 (London 1808, 2673-79); the *Eccentric Magazine*, Vol. 2 (London 1812-3, 241-48); Smeeton's *Biographia Curiosa* (London 1822, 249-53); Prest's *Magazine of Curiosity and Wonder* (1(3) [1835], 17-19); and Charles Dickens' *Household Words* (5 [1852], 546-48). His biography entitled *The Life of that Wonderful and Extraordinary Heavy Man, the late Daniel Lambert*, was first published in Stamford in 1809, and reprinted in 1892. On the Daniel Lambert tavern in London, see the articles in the *Daily Telegraph* of 9 Jan 1908, and the *World's Fair* of 12 May 1912. Later accounts of Lambert include those by O. Hill (*Middlesex Hospital Journal* 56 [1956] 74-76), R.B. Davis (*Tally Ho! Journal of the Leicester and Rutland Constabulary* 13(3) [1968], 61-66), and an anonymous pamphlet entitled *Daniel Lambert*, published by the Leicester Museums, Arts and Records Service, 1993. Valuable original material has been put at my disposal at the archives of the Newarke House Museum, Leicester, and the Stamford Museum, Stamford. The manuscript account of Lambert's death is in the Cambridge University Library (MSS Add 7221, pp. 117-118, section 160).

6 THREE EIGHTEENTH-CENTURY LONDON GIANTS

There are two biographical articles about Daniel Cajanus, written in Finnish and Dutch, respectively, by M. Tamminen (*Suomen Museo* 83 [1976], 93-108) and B.C. Sliggers (*Jaarboek Haerlem* 1978, 9-46). Other material includes C. Giörwell, *Thet Swenska Bibliotheket* (Stockholm 1757, 53-54) and T. Carpelan, *Finsk Biografisk Handbok* (Helsinki 1903, 313-319), a newspaper article in *Vasa Tidning* No. 52, 1839, as well as the scholarly papers by J.R. Aspelin (*Finskt Museum* 18 [1911], 30-34) and J. Finne & Y. Kajava (*Suomen Tiedakatemian Toimikutsa Sarja* A. 25 [1926], 54-56). On Cajanus' visits to Britain, see the *Daily Advertiser* of 23 and 27 September, 1742, E.J. Wood, *Giants and Dwarfs* (London 1868, 142-5), the *Biographical Dictionary of Actors* (Eds P.H. Highfill *et al.*), Vol. 3 (Carbondale 1975,

10-11) and W.M. Stone, *The Gigantick Histories of Thomas Boreman* (Portland 1933). His career in Holland has been described by W. Greve, *Natuur- en Geschiedkundige Verhandeling over de Reuzen en Dwergen* (Amsterdam 1816, 16, 32-38), by J. Marchant, *Verhaal van Reuzen* (Haarlem 1751, 109), by J.W. Stuffers, *De Groote of Sint-Bavo Kerk te Haarlem na de Resturatie* (Haarlem 1915, 25-27, 71-72), and by J.P. van Lennep (*Notes and Queries* 2s. 9, [1860], 423). A valuable modern source is the book by B.C. Sliggers & A.A. Wertheim (Eds), *De Tentoongestelde Mens* (Haarlem 1993, 24-25, 73-76). A short description of Cajanus' skeleton is included in the official guide to the Anatomical Laboratory of the Rijksuniversitet te Leiden, edited by T.J. Mulder (Leiden 1984, 23).

On Bernard Giglio, see A. Björklund, *Beskrifning öfver Kongl. Lust-Slotten Drottningholm och China* (Stockholm 1796, 51-52), E.G. Wood, *Giants and Dwarfs* (London 1868, 150-51, 456-57) and E. Garnier, *Les Nains et les Géants* (Paris 1884, 306-11), as well as the article by J. Bondeson (*Medicinskt Magasin* 2 [1997], 24-26).

The best modern biography of Hunter is *John Hunter (1728-1793)* by G. Qvist (London 1981). On the Irish Giant, the main sources are *Giants and Dwarfs* by E.G. Wood (London 1868, 157-65), C.J.S. Thompson, *The Mystery and Lore of Monsters* (London 1930, 163-75) and J. Dobson, *William Clift* (London 1954, 118-19) and *John Hunter* (Edinburgh and London 1969, 262-64); also the *Descriptive Catalogue of the Physiological Series in the Hunterian Museum*, Vol. 2 (London 1971, 199-206). There is also a biography of Patrick Cotter, *The Irish Giant* by G. Frankcom & H. Musgrave (London 1976) and a curious novel inspired by the life of Charles Byrne, H. Mantel, *The Giant, O'Brien* (London 1999). Articles on the Irish Giant include those by A.J.D. Dickens (*Black Bag* 5(3) [1959], 36-38), R.M. Bergland (*Journal of Neurosurgery* 23 [1965], 265-69), N.H. McAlister (*Canadian Medical Association Journal* 111 [1974], 256-57) and A.M. Landolt & M. Zachmann (*Lancet* i [1980], 1311-12).

7 THE KING OF POLAND'S COURT DWARF AND THE SICILIAN FAIRY

The Royal Museum at Drottningholm Castle has been described by A. Lindblom (*Nationalmusei Årsbok* 9 [1927], 85-123) and Y. Löwegren, *Naturaliekabinett i Sverige under 1700-talet* (Lychnos-Bibliotek 13, Lund 1952, 295-321). Important manuscript material is kept at the Riksarkivet (kungl. ark. [Dr. L. Ulrika] K268 fasc. 11), and the Drottningholm Castle inventories at the Slottsarkivet (DI:9-11,13-15,17-19,28,32,37). Two early guidebooks are those by A. Björklund, *Beskrifning öfver Kongl. Lust-Slotten Drottningholm och China* (Stockholm 1796, 50-68) and O Carlén, *Drottningholm. Dess historia och närmaste omgifningar* (Stockholm 1879, 38-39).

The four major biographical papers on Nicolas Ferry are those by A. Benoît (*Bulletin de la Société Philomatique Vosgienne* 9 [1883-4], 111-26) and Dr Liégey (*Annales de la Société d'émulation des Vosges* 16 [1889], 135-50), G. Richard (*Mémoires de l'Académie de Stanislas* (Sér. 6) 30 [1933], 97-114) and J. Avalon (*Aesculape* 29 [1939], 107-13). M. Kast's early account of him and Dr Morand's lecture were published in the Histoire de l'Académie Royale des Sciences (1746, 44-45 and 1764, 62-71). Anecdotes of Nicolas Ferry's life at Lunéville have been told by E. Garnier, *Les Nains et les Géants* (Paris 1884, 153-63), by G. Maugras in his books *La cour de Lunéville au XVIIIe siècle* (Paris 1904, 218-21) and *Dernières années de la cour de Lunéville* (Paris 1906, 236-39, 396-99), by P. Boyé, *La Cour Polonaise de Lunéville* (Nancy 1926, 230-37), and by J. Levron, *Stanislas Leszcynski* (Paris 1984, 286-91, 338-41, 396, 402).

Count de Tressan's lecture on Nicolas Ferry, extensively quoted by J. Avalon in the paper referred to earlier, was kept in the archives of the Académie des Sciences in the 1920s. The Princess de Talmont described Nicolas in another rare publication, *Lettre d'une personne de Lunéville à un de ses amis de Paris*, quoted by M. Richard in his aforementioned paper. Apart from the official autopsy report of Dr Morands, Count de Tressan published an addendum in the obscure collection *Aldovrandus Lotharingiæ de Bucholtz*, quoted by M. Richard. The important account by the surgeon M. Saucerotte was published in the *Journal Encyclopédique*, Sept 1768. An exhaustive account of Nicolas Ferry's skeleton was published by G.L. Buffon *et al.*, *Histoire Naturelle générale et particulière, avec la description du Cabinet du Roy*, Vol. 15 (Amsterdam 1771, 97-100). Other sources include I. Geoffroy Saint-Hilaire, *Histoire générale et particulière des anomalies de l'organisation*, Vol. 2 (Paris 1832, 148-53); the articles by R. Guérin (*Journal de la Société d'Archéologie Lorraine* 27 [1878], 78-79); Dr Porak (*Bulletin et Mémoires de la Société obstétricale et gynécologique de Paris* 6 [1890], 77-78); L. Manouvrier (*Bulletin de la Société d'Anthropologie de Paris* (Sér. 4) 7 [1897], 264-90); and P. Grace (*Metropolitan Museum Journal* 15 [1981], 175-82). M. Pierre Chanel, Conservator of the Castle Museum of Lunéville, and Frau Dr. J. Lessmann, Museum für Kunst und Gewerbe, Hamburg, are thanked for important information.

On the Sicilian Fairy, see the papers by E. Home (*Philosophical Transactions* 115(1) [1825], 66-80), H. Gilford (*Medico-Chirurgical Transactions* 85 [1902], 305-59) and J. Dobson (*Annals of the Royal College of Surgeons* 16 [1955], 268-72). The papers by J. Bondeson (*American Journal of Medical Genetics* 44 [1992], 210-19 and 46 [1993], 475) have an extensive list of references. On the 'Caroline Crachami syndrome', see the articles by G. Corsello *et al.* (*American Journal of Medical Genetics* 66 [1996], 265-68) and B. Boscherini *et al.* (*American Journal of Medical Genetics* 66 [1996], 269-72). The later investigations concerning Caroline Crachami's dentition are by B.K.B. Berkovitz *et al.* (*American Journal of Medical Genetics* 76 [1998], 343-48) and N. Jeffery & B.K.B. Berkovitz (*American Journal of Medical Genetics* 111 [2002], 260-70). Other literature on this subject includes the articles by H.J. Lin *et al.* (*American Journal of Medical Genetics* 58 [1995], 136-42), I. Kjaer *et al.* (*Cleft Palate–Craniofacial Journal* 38 [2001], 645-51) and P.N. Kantaputra (*American Journal of Medical Genetics* 111 [2002], 420-28).

Early sources on microcephalic primordial dwarfism include the books by H. Gilford, *Disorders of Growth and Development* (London 1911), A. Rischbieth & A. Barrington, *A Treasury of Human Inheritance*, Vol. 15 (London 1912) and H.P.G. Seckel, *Bird-headed Dwarfs* (Basel and New York 1960). More recent articles include those by N. Fitch *et al.* (*American Journal of Diseases of Children* 114 [1970], 260-64); B. Boscherini *et al.* (*European Journal of Pediatrics* 137 [1981], 237-42); F. Majewski & T. Goecke (*American Journal of Medical Genetics* 12 [1982], 7-21); E. Thompson & M. Pembrey (*American Journal of Medical Genetics* 22 [1985], 192-

201); F. Majewski (*American Journal of Medical Genetics* 44 [1992], 203-9); and F. Majewski & T. Goecke (*American Journal of Medical Genetics* 80 [1998], 25-31).

8 THE BIDDENDEN MAIDS

The older sources are generally referenced in the text. Four important papers on the Maids are those by J.W. Ballantyne (*Teratologia* 2 [1895], 268-74), G. Clinch (*The Reliquary and Illustrated Archaeologist* NS 6 [1900], 42-46), Marcel Baudouin (*Revue de Chirurgie* 25 [1902], 513-77) and J. Bondeson (*Journal of the Royal Society of Medicine* 85 [1992], 217-21). The latter has a full list of references. Important historical material on conjoined twins includes the articles by A.P. Chavarria & P.G. Shipley (*Annals of Medical History* 6 [1924], 297-302); A.F. Guttmacher (*Birth Defects* 3 [1967], 10-17); G.H. Schumacher *et al.* (*Anatomischer Anzeiger* 164 [1987], 225-36, 291-303); S. Geroulanos *et al.* (*Gesnerus* 50 [1993], 179-200); R.M.F. van der Werden (*Twin Research* 2 [1999], 30-32); and A.W. Bates (*Twin Research* 5 [2002], 521-28). I was also fortunate enough to possess an extra-illustrated, bound copy of Dr G.J. Fisher's *Diploteratology*, originally published in the *Transactions of the Medical Society of the State of New York* of 1865–1868. On Helen and Judith, see the article by J.J. Torkos (*Medical Proceedings* 9 [1963], 271-77); on Millie-Christine, see the excellent book by J. Martell, *Millie-Christine: Fearfully and Wonderfully Made* (New York 2000); on the Blazek sisters, see the articles by R. Henneberg (*Berliner Klinische Wochenschrift* 40 [1903], 798-801, 829-33), B. H. Breakstone (*American Medicine* NS 17 [1922], 221-26), and H. Schierhorn (*Anatomischer Anzeiger* 160 [1985], 353-65). On the Isle Brewers twins, see the article by J. Bondeson (*Journal of the Royal Society of Medicine* 86 [1993], 106-9) and its references. Some modern medical articles on conjoined twins and their surgical separation are those by R.G. Harper *et al.* (*American Journal of Obstetrics and Gynecology* 137 [1980], 617-29); R.M. Hoyle (*Surgery, Gynaecology and Obstetrics* 170 [1990], 549-62); G.A. Machin (*Birth Defects Original Article Series* 29(1) [1993], 141-79); R. Spencer (*Journal of Pediatric Surgery* 31 [1996], 941-44); and M.L. Hilfiker *et al.* (*Journal of Pediatric Surgery* 33 [1998], 768-70). Important information has also been derived from the pamphlet *The Story of Biddenden* and other local history sources. The Trustees of the Chulkhurst Charity and the Biddenden Local History Society are thanked for important information.

9 THE TOCCI BROTHERS AND OTHER DICEPHALI

The main sources on the Fair Maidens of Foscott are *Through Ten English Counties* by J.J. Hissey (London 1894, 141-44), and an anonymous article in the *British Medical Journal* (i [1902], 915-16). Other older historical instances of dicephali are described by G. Schwalbe, *Die Morphologie der Missbildungen* (Jena 1906, 75-79); E. Holländer, *Wunder, Wundergeburt und Wundergestalt* (Jena 1921, 64-71); and J.F.D. Shrewsbury (*Journal of Obstetrics and Gynaecology of the British Empire* 56 [1949], 67-85). On the Two-headed Boy of Bengal, see the article by J. Bondeson & E. Allen (*Surgical Neurology* 31 [1989], 426-34) and its references; recent cases have been described by D.B. Aquino *et al.* (*Pediatric Pathology & Laboratory Medicine* 17

[1997], 939-44) and J. Bondeson (*Fortean Times* 186 [2004], 46-49). The sad fate of Ritta-Christina was discussed in anonymous articles in *La Clinique* (1 [1829], 200, 254-55) and *Bulletin des Sciences Médicales* (18 [1829], 169-72), as well as by M. Saint-Ange (*Journal Hebdomadaire de Médécine* 6 [1830], 42-49), H. Danerow (*Litterarischen Annalen der gesammten Heilkunde* 16 [1830], 454-82) and E. Serres (Mémoires de l'Académie Royale des Sciences 11 [1833], 583-895). Later articles include those by P.J.S.Whitmore (*French Studies* 21 [1967], 319-22) and S.J. Gould (*Natural History* 91(11) [1982], 18-22).

Articles on the Tocci brothers include those by S. Fabini & A. Mosso (*Giornale della r. Accademia di Medicina di Torino* (Ser. 3) 23 [1878], 13-26); P. Colrat & F. Rebatel (*Lyon Médical* 29 [1878], 274-80); Dr Grünwald (*Virchows Archiv* 75 [1879], 561); R.Virchow (*Zeitschrift für Ethnologie* 18 [1886], 47-50 and 23 [1891], 245-46); Anon. (*Scientific American* 65 [1891], 374); R.P. Harris (*American Journal of Obstetrics* (NY) 25 [1892], 460-73); M. Baudoin (*Gazette Médicale de Paris* (Sér. 13) 4 [1904], 200); and L. Gedda (*Acta Genetica Medica e Gemellologica* 5 [1956], 1-13). The influence of the Tocci brothers on Mark Twain has been discussed by R.A. Wiggins (*American Literature* 23 [1951], 355-57); N. Fredericks (*Nineteenth-Century Literature* 43 [1989], 484-99); and M. Shell (*Arizona Review* 47(2) [1991], 29-75).

Later articles and reviews on dicephalus twins include those by G.B. Gruber & H. Eymer (*Beiträge zur Pathologische Anatomie und zur allgemeine Pathologie* 77 [1927], 240-76); G.B. Gruber (*Abhandlungen der Gesellschaft der Wissenschaften zu Göttingen*, Math.-Phys. Klasse III. Folge 4, 1931); G. Aschan (*Upsala Läkareförenings Förhandlingar* NF 47 [1941-42], 289-304); H. Scherrer (*Virchows Archiv* 323 [1953], 597-621); P.G. Brewster (*Acta Genetica medica e Gemellologica* 11 [1962], 450-56); G. Schnesinger (*Anatomischer Anzeiger* 143 [1978], 176-182); E.S. Golladay *et al.* (*Journal of Pediatric Surgery* 17 [1982], 259-64); and J.R. Siebert *et al.* (*Teratology* 40 [1989], 305-10). The separation of Katie and Eilish was described by L. Spitz *et al.* (Journal of Pediatric Surgery 29 [1994], 477-81) and later discussed by C. Myser & D.L. Clark (*Literature and Medicine* 17 [1998], 45-67), and in many newspaper and magazine articles. The information on the Hensel twins is from an article in the Swedish magazine *Exxet* (15 [1996], 6-17), for which the material had been fetched from an article in *Time* and a television documentary. On the recent debate on ethical aspects of surgery on conjoined twins, see the articles by D.C.Thomasma *et al.* (*Hastings Center Report* 24 [1996], 4-12), J. Raffensperger (*Pediatric Surgery International* 12 [1997], 249-55), and A. Domurat Dreger (*Studies in the History and Philosophy of Science* 29 [1998], 1-29).

10 CAT-EATING ENGLISHMEN AND FRENCH FROG-SWALLOWERS

Lysons' *Collectanea* contains much valuable information about the old English gluttons and cat eaters. The polyphagi of olden times have been described by E.G. Happel in Vol. 1 of the *Relationes Curiosae* (Hamburg 1683, 375-79) and D. Biett (*Dictionnaire des Sciences Médicales* 4 [1813], 197-202). Charles Domery was described by J. Johnston in the *Medical and Physical Journal* (3 [1800], 209) and Charles Dickens' comments were in his *Household Words* (5 [1852], 546-48). Jacques de Falaise was described by J.P. Beaudé in the *Revue Médicale Française et Étrangère* (3 [1826], 521-26) and in an anonymous article in the Norwegian journal *Eyr* (3 [1828], 292-96). Professor Percy's paper on Tarrare originally appeared in the *Journal de Médecine, Chirurgie, Pharmacie &c* (9 [1805], 87-106). It was commented on by J.G. Millingen in his *Curiosities of Medical Experience* (London 1839, 196-202), and in an anonymous article in *Aesculape* (20 [1930], 292-301). On Antoine Langulet, see M. Berthollet's paper in the *Archives Générales de Médecine* ((Sér. 1) 7 [1825], 472-73), and P. Haining, *The Flesh Eaters* (London 1994, 125-32). A particularly well-written account of 'human ostriches' and similar performers is that of Ricky Jay, *Learned Pigs and Fireproof Women* (London 1987, 276-99). Further material is provided by J. Boullet (*Aesculape* 34 [1953], 164-65) and R. Bogdan, *Freak Show* (New York 1988, 263-64).

LIST OF
ILLUSTRATIONS

the author's collection.

15 Shwe-Maong, the king's favourite, and his daughter Maphoon, from John Crawfurd's *Journal of an Embassy from the Governor-General of India to the Court of Ava*, Vol. 1.

16 Maphoon at thirty-one years of age, with her fourteen-month-old younger son on her lap.

17 Maphoon, Moung-Phoset and Mah-Mé in 1872. From the collection of Professor A.E.W. Miles, reproduced with permission.

18, 19 Close-ups of Maphoon and Moung-Phoset from the Goss photographs. From the collection of Professor A.E.W. Miles, reproduced with permission.

20 A drawing of Julia Pastrana by the German artist Herbert König.

21 A Russian drawing of Julia Pastrana. Reproduced by permission of the St Petersburg Circus Museum.

22 A caricature drawing of Julia Pastrana, made in 1859 by the Warsaw artist Kostrzewski.

23 A photograph of Julia Pastrana, taken when she was exhibited in London in 1857.

24 A Russian caricature of Julia Pastrana exhibited together with a very fat man. The individual on the extreme left is probably Mr Lent. Reproduced by permission of the St Petersburg Circus Museum.

25 Julia Pastrana's mummy photographed during the early 1860s. From the author's collection.

26 A very good drawing of Julia Pastrana during life, from a German circus poster dated 1857. Reproduced by permission of the St Petersburg Circus Museum.

27 A German advertisement, probably from the 1890s, to see the mummy of 'the most interesting woman in the world', as Julia Pastrana was called.

28 'Zenora Pastrana', Mr Lent's second bearded wife. She suffered from secondary hirsutism, quite a different condition from that of poor Julia.

29 A drawing of Julia Pastrana's mummified son.

30 A drawing of Adrian and Fedor, from an article in the *Lancet* of 1873.

31 Jo-Jo as an adult, a photograph taken in the late 1880s. From the author's collection.

32 Fedor, alias Jo-Jo, as a boy. From the author's collection.

33 One of Krao's exhibition posters.

34 An early photograph of Krao with her manager Mr Farini.

35 Lionel, the Lion-Faced Boy, from an old photograph in the author's collection.

36 Lionel, the favourite of women and children. A poster from 1909 in the author's collection.

37 The title page to the original London pamphlet about Tannakin Skinker, published in 1640. Reproduced by permission of the British Library.

38 A fierce-looking pig-faced lady, from a German print issued in 1717. From the author's collection.

Newarke House Museum, Leicester.

58   Daniel Lambert attacks Napoleon Bonaparte in the caricature 'The Two Wonders of the World'. Reproduced by permission of Newarke House Museum, Leicester.

59   A stone statuette of Daniel Lambert. Reproduced by permission of Newarke House Museum, Leicester.

60   A portrait of Daniel Lambert, by his friend Benjamin Marshall, painted in 1806 during his first season in London. Reproduced by permission of the Newarke House Museum, Leicester.

61   Another portrait of Daniel Lambert, owned by the Stamford Town Council. Reproduced by permission.

62   Enoch Seeman's portrait of Daniel Cajanus, reproduced by permission of the National Museum of Finland, Helsinki.

63   A Dutch engraving made in 1749 to commemorate Cajanus. Reproduced by permission of the Gemeentearchief of Haarlem.

64   Daniel Cajanus plays draughts at the Blauw Jan; a contemporary drawing later published in the *Almanak tot Nut van't Algemeen* of 1802.

65   A watercolour by T.H. Shepherd of part of the Hunterian Museum, *c.*1860.

66   Henry Blacker, the English Giant, an engraving from Caulfield's Remarkable Persons. From the author's collection.

67   One of Daniel Cajanus' enormous shoes, together with one of ordinary dimensions. Reproduced by permission of the Anatomical Institute of Leiden.

68   An engraving of Bernard Giglio, Henry Blacker's competitor, at the age of nineteen, by Fougeron after Millington. From the author's collection.

69   The Irish Giant being exhibited.

70   An etching by John Kay of Charles Byrne and the two gigantic Knipe brothers.

71   John Hunter's portrait by Sir Joshua Reynolds, from a print in the author's collection.

72   A drawing of the Irish Giant by Thomas Rowlandson.

73   John Hunter receiving a giant and two dwarfs: an illustration from Jesse Foot's *Life of Hunter*.

74   A contemporary engraving of Nicolas Ferry, from a print in the author's collection.

75   A print of Nicolas Ferry standing in the remnants of the pastry he had been 'served' in, before the admiring eyes of King Stanislas. A tinted lithograph from Maison Aubert, after A. Géniole. Reproduced by permission from the Wellcome Trust.

76   Thérèse Vouvray, the alleged Madame Bébé. from the author's collection.

77   A portrait of Nicolas Ferry together with a large dog, by an unknown artist. From an early nineteenth-century engraving in the author's collection.

78   The statue of Nicolas Ferry at Drottningholm Castle. Reproduced

INDEX

TEMPUS – REVEALING HISTORY

D-Day
The First 72 Hours
WILLIAM F. BUCKINGHAM
'A compelling narrative'
The Observer
£9.99
0 7524 2842 X

The London Monster
Terror on the Streets in 1790
JAN BONDESON
'Gripping'
The Guardian
£12.99
0 7524 3327 X

London
A Historical Companion
KENNETH PANTON
'A readable and reliable work of reference that deserves a place on every Londoner's bookshelf'
Stephen Inwood
£20
0 7524 3434 9

M: MI5's First Spymaster
ANDREW COOK
'Well-researched, penetrating and engagingly written'
Andrew Roberts
£20
0 7524 2896 9

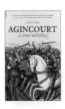

Agincourt: A New History
ANNE CURRY
'A highly distinguished and convincing account of one of the decisive battles of the Western world'
Christopher Hibbert
£25
0 7524 2828 4

William II
Rufus, the Red King
EMMA MASON
'A thoroughly new re-appraisal of a much maligned king. The dramatic story of his life is told with great pace and insight'
John Gillingham
£25
0 7524 3528 0

The English Resistance
The Underground War Against the Normans
PETER REX
'An invaluable rehabilitation of an ignored resistance movement'
The Sunday Times
£17.99
0 7524 2827 6

Elizabeth Wydeville
The Slandered Queen
ARLENE OKERLUND
'A penetrating, thorough and wholly convincing vindication of this unlucky queen'
Sarah Gristwood
£18.99
0 7524 3384 9

If you are interested in purchasing other books published by Tempus, or in case you have difficulty finding any Tempus books in your local bookshop, you can also place orders directly through our website

www.tempus-publishing.com

TEMPUS – REVEALING HISTORY

Quacks
Fakers and Charlatans in Medicine
ROY PORTER
'A delightful book'
The Daily Telegraph
£12.99
0 7524 2590 0

The Tudors
RICHARD REX
'Up-to-date, readable and reliable. The best introduction to England's most important dynasty'
David Starkey
£9.99
0 7524 3333 4

The Kings & Queens of England
MARK ORMROD
'Of the numerous books on the kings and queens of England, this is the best'
Alison Weir
£9.99
0 7524 2598 6

The Covent Garden Ladies
Pimp General Jack & the Extraordinary Story of Harris's List
HALLIE RUBENHOLD
'Has all the atmosphere and edge of a good novel… magnificent'
Frances Wilson
£20
0 7524 2850 0

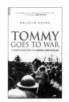

The Wars of the Roses
The Soldiers' Experience
ANTHONY GOODMAN
'Sheds light on the lot of the common soldier as never before' *Alison Weir*
£25
0 7524 1784 3

Sex Crimes
From Renaissance to Enlightenment
W.M. NAPHY
'Wonderfully scandalous'
Diarmaid MacCulloch
£10.99
0 7524 2977 9

Ace of Spies The True Story of Sidney Reilly
ANDREW COOK
'The most definitive biography of the spying ace yet written… both a compelling narrative and a myth-shattering *tour de force*'
Simon Sebag Montefiore
£12.99
0 7524 2959 0

Tommy Goes To War
MALCOLM BROWN
'A remarkably vivid and frank account of the British soldier in the trenches'
Max Arthur
£12.99
0 7524 2980 4

If you are interested in purchasing other books published by Tempus, or in case you have difficulty finding any Tempus books in your local bookshop, you can also place orders directly through our website

www.tempus-publishing.com

keep the boys immobilised, since this made the exploitation of them much easier. Their failure to walk diminished their quality of life immeasurably.

It is also clear that Professor Gruber was right when he postulated that all subcategories of dicephali can be capable of prolonged life. The main predictor of survival is the degree of conjunction and deformity of the hearts. The stillborn majority usually have cardiopulmonary malformations that are incompatible with extrauterine life. In other instances, like Ritta-Christina and the 1952 US twins, the left twin has a functional heart, but the right twin's heart is malformed. In a few cases, like the Scottish Brothers and the Tocci and Hensel twins, there are two fully functional hearts, as evidenced by the absence of cyanosis and heart murmurs, and by the prolonged survival of the twins.

The fact that a pair of dicephalus conjoined twins may live for a prolonged period of time – sixty-three years in the case of the Tocci brothers – has importance for the question on whether surgical separation of dicephali should be performed. As we have seen, the separation of several other types of conjoined twins is a well-established procedure, and enjoys considerable success. It is clear, from all standpoints, that it is desirable to separate less extensively conjoined twins, like the pygopagus and omphalopagus types discussed earlier, and that the children's quality of life is definitely much improved. In dicephali, and also in certain more extensively conjoined types of twins, like the thoracoabdominopagus variety, the anatomical structure is often such that it is unlikely that both twins could survive an attempt at separation. This has led to the concept of 'sacrifice surgery' being introduced: one twin is deliberately killed to save the other, and used as a donor of shared organs. By 1996, sacrifice surgery on conjoined twins had been performed nine times. A much publicised case was that of the extensively conjoined Lakeberg twins, who had a common liver and a shared, six-chambered heart. Nevertheless, the parents pressed for an operation. One of the twins was 'sacrificed' by the surgeons, but the operation was still a failure; the surviving twin died before her first birthday, having been hospitalised and ventilator dependent her entire life. The Lakeberg case triggered an unprecedented debate about the ethical issues involved. It was reasoned that the only way to justify taking one life to save another was by informed consent: one twin must voluntarily give his or her life to save that of the other. Since newborn twins cannot speak for themselves, the assumption is that the parents make this choice on behalf of their children. At various times, Protestant, Roman Catholic, Rabbinical and Islamic theologians have been consulted in these difficult cases: they have agreed that the sacrifice of one twin to save another is ethical.

If a decision had been made to separate, at all costs, a pair of dicephalus twins like Abigail and Brittany Hensel, the extremely unlikely best-case scenario would be that, after a lengthy course of operations and years of hospital stays, a mobile, vigorous body with two minds would be changed into two one-armed, one-legged invalids, with half a pelvis each. They would both be likely to be sterile, probably incontinent, with grossly deformed thoracic cavities, extensive scarring, and vast cosmetic defects. It is unlikely that both twins would survive, and quite likely that neither twin would survive the attempt. Sacrifice surgery would surely be unethical in a pair of equally strong, viable twins, but if the decision were to sacrifice one twin as an organ donor to the other, the odds of survival would be unlikely to improve greatly. A danger in all advanced, high-technology medical procedures is the attitude that all that *could* be done also with necessity *should* be done. There is good reason to doubt, for both medical and ethical reasons, whether surgical separation of dicephalus conjoined twins should at all be attempted, except in a situation in which one twin is clearly dying. In such a situation, both medical and ethical issues should be considered before surgery is attempted, and the situation with regard to quality of life for the survivor of the operation given as much (if not more) consideration as the quantity of life. In the 1977 Arkansas case, the surgeons actually stated as one of the arguments to operate that the twins might survive for a prolonged period of time, but this attitude that life as a conjoined twin is literally a fate worse than death is highly questionable. Although an adult person would find it intolerable to be linked for life to another individual, things are very different when the conjunction is present from birth. Many of the historical cases discussed in this book, like Helen and Judith, Rosa and Josefa Blaczek, and of course the original Siamese twins Chang and Eng themselves, would hint that the twins themselves would not agree that their lives were a complete, utter misery – many of them grew up to be stable, socially well-adjusted people. They knew no other life than to be a conjoined twin, and accepted its limitations; in fact, both Millie-Christina and Rosa-Josefa Blaczek themselves refused to be separated.

The life story of the Tocci brothers is a more tragic one, however. Until they were twenty years old, they knew no other life than that of an interesting object on show before the curious. Already at the age of four weeks, their father took them to Turin for exhibition, and they had few holidays thereafter. According to their Austrian handbill, the brothers were on show six hours every day, seven days a week. To spend one's teenage years as a 'freak' in the American sideshow of the 1890s is unlikely to be an uplifting experience. Every day, goaded by their possessive and avaricious parents, the boys were put on show before a coarse, unfeeling audience of carnival 'rubes'. They were not cute little children any more, like a funny little two-headed puppet, but had grown up to be a near-adult, humanoid 'monster' with whom people could identify. Like their contemporary, the original 'Elephant Man' John Merrick, they must have been sickened by people exclaiming in horror, 'What a monster!' 'What a freak!' After this kind of experience, their decision never to be seen by a stranger again seems quite rational. John Merrick asked his benefactor Frederick Treves if he could be sent to a solitary lighthouse, or a blind asylum; the Tocci brothers had ample money from their tours, which they put to good use. It is to be hoped that at the end of their lives, living in their villa in Venice, Giovanni Baptista and Giacomo found some happiness.

CAT-EATING
Englishmen
AND
French
FROG-SWALLOWERS

Among the vast collections of the British Library are seven large folio volumes full of press cuttings, handbills and advertisements, collected by the clergyman Daniel Lysons in the late eighteenth century. Lysons was a distinguished scholar and clergyman, but he was also a habitué of London low life. In the gloomy backstreets of the metropolis, he hobnobbed with quacks, mountebanks, jugglers and exhibitors of animals and human 'freaks'; in his huge scrapbooks, he collected all the information he could procure about them. Antiquaries and historians recognise Lysons' *Collecteana* as a valuable source of material on cultural history. When studying these immense scrapbooks, one is constantly impressed with the wealth of interesting material, which tempts the mind to stray towards novel attractions, and the eccentricity of intellect required to form such a bizarre and multifarious collection. In one of the volumes, a startling newspaper cutting from the *World*, of 13 March 1788, has been pasted in:

> Amongst the curious Betts of the day, may be reckoned the following: The Duke of Bedford has betted 1,000 guineas with Lord Barrymore, that he does not – eat a live Cat! It is said his Lordship grounds his chances upon having already made the experiment upon a Kitten. The Cat is to be fed as Lord Barrymore may choose.

The Londoners greeted this bizarre report from the upper-class sporting circles with immediate interest. Several letters and articles were submitted to the Editor of the *World*, and published under the heading 'Cat Eating'. An authority on blood sports pointed out that 'the bet of his Grace of Bedford, that Lord Barrymore will not eat a live Cat, is not without precedents in the annals of sporting'. He had himself, at a racecourse near Kildare, witnessed an imbecile Irishman devouring five fox cubs, after £50 had been wagered by the spectators. Another correspondent had seen a Yorkshire shepherd eat a live black tom cat, which had been carefully selected for its size and tenacity. This had happened in 1777, and it was remarked that the callous snobs responsible for this outrage had rewarded the wretched shepherd with the princely sum of 2 guineas. Lord Barrymore seems to have become rather worried when he saw his bizarre wager being much publicised in the papers, and he sent an official disclaimer to the Editor of the *World*:

> In the Bett that was stated in this Paper, we understand that there was a mistake – as Lord Barrymore only betted, that he found a man who would eat a Cat.

Richard Barry, the seventh Earl of Barrymore, was established as one of the leading rakes of London when he was hardly out of his teens: in a contemporary peerage, he was stated to have 'wasted his fortune and his health among gamblers, pimps, and players'. He raced horses, bet on pugilists, and roamed about the streets of London with his cronies, drinking, fighting, whoring and spending recklessly out of the family fortune. The earl was nicknamed 'Hellgate' for his rakehellish ways and his clubfooted, evil brother the Hon. Henry Barry was called 'Cripplegate'. His other brother, the Hon. Augustus Barry, was nicknamed 'Newgate' since this was the only prison with which this learned cleric, who shared Lord Barrymore's taste for low life to no little extent, had not yet made a personal acquaintance. Their sister, Lady Caroline Barry, was nicknamed 'Billingsgate' after the foul-mouthed fishwives who congregated at this old London gate, for her coarse language. The Barrymore siblings had the run of London until 1793, when the earl was shot dead by accident. By this time, he had spent the major part of the family fortune on his amusements and various hare-brained schemes of his own invention.

Francis Russell, the fifth Duke of Bedford, was a wealthy magnate who was often seen at the racecourse and in the gambling parlours; he bragged that at the age of twenty-four he had scarcely opened a book. He was a long-standing crony of Lord Barrymore. The two noblemen, who were both courtiers to the extravagant Prince of Wales, had betted 500 guineas against 400, a sum exceeding the life earnings of a day labourer. The duke's comments on hearing of Lord Barrymore's unsporting *volte-face* have, perhaps unfortunately, not been recorded for posterity, nor is it known whether Lord Barrymore ever managed to recruit a man willing to eat a cat. According to Mr J.F. Robinson's well-informed book *The Last Earls of Barrymore*, the wager was put at the first spring meeting at the racecourse, on 12 March 1788, and the earl did, from the beginning, point out that *he would procure* a man willing to eat a live cat.

But although Lord Barrymore was never to sink his teeth into a cat's body, it is certain that a similar wager was made in January

1790, and that a live cat was eaten at a public house in Windsor. A correspondent of the *Sporting Magazine* was there to witness the disgusting proceedings. A nine-pound cat had been selected as the victim, and 'the Man-monster... made a formidable attack on the head of his antagonist, and with repeated bites, soon deprived it of existence'. He then devoured his prey without even stripping off the skin, leaving only the bones 'as memorials of a most astonishing instance of the exercise of a brutal appetite, and the degradation of human nature'. According to the *Public Advertiser* of 3 February 1790, the notorious Cat-eater of Windsor had later 'given another proof of the brutality of his disposition – an instance too ferocious and sanguinary, almost, to admit of public representation.' At a public house, perhaps the same one where he had eaten the cat, he had suddenly, and without reason, hacked off one of his hands with a billhook. He gave no reason for this depraved action, except 'his total disinclination for work' and that he hoped that this desperate deed would induce the overseers of his parish to provide for him during the remainder of his life. For many years thereafter, lurid newspaper stories about men eating live cats abounded. In 1820, the philanthropist Mr Henry Crowe M.A., an early champion of animal rights, held this up as one of the worst outrages of all in his book *Zoophilos*: 'Is it conceivable that the wretch who could EAT A LIVE CAT for a wager, or that another, who could do the same to *amuse* the populace as a mountebank (anecdotes said to be well attested), should either of them feel qualms or compunction at adding even cannibalism to murder?'

The scholars of olden times have supplied many more or less trustworthy accounts of the great eaters, or polyphagi, of olden times. According to the learned Vospicius, the Emperor Aurelius once amused himself by watching a peasant devouring in turn a roast suckling-pig, a roast sheep and a roast wild boar, all served with a generous supply of bread and wine; the man coped with this formidable task within one day. In the year 1511, another gluttonous peasant performed before the court of the Emperor Maximilian: he ate a fatted calf raw, and started tearing a sheep's carcass with his powerful jaws, before the courtiers interrupted this somewhat monotonous amusement, at the Emperor's request. The Danish anatomist Caspar Bartholin once saw a student who could drink copious amounts of wine; at autopsy, the stomach of this individual was observed to be of enormous size. Helwigius claimed to have seen a man who could devour 90 pounds of food for his dinner, and Professor Martyn, of Cambridge University, had observed a boy who could consume 370 pounds of food in a week. A pig was fattened on the vomits of this boy and sold at the market for a good price, although one would rather suspect that this porker's unusual diet was not disclosed to the unsuspecting buyer.

In early seventeenth-century England, a glutton named Nicholas Wood, who was known as 'The Great Eater of Kent', performed at many country fairs and festivals. He was a native of the village of Harrietsham near Maidstone in Kent. In his youth, Nicholas Wood was employed as a servant of a local gentleman, but the rumour of his prodigious appetite was soon widespread, and he became a local hero. It was said that he had once eaten a whole hog, and that although he was a strong, stoutly built labourer, he had to spend all his estate to provide food for his insatiable belly. Once, when invited to Leeds Castle by Sir Warham St Leger, Nicholas Wood won a bet by eating a dinner intended for eight people. Another local gentleman, Sir William Sedley, laid an even more magnificent table for the Great Eater; this was the first time this celebrated glutton had been defeated. After a valiant effort, Nicholas Wood fell to the floor in a deathlike trance, his stomach distended like a huge balloon. Fearing that the glutton would die, Sedley's servants laid him down near the fireplace, and smeared his belly with fat to make it more readily distensible; the insensible glutton was then carried up to bed, many spectators fearing for his life. The day after, the Great Eater revived, but his fickle benefactor decided to mock the once famous performer. Sir William Sedley's stewards dragged him outside, and he was put in the stocks to be jeered by the populace. At the castle of Lord Wotton in Boughton Malherbe, Nicholas Wood got his own back; he won a bet by eating seven dozen rabbits, and was again celebrated by his friends for using his unique talent to score off those above him in society. Nicholas Wood's greatest misfortune occurred at the market of Lenham, where a cunning trickster named John Dale had made a bet that he could fill the Great Eater's belly for the price of a mere 2 shillings. He accomplished this feat by soaking twelve one-penny loaves of bread in six pots of very strong ale; Nicholas Wood fell asleep, and remained insensible for nine hours, after finishing only half of this highly alcoholic meal.

In 1630, Nicholas Wood met the poet John Taylor, who was visiting a country inn in Kent. The poet watched the Great Eater win a bet by devouring a breakfast consisting of a leg of mutton, sixty eggs, three large pies and an enormous black pudding. This was all the food in the inn's larder, but Nicholas Wood was still hungry. The waiter ran out to fetch a large duck, which the Great Eater tore to pieces and ate, leaving only the beak and quills. John Taylor was deeply impressed by this exhibition of brutal appetite: with his poetic imagination, he could envisage that the duck, which, a mere minute ago, had been peacefully swimming in the pond of the tavern, now 'swomme in the whirlepole or pond of his mawe'. John Taylor paid Wood 20 shillings to visit him in London some time later. In the meantime, the shrewd poet had made up a cunning plan to cash in on his new acquaintance. Nicholas Wood had never performed in London, and his gluttonous orgies would be a novelty even for the blasé citizens of the metropolis. After a grandiose advertisement campaign, the Great Eater was to make his bow to the London audience at the Bankside bear-garden. At the first show, he would wolf down a wheelbarrow full of tripe, at the second devour 'as many puddings as would reach over the Thames'. At the subsequent shows, he would eat a fat calf worth 20 shillings, and then twenty sets of sheep's innards. Initially, Nicholas Wood felt disposed to accept this plan, hoping, perhaps, to become a superstar of gourmandising. His literate agent wrote a pamphlet to celebrate 'the Admirable Teeth and Stomachs Exploits of Nicholas Wood'; it was widely spread among the Londoners, who were soon curious about this novel attraction. The eloquent John Taylor spared no superlatives to describe his artist's enormous powers of digestion. His intestinal tract was a stall for oxen, a sty for hogs, a park for deer, a warren for rabbits, a pond for fishes, a storehouse for apples, and a dairy for milk and honey. His jaws were a mill of perpetual motion, and his capacious stomach the '*rendez-vous* or meeting place for the Beasts of the Fields, the Fowles of the Ayre, and Fishes of the Sea'. But when the day of the grand opening was imminent, the Great Eater's mind became increasingly worried: he suffered from stage fright, and remembered, with horror and apprehension, the many distasteful and dangerous practical jokes he had encountered during his long and perilous career. The embarrassing anaesthesia in Lenham had not been forgotten, and shortly before he left for London, he had lost all his teeth but one at the market of Ashford, after being tricked into eating a shoulder of mutton *with bones and all*. One day, Nicholas Wood escaped from his lodgings in London, never to be heard of again. His prospective manager, John Taylor, had to be content with the publication of his long complimentary poem to 'the Great Eater of Kent', containing the lines:

> Thou that putst down the malt below the wheat,
> That dost not eat to live, but live to eat,
> Thou that the sea-whale and land-wolf excells,
> A foe to Bacchus, champion of god Bael's:
> I wish if any foreign foes intend
> Our famous isle of Britain to offend,
> That each of them had stomachs like to thee,
> That of each others they devoured might be.
> Though Maximus, Rome's great emperor
> Did forty pounds of flesh each day devour,
> Albinus the emperor did him surpass:
> Five hundred figs by him down swallowed was,

Of peaches he consumed one hundred more,
Of great muskmellons also half a score,
One hundred birds, all at one meal he cast
Into his paunch, at breaking of his fast.

∾

In the early 1700s, a Bohemian countryman became famous for
his capacity to eat great amounts of raw meat. He performed
widely in Germany and Austria. Once, he breakfasted on a calf
roasted whole, and he was able to devour a leg of mutton in a
matter of minutes. In 1709, this Bohemian glutton was advertised
in a handbill, which depicted him seizing a puppy between his
powerful jaws. He holds a large ham and a goblet of ale in his
hands. At his feet lies a cat, happily unaware of the fate he has in
store for it. Another feat of this disgusting performer was that he
could crush a large stone between his powerful jaws.

An imbecile Irishman named Thomas Eclin performed similar
wonders in London of the 1740s and 1750s. According to the
newspapers, he was 'remarkable for his Vivacity and Drollery in
the low Way'. His feats included eating live dogs and cats and
leaping head first into the Thames when the weather was freezing
cold. Thomas Eclin was fond of drinking copious amounts of
gin, and after his death from vomiting blood, the *Daily Advertiser*
announced the sale of a drawing in his honour, depicting the
cat-eater 'with the just Emblems of his Ambition: a Decanter
and a Glass at his Elbow, and Pipe in his right Hand'. There were
numerous other performers in the same vein. The *Annual Register*
of 1765 tells that a brewer's servant named Walter Willey ate a
roasted goose of 6 pounds and a quartern loaf, and drank three
quarts of porter; he accomplished this feat in little more than an
hour, and won a bet of 2 guineas. According to the *Cambridge
Chronicle* of 13 September 1770, a young country lad won a
wager through eating an 8-pound leg of mutton, with a quantity
of bread and carrots. The next day, he ate 'a whole cat, smoth-
ered with onions.' Another glutton, Charles Tyle, of Stoke Abbott

in Dorset, ate 133 eggs within one hour, with a large piece of bacon and a quantity of bread. According to the *Bristol Gazette* of 13 March 1788, he afterwards complained that there had not been enough eggs, and that he had not yet had a full supper.

There are many other instances of British gluttons making wagers to consume prodigious amounts of food and drink; these unsavoury amusements seem to have been relished both in London and in the countryside, and survived well into the nineteenth century. According to the *World* of 11 March 1790, a man at Stillington in Lancashire drank five quarts of ale, and then masticated and swallowed the earthen mug. He did not have long to celebrate winning his bet, since he died two days later, probably of intestinal obstruction caused by the fragments of the mug. The *London Packet* of 2 March 1804 told that one glutton had just eaten his length in pork sausages, 2 pounds of new bread, and drunk a quart of porter and two glasses of brandy, all in twenty-two minutes. Another voracious eater, who obviously had a strong predilection for greasy food, ate a pound of butter and a 1-pound dumpling. The *Observer* of 24 March 1811 reported that a countryman had just eaten sixty-five raw eggs in eight minutes, for a trifling wager. Another man had eaten a pint of periwinkles, with shells and all, in ten minutes. Encouraged to repeat the performance, he did so, but fell violently ill after accomplishing his feat, and was not expected to recover. The *Times* of 26 August 1824, reported another melancholy event. A man from Jersey ate six raw eggs mixed with half a pint of gin. As the wager was renewed, at a higher amount each time, he repeated this performance three times. With two pints of gin within him, he tore into a quantity of raw bacon, and drank two large glasses of brandy. Then he 'felt indisposed', went home and died. Another glutton, William Webber, undertook to eat a roast pig of 10 pounds' weight, served with two quartern loaves and a quantity of potatoes. Having 'cleared' an 8-pound pig on Christmas Eve the year before, he began in a capital manner, and drank beer and smoked his pipe in between the generous helpings, but had to give up, according to the *Times* of 3 March 1840, with 1½ pounds of meat still on the table before him.

Some years after Nicholas Wood had withdrawn from show business, an Irish soldier named Francis Battalia appeared in London. This individual had a unique talent: he could chew and swallow large plates full of stone and gravel. After his meal, he shook his body violently, making the stones rustle from the depths of his stomach. The advertisements claimed that as an infant, Battalia had refused all kinds of food until the wet nurse mixed his gruel with small pebbles. He had subsequently, it was claimed, relied on the productions of the mineral kingdom for his daily nourishment, growing up to be a vigorous and active fellow, although of short stature. Francis Battalia's performances were described in John Bulwer's *Anthropometamorphosis*, and his portrait, by Hollar, was engraved and widely distributed. An artist rather resembling Francis Battalia was performing in the late 1770s, under the short but self-explanatory stage-name 'The Stone Eater'. This time, his partiality for hard-to-chew food was explained by his having been shipwrecked off the Norwegian coast in 1761. Sitting on an uninhabited, rocky islet, he had munched gravel for thirteen years before being saved by a passing ship. He claimed that his intestinal tract had become used to minerals as the principal source of nourishment. Those who doubted this were invited to his shows, where he ground stones and pebbles between his powerful jaws, with a horrible crunching sound. The Stone Eater was much noticed by the medical establishment: the advertisements bragged that Sir Joseph Banks and the great John Hunter had been attracted by his unique accomplishments, but neither of these gentlemen described him in print. It is true, however, that Dr Munro wrote a short article about the Stone Eater in his *Medical Commentaries*. Soon, a rival stone eater appeared in London: this fellow called himself Siderophagus, and he munched iron as well as chewed pebbles. His wife was in the same line of business: under the stage name Sarah Salamander, she drank aqua fortis and oil of vitriol as if it had been a small beer. Another stone eater, either the original one or an usurper of that title, surfaced in 1788 and was still active in the early 1790s; he was immortalised by the comic poet Mr O'Keefe:

Make room for a jolly Stone-eater,
For Stones of all kind I can crunch;
A nice bit of Marble is sweeter
To me than a Turtle or Haunch.
A Street that's well pav'd is my larder –
A Stone you will say is hard meat,
But, neighbours, I think 'tis much harder
Where I can get nothing to eat!
With my crackeldy mash, ha! ha!

London Bridge shall just serve for a luncheon –
Don't fear – I would make it a job:
The Monument next I will munch on,
For fear it would fall on my nob:
Ye Strand folks, as I am a sinner,
Two nuisances I will eat up;
Temple-Bar will make me a good dinner,
Because on St. Clement's I'll sup!

Another contemporary of the Stone Eater was a French glutton named M. Dufour. At one of his shows in 1792 he ate a specially composed banquet before a large and admiring house. As an hors d'oeuvres, he had soup of asps boiled in simmering oil, with thistles and burdocks as a salad. Then, he ate dishes of tortoise, bat, rat and mole; the main course was a roast owl served in a sauce of glowing brimstone. For dessert, he supped on toads decorated with flies, crickets, spiders and caterpillars. As an encore, M. Dufour swallowed the still burning candles on the table, and washed them down with a flaming glass of brandy. Finally, he swallowed the oil lamp, and the flames glowed from his wide mouth when he made his bow to the enraptured audience.

In February 1799, the French ship *Hoche* was captured by the Royal Navy off the coast of Ireland. One of the soldiers on board was named Charles Domery. In the military prison, the English guards were amazed by the Frenchman's voracious appetite. Although he received double rations, he kept begging food from the other prisoners, and did not refuse dead cats and rats delivered to him as presents by the curious turnkeys. The other French soldiers said that Charles Domery had always eaten a prodigious amount of food: he had eight brothers, all of them soldiers, with similar voracious appetites. When staying at an army camp outside Paris, Charles Domery had eaten 174 cats in one year. Dogs and rats equally suffered from his merciless jaws, and he also ate 4 or 5 pounds of grass each day, if bread and meat was scarce. He liked raw meat better than meat cooked or boiled, and a raw bullock's liver was his favourite dish. When, in action on board a ship of the line, another sailor's leg was shot off by a cannon ball, Domery grasped it and began feeding heartily, until another mariner tore it away from him in disgust, and threw it into the sea. In spite of his gluttonous habits, Charles Domery was of normal build and stature; although he was completely illiterate, the prison doctors considered him to be at least of average intelligence. In September 1799, Dr Johnston, the Commissioner of Sick and Wounded Seamen, decided to perform an experiment to test the Frenchman's preternatural appetite. At four o'clock in the morning, Charles Domery breakfasted on 4 pounds of raw cow's udder, and at half past nine, Dr Johnston and Admiral Child had prepared a suitable luncheon for him, consisting of 5 pounds of raw beef, twelve large tallow candles and a bottle of porter. At one o'clock, the glutton again devoured 5 pounds of raw beef, 1 pound of candles and three large bottles of porter. At five o'clock, he returned to the prison; it was recorded that he was of particularly good cheer after his great feast: he danced, smoked his pipe and drank another bottle of porter. The following morning, he awoke at four o'clock, eager for his breakfast. None less than Charles Dickens had read an account of Domery's voracious gluttony, and in his *Household Words*, he wrote that Charles Domery 'dining in public on the Stage of Drury Lane, would draw much better than a mere tragedian, who chews unsubstantial words instead of wholesome beef'.

Another celebrated French glutton, M. Bijoux, was a porter at the zoological garden of the Jardin des Plantes in Paris. He believed himself to be a great naturalist, and even called himself the French Linnaeus, since he had made up an elaborate system of classifying all animals from the appearance of their excrements. To support his studies, he kept a large collection of faecal matter in his private museum. M. Bijoux ate the most disgusting objects without hesitation: he even consumed the body of an old lion that had died of disease in its cage. Once, a sporting nobleman made a bet with Bijoux that he could not devour 9 pounds of hot bread within two minutes. After a frenzied performance, the glutton won his bet, but with the cost of his life: immediately after swallowing the last morsel, he dropped dead. The intestinal tract capable of digesting the King of Beasts thus had to capitulate before a mere *pain riche*!

In the early 1820s, a glutton named Jacques de Falaise performed at M. Comte's theatre in Paris. A native of the Montmartre district, he was a time-honoured attraction at various sleazy taverns. His career apparently had its ups and downs: at least twice he rose from obscurity to be widely advertised by his managers. He reached some fame among the Parisians, and was interviewed several times by curious members of the medical profession. During his shows, Jacques swallowed eggs and walnuts whole, and ate live sparrows, crawfish, mice, adders and eels. Once, after a wager had been entered into, he swallowed fifty five-franc pieces, which nearly killed him, since these coins were as large as half-crowns. Some years later, poor Jacques hanged himself; at autopsy, it was noted that his stomach had many scars of older injuries from the sharp and corrosive substances he had swallowed.

❧

These unsavoury tales from the annals of polyphagy would perchance have seemed exaggerated, had they not been surpassed by the foremost glutton of all times, a Frenchman known to his contemporaries as Tarrare. It is not known if Tarrare was his real name or a nickname bestowed on him at some time during his astounding career. The expressions 'Bom-bom tarrare!' and 'Tarrare bom-de-ay!' were used at this time to describe powerful explosions or fanfares, and it may be speculated that the name Tarrare was bestowed upon him to ridicule his prodigious flatulence. Tarrare was born in the French countryside, just outside the city of Lyon. Already as a child, he had an enormous appetite. When he was in his teens, his parents could not feed this monster any more, and turned him out of the house. For several years, he scoured the French provinces, in the company of robbers, whores and vagabonds. Later, he was employed as a clown by an itinerant quack: by swallowing stones, corks and live animals, he attracted the attention of the curious populace towards the mountebank's spiel about his nostrums and wonder drugs. Tarrare could devour a whole basketful of apples, by swallowing them one by one. In 1788, he left his employer and moved to Paris, to earn a perilous living by means of similar performances in the streets of the French capital. Once, he was struck by acute intestinal obstruction after one of the shows. In agony, Tarrare was carried away to the Hôtel Dieu hospital, there he was treated with a powerful purgative, which had the desired effect. This experience did not induce him to give up his career. Just after having recovered, he volunteered to swallow the surgeon M. Giraud's watch and chain to demonstrate his talents, but the forthright surgeon replied that in that case, he would cut Tarrare's belly open with his sword to recover his valuable timepiece.

At the advent of the revolutionary wars in France, Tarrare joined the army as a recruit, but the frugal diet of the troops did not suffice to quench his insatiable hunger. He was again taken into hospital, in a state of extreme exhaustion. At the doctor's orders, he was given quadruple rations, but to little avail: Tarrare still lurked about, looking for food in the gutters and dustbins. The military surgeons were amazed by Tarrare's immense appetite. They ordered that he was to remain in hospital to take part in some physiological experiments designed by M. Courville, surgeon to the 9th Regiment of Hussars, and Professor Percy, the surgeon-in-chief of the hospital. Many years later, Baron Percy summarised the results in a scientific treatise. Once, during Tarrare's residence in the hospital, a table had been laid for fifteen German labourers just outside the hospital gates. Tarrare spied the table, and the porters had great difficulties in keeping him at bay. Dr Courville, who had observed the glutton lurking nearby, decided to put his digestion to the test. The luncheon of the German labouring men, who were apparently not consulted when the disposal of their food was decided upon, consisted of two enormous meat pies, served with huge plates full of grease and salt, and a pair of 2-gallon jugs full of milk and soured milk. The voracious Tarrare ate everything on the table, not leaving even a breadcrumb or a drop of milk. After this orgy, he immediately fell asleep. Dr Courville noted that the skin of his paunch, normally lax and flabby in texture, had become widely distended like a huge balloon. In another experiment, Tarrare was given a live cat, which he devoured after tearing its abdomen with his teeth and drinking its blood. He later vomited the fur and the skin. The doctors also fed him live puppies, snakes, lizards and other animals, and Tarrare did not refuse any of their offerings.

Tarrare's appearance did not betray his voracious appetite: he was pale, thin and of medium height, and his temperament was apathetic. His fair hair was uncommonly thin and soft. His mouth was enormously wide, and the enamel of the teeth much stained. He sweated profusely, and was constantly surrounded by a malodorous stench. When Tarrare was starving, the abdominal skin hung like a huge leather bag, which he could wrap round his waist, but when he had eaten a hearty meal, his paunch could distend in a remarkable manner. After one of his feasts, he smelt worse than ever, and his eyes and cheeks became blood-shot. Professor Percy wrote that the methods utilised by 'this filthy glutton' to make his rations last were too disgusting to be described in detail. All creatures great and small were in constant danger from his ravenous jaws: 'the dogs and cats fled in terror at his aspect, as if they had anticipated the kind of fate he was preparing for them'.

After the experiments at the military hospital had been going on for several months, the French military board inquired how soon Tarrare would be fit for active duty again. The doctors were quite unwilling to lose touch with their valuable 'guinea pig', however, and Dr Courville came up with a bizarre idea. He had persuaded Tarrare to swallow a wooden box with a document inside; it turned out that two days later, after a visit to the hospital latrines, the glutton could deliver the box with the document in good condition. Dr Courville went before the army commander, General de Beauharnais, to suggest that Tarrare be recruited into the French secret service as a master spy. Using the wooden box, he could smuggle top secret documents through enemy territory without even risking getting caught! Vicomte de Beauharnais was apparently quite intrigued by this plan, since he ordered that Tarrare was to perform before several top-ranking officers at the headquarters of the French army at the Rhine. It is unlikely, but by no means impossible, that Napoleon Bonaparte was one of those present. After swallowing the wooden box with ease, Tarrare was rewarded with a wheel-barrow full of raw bull's liver and lungs, which he devoured on the spot, to the consternation of the generals.

After this performance, Tarrare was officially employed as a spy. His first assignment was to deliver a secret letter to a French colonel held captive by the Prussians in a fortress near Neustadt. General de Beauharnais was much less impressed with Tarrare's mental abilities than with his powers of digestion, however, and he did not want to entrust him with any documents of real importance. Although the glutton was tricked into believing that he carried papers of vital importance for the outcome of the war, the general ordered that a a note telling the imprisoned French colonel to send back, by the same messenger, all possible information about Prussian movements of troops, was all that was to be put into the box swallowed by Tarrare.

In the middle of the night, Tarrare was sent off from the French entrenchments, disguised as a German peasant. He did not know a word of German, however, and soon attracted attention. Outside the city of Landau, he was arrested by a patrol of soldiers, who had been called by some watchful countrymen. After the Frenchman had been strip-searched and interrogated, the soldiers gave him a sound whipping, but Tarrare did not betray a word about his mission. He was then taken before General Zoegli, the Prussian military commandant, but Tarrare again gave nothing away, although the sinister Germans assured him that once he was installed in their prison, they had ways of making him talk.

Tarrare was not cut out to be a war hero, and after twenty-four hours in the hands of the Prussian counter-espionage, he confessed all about the bizarre scheme concocted by the doctors and General de Beauharnais. He was chained to a bog-house, and his tormentors were overjoyed when, at last, he delivered the wooden box. They had expected that the box would contain top-secret files, as Tarrare had promised them, and were furious when General de Beauharnais' curt letter was read out. Their disappointment was taken out on the wretched Tarrare, who was put on a scaffold with a noose around his neck, and asked to make his peace with the Almighty. At the last minute, General Zoegli, who had had a good laugh at the Frenchman's expense, ordered that his life was to be spared. Before he was ignominiously driven off near the French lines, Tarrare was given another brutal thrashing, in order to put him off secret service work for all time.

❧

After his brief and disastrous career as a secret agent, Tarrare was willing to do anything to evade being conscripted into military service. After he had been readmitted into the military hospital, he told Professor Percy that he was ready to try any possible cure to rid him of his gluttony. The professor first tried tincture of opium, but without success; he then fed Tarrare sour wine and tobacco pills, but without affecting his preternatural appetite. Professor Percy had read a case report stating that large amounts of Levantine soft-boiled eggs were a powerful appetite suppressant, but Tarrare was resistant even to this exotic cure. All attempts to make him keep a controlled diet were fruitless: Tarrare sneaked clandestinely out of the hospital to lurk outside the butchers' shops; in the dark back alleys of Paris, he fought the street mongrels for the possession of disgusting carrion found in the gutters and refuse heaps. Within the hospital, he sometimes skulked into the wards to drink the blood from patients treated with venesection. Several times, he was kicked out of the morgue after having taken liberties with the corpses. Some of the doctors requested that Tarrare should be committed to a lunatic asylum, but Professor Percy had, in some strange way, grown attached to his former 'guinea pig', and still wanted to keep him under observation at the hospital. Some time later, however, a fourteen-month-old infant suddenly disappeared from its hospital bed. Everyone suspected Tarrare of being responsible, and this time not even the professor could save him; the enraged doctors and porters chased Tarrare away, and he was never seen at the hospital again.

Subsequently, Professor Percy lost sight of his patient for several years. One can only speculate how this monstrous glutton had managed to stay alive in a France ravaged by war and revolution. Four years later, Professor Percy heard from M. Tessier, the chief surgeon of the hospital in Versailles, that Tarrare had been admitted to one of his wards. The once-celebrated glutton was in a miserable state of feebleness, and he could hardly rise from his hospital bed. Tarrare had himself asked to see the professor, for the reason that two years earlier he had swallowed a stolen gold fork, which he was sure still resided within his intestinal canal; now, he wanted to hear if the knowledgeable physiologist knew of some way to dislodge it from its lair within him, by means of some powerful emetic or laxative! It was apparent to Professor Percy that Tarrare was badly ill, in the last stage of tuberculosis; he was a mere shadow of the vigorous glutton he had been just a few years before. A month later, Tarrare was struck by a continuous, purulent diarrhoea, and died within a couple of days. The corpse putrefied uncommonly quickly, and even the surgeons of the hospital, who were used to dealing with rotting corpses, were unwilling to dissect him. Tessier had heard of Tarrare's former glory, and he decided to find out what this monster looked like inside, and also to determine whether he really had a golden fork within him as he claimed. At the autopsy, the rotting entrails were bathing in pus. The liver was very large, and the gallbladder distended. The stomach was enormous, and filled the major part of the abdominal cavity. No gold fork was found inside Tarrare's intestinal tract. The gullet was uncommonly wide, and when the huge jaws had been forced open, the surgeons could see a broad canal down to the stomach.

One would have thought that a ghoul like Tarrare would be absolutely unique in history, but less than thirty years later, a veritable soulmate of his was arrested by the Paris police. His name was Antoine Langulet, and an account of his career was drawn up by a certain Dr Berthollet in 1825, after Langulet had been committed to an asylum for the criminally insane. Antoine Langulet lived in a hovel near the Avenue de l'Opéra, not far from the Opera House itself. It is stated that he was not a vagabond, but he did no work, and it is not known how he supported himself. At the time of his arrest, he was 5 foot 10 inches tall, and weighed a little under 170 pounds. Antoine Langulet had, from an early age, been in the habit of eating the most disgusting substances. He liked putrid meat from a fly-blown cadaver better than a fresh beef steak. He spent the daytime lurking inside his humble abode, but after dusk he ventured out to scavenge the streets, collecting offal and rotten meat from the gutters, and stuffing his pockets with his foul-smelling treasures. Normally, he liked to cook his meat over an open fire, and was proud of his ability to tell the difference between different animals. He was a friend of the Paris horse knackers, and they sometimes allowed him to feed on the sick old horses they had killed. He was sure to seek out the most inflamed, livid tissues, or those most altered by disease.

Had Antoine Langulet been content with rotten horseflesh for dinner, he would never have come into contact with Dr Berthollet and his fellow alienists at the Bicêtre prison. But Langulet had discovered another source for his favourite food: an old cemetery near the Rue de Clichy. After midnight, he left his house and climbed the cemetery gates under the cover of darkness; he had brought with him a spade, a maul and a sledgehammer. With these implements, he unearthed and broke open the coffins of recently buried people, and feasted on the rotting corpses. He ate the intestines in preference to anything else. After some months of these outrages, there were rumours that grave-robbers were at large in the cemetery, but a doctor who had examined the contents of the unearthed coffins and what remained of their occupants said that this was definitely the work of a human ghoul. The cemetery was guarded in the hope of catching this monster, but the voluntary policemen who were posted to stand guard over the eerie graves were probably just as pleased that their quest was unsuccessful. Finally, a verger saw a creature pulling the body of a young girl from her grave, and bravely pursued it. The ghoul outran his pursuers and, still carrying the corpse, climbed the cemetery gates with great agility. He would have been safe, had not someone noted some pieces of female apparel outside Langulet's house. As the police burst in, they discovered him feeding from the corpse, and he was of course arrested. Dr Berthollet had expected to find a raving lunatic, but Langulet turned out to be a sensible, rational man, except for his depraved appetite. Antoine Langulet did not consider that he had committed any crime. He freely admitted that, ever since his childhood, he had been in the habit of eating what others termed disgusting food, but this taste was perfectly natural to him. More sinisterly, Langulet also admitted that he had often wanted to eat the bodies of young children, but he had never been able to summon courage enough to kill them, he said. Bearing this ill-judged remark in mind, Dr Berthollet recommended that he should be imprisoned indefinitely.

The tales of Tarrare and Langulet will raise a *frisson* of horror even in the most devoted students of the macabre: the bizarre antics of the French gluttons are almost unbelievable, and one would at first be tempted to suspect that their biographers had been guilty of exaggeration. This does not seem to be the case, however. Dr Berthollet's report is brief and matter-of-fact, and Mr Peter Haining has discovered independent evidence of Langulet's career, particularly an account in *Le Figaro*. George Didier, Baron Percy, was one of the leading military surgeons of his time; in his list of publications, the case report about Tarrare seems out of place among his many valuable surgical articles and monographs. Tarrare was widely famous among the Parisians, who delighted in the demented glutton's macabre display of his powers of deglutition.

The gluttons Charles Domery, Tarrare and Antoine Langulet not only share their French nationality, but have several other characteristics in common. Neither, in spite of their singular behaviour, seemed apparently insane to their contemporaries. Domery's gluttony had begun at the age of thirteen, and the disgusting habits of Tarrare and Langulet had been established at an even earlier age. Although they could eat enormous amounts of food, they never vomited it and did not gain in weight. They had a particular preference for raw, or even rotten, meat, and preferred it to meat cooked or fried. Their gluttony enabled them to devour the most disgusting food with alacrity. Both Tarrare and Domery would sweat profusely, particularly after a feast, and were continuously surrounded by a nauseating odour.

the local surgeon, who marvelled that from the navel upwards they were two complete children, from the umbilicus downwards just one. They had two hearts, two livers that were united in the middle, two pair of lungs, two stomachs and two spleens. It is remarkable that they were not considered as a portent or even as a 'horrible monster', but instead called 'these beautiful twins' and a marvellous prodigy of nature. The reason is probably that they were not described by a chronicler or theologist, but by a certain Dr Wilhelm Rosenzweydt, surgeon and anatomist, who was capable of seeing beauty in God's creation, even in an unusual form.

Gould and Pyle, in their *Anomalies and Curiosities of Medicine*, abstracted two curious sixteenth-century reports from Bateman's *The Doome* in the British Library. One concerns a 'double-headed male monster' in Switzerland. Observed in 1538 at the age of thirty, each head possessed a beard, and the faces resembled each other in appearance. The two bodies fused at the umbilicus into one single lower body. The twins had one single wife, with whom they were said to live in harmony. Bateman also describes a German woman with two heads, who begged from door to door. One of the heads was deformed, and her countenance was altogether so frightening that she was given her expenses to leave the country, since it was believed that women would miscarry or receive dreadful 'maternal impressions' at the sight of her. Other writers on monstrosities also mention this Bavarian woman, providing much-needed additional credibility to Bateman's account.

Liceti and other seventeenth-century writers on teratology report several contemporary cases of dicephalus conjoined twins, all of them stillborn or less viable. Two of the most interesting instances were described by Dr Andreas Emmenius in a thesis entitled *Abbildung und Beschreibung zweier Wunder-geburten*, published in Leipzig in 1627. One pair of dicephalus twins, baptised Sara and Anna, lived just half an hour. They had three arms, one on each side and a third between the two heads. At autopsy, the two hearts lay close to one another, in a common pericardium. A four-armed pair of dicephali, named Justina and Dorothea, actually lived six weeks. They died in an attack of seizures without previously seeming unwell. Autopsy showed that their hearts were separate and distinct, but the right one was malformed.

Probably the most curious illustration of a dicephalus of all is the 'Turkish Archer' depicted in an old German print. This striking-looking individual is clearly an adult; he is said to have been captured by the troops of Doge Morosini in 1697, in the Peloponnesian war between the Austrians and the Turks. In contrast to the living dicephali described earlier, he has only two arms, and the two necks are attached to a common trunk. He is thus a dicephalus dibrachius. There is no other mention of this Turkish archer in the late seventeenth-century literature on monstrosities, however, and some scholars have presumed that he was a product of early wartime propaganda, aimed to show the Turks as monstrous, sub-human creatures. It is amazing, in that case, that the artist has produced the portrait of a teratologically fully correct dicephalus rather than some fanciful imaginary creature.

Another remarkable specimen in the aforementioned Hunterian Museum is a child's skull of most bizarre aspect, which had belonged to the famous Two-headed Boy of Bengal. In 1790, this boy was described by John Hunter's principal assistant Everard Home, who rightly claimed that the Two-headed Boy was 'a species of *lusus naturae* so unaccountable, that, I believe, no similar instance is to be found upon record.' This was a very different kind of two-headed child than those we have encountered previously: his two heads were actually on top of each other, joined by the crowns of the skulls! Everard Home never went to India to see the boy, but collected several descriptions and drawings of him from laymen. The Two-headed Boy was born in May 1783 in the village Mundul Gait in Bengal; his parents were poor farming people. Immediately after the child had been delivered, the midwife, who was greatly terrified by its strange appearance, tried to destroy the two-headed infant by throwing it into the fire; the boy was saved from the flames with burns to one eye and one ear on the upper head. The parents soon realised the possibility of earning money by exhibiting their child in Calcutta, where he attracted much attention. So large were the crowds which gathered to see the Two-headed Boy that his parents had to cover him up between shows. In this way the boy spent his short and miserable life; his emaciated and sickly appearance, Home thought, was caused by his being covered by sheets most of the time. The Two-headed Boy's fame soon spread all over India, and several noblemen and civil servants had him exhibited in their houses. One of these, Colonel Pierce, described him in a letter to the President of the Royal Society, Sir Joseph Banks, who later gave the letter to Everard Home.

The two heads were of equal size and covered with black hair at their junction; the upper head ended in a neck-like stump, which one observer likened to a small peach. When the boy cried or smiled, the features of the upper head were not always affected, and their movements seem to have been purely reflex: a pinch in the cheek produced a grimace, and when it was given the breast, its lips attempted to suck. The natural head and body were quite normally developed, but a number of anomalies were noted in examining the parasitic head: the corneal reflexes were absent and the eyes' reaction to light was weak. No pulsations could be felt in the temporal arteries of the parasitic head, but its superficial facial veins were well filled with blood. The ears were malformed, and the tongue small. The lower jaw was rather small, but capable of motion. The secretion of tears and saliva was plentiful. When the child slept, the eyes of the parasitic head could be observed to be open and moving. When it was first awakened, all four eyes moved in the same direction, but normally the two heads' eye movements were independent.

When the Two-headed Boy of Bengal was four years old and in good general health, his mother left him one day to fetch water. When she returned, her son was dead from the bite of a cobra. Several scientific amateurs made offers to purchase the corpse, but the religious parents did not allow it; instead, they buried their child near the Boopnorain river, outside the city of Tumloch. The grave was later plundered by Mr Dent, the East India Company's agent for salt in this city. He dissected the putrefied body and kept the skull, which he gave to Captain Buchanan of the same company. The captain brought the skull to England, where he gave it to his friend Everard Home. When Mr Dent had dissected the heads, he had noted that the brains were separate and distinct, each enveloped in its proper coverings. The dura mater of each brain adhered firmly and contained many large vessels, supplying the nutrition to the upper head. In his examination of the double skull, Everard Home noted that the halves were nearly of the same size. No septum of bone existed between the two brains. The natural skull was quite normal, but the parasitic one was imperfect in a number of particulars, and its facial bones were generally smaller.

Everard Home much regretted that men of observation never got the opportunity to examine the boy. The two brains and their influence on the intellectual principle fascinated him. Neither Home nor John Hunter speculated about how the Two-headed Boy should be classified in the system of teratology. They do not seem to have noted the similarity between the boy and the symmetrical conjoined twins of the type craniopagus, which are joined at the crowns of the heads. The junction may be more or less extensive: in partial craniopagi, the crania are intact or simply fused, while in total craniopagi, the two brains are encased in a common cranium. While in the former subgroup the brains are often quite intact, those of the latter subgroup are sometimes malformed. Craniopagi had been described several times in the old annals of teratology. The famous twins of Worms, born in 1495 and depicted in several crude woodcuts of the time, were frontal craniopagi and lived for ten years. During the eighteenth century, several well-attested cases were reported. Today, at least eighty bona fide cases of craniopagus conjoined twins have been described; this type represents 6% of this type of condition,

making the incidence 0.6 per million births. The surgical techniques for separating craniopagus twins have improved much
during the last decades, but the operation is still a most uncertain
and difficult venture, especially in cases with total conjunction
and malformations of the brains and their vascular supply.

In his *Traité de Tératologie*, published in 1836, the famous
French anatomist Isidore Geoffroy Saint-Hilaire was the first to
note the similarity between the Two-headed Boy of Bengal and
the craniopagus conjoined twins. He suggested that the Two-
headed Boy belonged to a special group of parasitic craniopagi,
and quoted a similar French case, described by the Liège surgeon
M. Vottem in 1828. Here, the parasite had been much larger
than in Home's case, with incompletely developed arms and a
rudimentary spinal column. The monstrous foetus was seen to
gasp for breath and move slightly for about half an hour; after
its death, the mother was told she had given birth to a stillborn
normal child, in order not to disturb her. In all, ten cases of this
teratological type have been reported to this day. Home's case
was the first of these, and the only one capable of prolonged
extrauterine life. The most likely teratogenetic mechanism is that
the two foetuses are originally conceived as symmetrical craniopagus conjoined twins, but that one twin loses its contact with
the umbilical vesicle, which explains the underdevelopment of
the parts not directly supplied with blood through anastomoses
from the healthy twin. This theory is supported by the fact that
in several cases, the neck-like stump on top of the parasite's head
has proved to contain a small sternum, clavicles and a number
of underdeveloped ribs, as well as a rudimentary heart, pharynx
and lungs.

Had the Two-headed Boy lived today, it would certainly have
been attempted to remove the parasite, and thus restore him
to a near-normal life, at least if the legal status of the parasitic
head, which seems to have given some signs of independent
life, could be resolved in this unprecedented case. The operation
would have been facilitated by the brains being separate and
distinct; the skull defect was relatively small, and the tissues of

the parasite could be used to cover it. Thus, if he had had the
fortune of being born 200 years later, the Two-headed Boy of
Bengal would have met with a more appealing future than that
of a miserable object of exhibition. It is curious that there have
been two recent instances of live-born parasitic craniopagi. The
first one was born in the Dominican Republic in December
2003, and bore a marked resemblance to the Two-Headed Boy
of Bengal. American neurosurgeons tried surgical separation, but
the unfortunate little girl expired from a heart attack caused by
the massive loss of blood. The second one was born in Egypt in
April 2004. The conjunction appears to have been less extensive
than in most other cases, and surgical separation was successful. The girl was still alive in late 2005, hopefully indicating a
favourable prognosis. In both these twenty-first-century cases,
the parasitic head showed some signs of independent life.

In the nineteenth century, there was a great upsurge in the
interest and knowledge in both normal and abnormal human
anatomy. This was the heyday of scientific teratology, particularly in Germany and France. In addition to dissecting every
malformed infant that came into their hands, the pioneer teratologists reviewed the old annals of strange births to discover
historical cases of rare malformations. There had by this time
been several dissections of stillborn dicephali; one of the most
detailed ones, by the obstetrician Dr Bland, had been published
in the *Philosophical Transactions* of the Royal Society of London
in 1781. Although some of the older instances of dicephalus
twins, like the Scottish Brothers, had been capable of prolonged
extrauterine life according to the original sources, many of the
sceptical teratologists tended to doubt the veracity of this ancient
tale, particularly as there had not been a single eighteenth- or
early nineteenth-century instance of viable dicephalus twins.

All of this would change when 'Ritta-Christina, l'Enfant
Bicéphale' appeared in Paris in October 1829. These little girls

had been taken to Paris for exhibition when they were just six or seven months old. They were born in Sassari, Sardinia, and their mother, thirty-two-year-old Maria Teresa Parodi, had previously given birth to eight other children. Like the Scottish Brothers, Ritta-Christina had a common waist, one pelvis and two legs, but two upper bodies, four arms and two heads. It was soon noticed that the right twin, Ritta, was weaker and more delicate than her sister Christina; as the twins grew older, this difference increased. Christina seemed like a vigorous and healthy child, but Ritta, who had much the smaller appetite of the two, was pale and sickly. At times, she had alarming attacks of cyanosis and difficulties in breathing. The parents of Ritta and Christina were desperately poor. Much impressed by the great interest in their extraordinary twins from both the medical profession and the general public, they decided to make money from the children while they still could. After a brief tour of some Italian cities, they set out for Paris.

The civic authorities were averse to such a degrading monster show, however, particularly as the children were of a tender age, and after some deliberation, the magistrates decided to shut the show down. The parents, still in dire financial straits, had to move to a derelict house in Paris, where they clandestinely showed the twins, for a fee, to journalists and members of the medical profession. The newspapermen wrote flippant articles, inquiring whether this monster was really one child or two, and whether they had one or two immortal souls. Several Parisian lovers of curiosities urged the authorities to allow the parents to put Ritta-Christina on show again, but while the magistrates debated this issue, the health of the twins rapidly deteriorated. For want of money to purchase coal or firewood, their parents had to put the twins' cot into a room without a fire during a cold winter evening. Christina withstood this exposure to the elements without ill effects, but Ritta developed acute bronchitis and was soon in a critical state. The medical men were amazed to see that when Ritta was *in extremis* and gasped desperately for breath, her sister was playing and laughing. These doctors may have been benevolent enough to have offered their professional assistance for nothing, but, rather sinisterly, there is no mention of this in either the popular or the medical press, and instead much speculation on what the autopsy would show and what museum would get the skeleton of such an anatomical rarity.

On 23 November 1829, three days after Ritta had been taken ill, she finally gave her final gasp for breath, after a long struggle. At the same instance, her sister, who had previously appeared completely unaffected, gave a cry, let go of her mother's hand, and died. The twins were then eight months and eleven days old. The local *curé* had barely had time to finish his duties, when a deputation of members from the Académie Royale de Médécine came in with a large cask of plaster of Paris, to make a cast of the tiny corpse. According to a newspaper report, dated the day after the demise of Ritta-Christina, the distraught father had not yet decided whether he would allow the anatomists to dissect his daughters. The next day, he was prevailed upon by the distinguished anatomist Isidore Geoffroy Saint-Hilaire, who had seen Ritta-Christina alive more than once. It is, again sinisterly, reported that Geoffroy Saint-Hilaire arrived in the company of the police, and that later the same day his assistants transported the remains of Ritta-Christina to the amphitheatre of the Jardin du Roi. According to another account, which the *Times* had obtained from the *Courier Français* newspaper, Ritta-Christina's father 'refused for a long time to suffer the monster to be dissected, but the solicitations of Geoffroy Saint-Hilaire, and the injunctions of the Police, overcame his repugnance, and the bicephalic infant has been taken to the Theatre of Anatomy of the Jardin du Roi'. Exactly by what means the father was persuaded is not stated (threats and/or bribes?); it is unlikely that the wretched man was moved by zeal for the science of teratology. At any rate, the anatomists had won, and the twins' body was prepared for dissection. An exulting medical journal promised that 'Nous ferons connaître cette autopsie curieuse' – We will make known the result of this curious autopsy.

There was a good deal of bickering in the French newspapers about who was to blame for the premature death of
the two-headed phenomenon. Ritta-Christina's parents were
blamed for putting their children on show, and there were lurid
rumours that the twins' death was due to overexposure and a
too fatiguing exhibition schedule. The doctors and anatomists
involved, particularly a certain Dr Martin Saint-Ange, were also
roundly criticised for their callous attitude, and it was asserted
(probably with some right) that they had been more interested
in Ritta-Christina's anatomy than in caring for the twins' well-
being. Dr Saint-Ange retorted that, in fact, Ritta-Christina's
condition had deteriorated over a considerable period of time.
Furthermore, had the parents been allowed by the magistrates
to put Ritta-Christina on show before the (paying) multitudes
eager to see the twins, this would have solved their financial
difficulties and enabled them to keep their children warm and
well fed.

The autopsy of Ritta-Christina was performed by a certain
Dr Manel, in the presence of Baron Dubois, Isidore Geoffroy
Saint-Hilaire, Dr Étienne Serres, Baron Cuvier and many other
French medical luminaries. After all, this was the first dissection
of viable dicephali in several hundred years, and the occasion
had certainly been well advertised in the newspapers. It was seen
that the twins were each other's mirror images: all Ritta's internal
organs were transposed. The two hearts were situated next to
each other within a common pericardium. Ritta's heart was
severely malformed: there were two ascending cavernous veins
leading to the auricles of the heart, and the septum between the
auricles was perforated in three places. This must have led to a
considerable admixture of arterial and venous blood, to a degree
that might actually have been fatal in a normal child. Christina
had a perfectly normal circulatory system, however, and large
branches of the twins' iliac arteries were connected, thereby
ensuring that oxygen-rich arterial blood from Christina could
be shunted into Ritta's circulation. The defective appetite of the
ailing Ritta was compensated for by the fact that the twins had

a common large intestine, from which the partly digested food eaten by Christina could be absorbed also by Ritta. The liver was common, with a central furrow, and there were two gallbladders. The twins each had a stomach, spleen, pancreas and larger part of the small intestine. The two spinal columns fused into a common pelvis. There were two uteri, one of them imperforate, but both with its normal appendages, though only one set of external genitals. The anatomist Étienne Serres, who published a lengthy study on the anatomy of Ritta-Christina in 1833, was amazed that the larger uterus of the twins appeared to be fully functional. If the twins had survived to a mature age, he speculated, conception might have occurred, and a single child would have had two distinct mothers. The major part of Dr Serres' 300-page article is an attempt to prove, using a novel system of teratology of his own construction, that Ritta and Christina were two persons with fused lower extremities. The same system of teratology led him into some absurd reasonings, and he even stated that in a dipygus creature – an individual malformed in exactly the opposite way to Ritta-Christina, with double lower bodies, four legs and only one head – the single brain must share the combined thoughts of two personalities. In contrast to his theoretical reasoning, Dr Serres' anatomical description of the twins is excellent, and illustrated with beautiful plates. The skeleton of Ritta-Christina, figured on one of them, was for many years exhibited among the skeletons of animals at the Musée d'Histoire Naturelle. It made a lasting impression on no less an observer than Stephen Jay Gould, when he saw it there in 1982.

In his novel *Une Fille d'Ève*, published in 1838, Honoré de Balzac described the strictly religious upbringing of two sisters with the words: 'Cette sévère et religieuse éducation fut la cause des mariages de ces deux sœurs, soudées ensemble par le malheur, comme Ritta-Christina par la nature.' Such had been the fame of 'La Fille Bicéphale' that even nine years after their death, Balzac did not need to explain this reference to his readers. It is very likely that he had read Isidore Geoffroy Saint-Hilaire's *Histoire Générale des Anomalies de l'Organisation*, which was completed in 1836, and seen the illustration of Ritta-Christina in the atlas volume of this famous work. Geoffroy Saint-Hilaire marvelled that dicephalus twins could live as long as eight months. He proposed that this certainly gave an appearance of truth to some of the older tales of viable dicephali, the Scottish Brothers in particular. Less than fifty years later, another pair of dicephalus twins would prove him right.

❧

The most celebrated pair of dicephalus conjoined twins of all time, the brothers Giovanni Baptista and Giacomo Tocci, were born in Locana,a town in northern Italy, on 4 October 1877. Their father was the thirty-two-year-old workman Giovanni Tocci and their mother the nineteen-year-old Maria Luigia Mezzanrosa. Unlike the situation for the majority of other con-joined twins, the labour was easy, since the twins were very small, and the mother's pelvis wide. The head of one twin presented first, followed by the other head and upper body, and finally the lower body and legs, with one umbilical cord and placenta. The midwife, who had practised in Locana for many years, gave a shriek of horror and astonishment when she saw the twins, whose bodies seemed to blend together at the level of the navel – was this one or two children? Poor Signor Tocci was affected even worse: he fainted dead away when his first-born children were held up before him. One source states that he had to be restrained in a lunatic asylum to gather his wits after this shock to the system. The twins had two heads, two necks and four perfect arms, but only one lower body and one pair of legs. The two upper bodies fused into each other at the level of the sixth rib, to give the impression of just one lower body underneath a double thorax.

Having recovered from the nervous attack, Signor Tocci decided to make his extraordinary children the family bread-winners: when they were just four weeks old, he took them to Turin to exhibit them for money.They became quite an attraction in show business, being absolutely unique in the world. When the Tocci brothers were just one month old, they were examined by Professors Fubini and Musso, from the Turin Academy of Medicine. In spite of their deformity and small size, the twins appeared vigorous; together they only weighed 8 pounds. Using a stethoscope, Fubini and Musso established that the boys had two separate hearts, which were beating independently: one with a frequency of 152 heartbeats per minute, the other with 154. Importantly, they do not mention any heart murmur. The pulse in each leg was synchronous with the heartbeat on the same side. Their movements of respiration were not synchronous, indicating that the twins had a pair of lungs each. Fubini and Musso were doubtful whether the Tocci brothers would live long: they knew the tragic story of Ritta-Christina, and thought that these tiny twins were as unlikely to survive.

In May 1878, the twins were exhibited in Paris, and in October that year, when they were just one year old, they came to Lyon. Here, two local doctors described them thoroughly in the *Lyon Médical* magazine. Some of their attention was apparently usurped by the charming Signora Tocci, whom the doctors approvingly described as being 'une belle et vigoureuse femme, brune comme une Italienne, parfaitement constituée.' The twins were vigorous and agile, with blonde hair and greyish blue eyes. Giovanni Baptista was a little smaller and more slender than his brother. Although small at birth, they had grown into strong and healthy-looking children: the doctors attributed this to the nourishing effects of the milk of a sturdy wet nurse employed by Signor Tocci. The doctors did not hesitate to declare that their general development, both bodily and intellectually, was well in line with that of a normal infant of the same age.

Throughout the 1870s and 1880s, Signor Tocci and his wife toured Europe with their extraordinary children. They visited most larger cities in Italy, France, Switzerland, Poland, Austria and Germany. They were always on the move, and the exhibition schedule was strenuous, with the twins on show almost every day of the week. Signor Tocci had been very much affected by

Fubini and Musso's opinion that his children would not live long: he decided to get as much money as possible out of them while they were still alive. All accounts agree that the Tocci family made considerable sums of money and could live in relative luxury. In August 1879, the twins were demonstrated before the Swiss Society for Natural Science in Berne. A certain Dr Grünwald described the twins, and agreed with the French doctors that they looked healthy and likely to live. He was much amused when both twins eagerly tried to grasp a spoonful of food held out between them, and has this scene drawn as an illustration for his article.

In 1881, the Tocci twins were exhibited in Vienna. They were billed as 'The Greatest Wonder of Nature', and in the exhibition handbill, Dr Richard Hescht, Professor of Pathological Anatomy in Vienna, affirmed that they were genuine united twins, and probably unique in the world. They were on show in the sessions room of the Vienna Gardening Society from ten to twelve o'clock and from one to five o'clock every day of the week. A visiting English doctor bought a large photograph of the twins, on the back of which he made some notes about their development. At the time they were on show in Vienna, the twins were three years and four months old. Both spoke Italian, but while Giovanni Baptista, the right twin, seemed clever and alert, poor Giacomo was described as 'somewhat idiotic'. The doctor was amazed that each child could see, hear, feel, think, eat, drink and cry, and that their mental activity was completely independent. Two heartbeats could be heard with the stethoscope, and again there was no mention of any heart murmur. The breathing of the twins was also distinct, and in swallowing each moved his individual thorax half, indicating two separate diaphragms. One twin might vomit while the other sucked, so there must have been two stomachs. The intact penis and anus served for both children; posteriorly, there was a rudimentary second male sexual organ.

In 1886 and 1891, the celebrated pathologist Rudolf Virchow saw the Tocci brothers and left a very good description of them. Shaming the gloomy prophesy of Fubini and Musso, the twins appeared healthy and strong and gave every indication that they would live to an advanced age. In 1891, the Tocci brothers were hired by a German impresario, who exhibited them at the Panoptikon in Berlin. Rudolf Virchow was interested to note that by this time, the Toccis had several other children. Signor Tocci was a thin, swarthy man with typical Italian features. His thirty-three-year-old wife, who had been admired by the French doctors just thirteen years earlier, was described as a very robust-looking, corpulent woman. A contemporary photograph verifies this unflattering description, and it is clear that her several childbirths, and the free access to calorie-rich food allowed by the family's recent affluence, had destroyed whatever good looks she had once possessed. The Toccis' other children were perfectly normal; one of them, a sturdy boy, was exhibited together with the twins.

Each of the Tocci brothers had control of the leg on his side. Both legs were weak from want of muscular training, and Giacomo's foot had so-called talipes equinovarus, a form of club foot that disabled him from resting it flatly on the floor. Thus the twins could not stand up independently, unless they supported themselves with their arms, or were held by some other person. They could also stand up using a ring perambulator, but the lack of co-ordination disabled them from walking. All available photographs of them as adolescents represent them standing supported by a chair, which they grip with the hands of their outer arms; their inner arms are stretched up over their heads to hold a nosegay or a toy. Amiable and eager to please, the twins willingly replied to questions from their audience; in addition to their native Italian, they could speak French and German. They both had a liking for music, and had readily learnt to read and write. Their mentality and external appearance varied a good deal. Giovanni Baptista was the stronger and better formed, with a more alert expression; he was also the more intelligent and had a natural talent for drawing, for which his brother had no taste. In spite of the harsh judgement of the English medical man quoted earlier, Giacomo was by no means idiotic. The German showman H.W. Otto, who saw the twins in 1886, considered their mental condition to be perfectly normal. Although the Tocci brothers normally got along quite well, they had their regular disputes, which they sometimes settled using their fists.

Late in 1891, the Tocci brothers came to America, where a showman had planned an extensive tour for them. They were promoted as 'The Two-Headed Boy', as 'The Wonderful Blended Twins', or even as 'The Greatest Human Phenomenon Ever Seen Alive'. They were paid not less than $1,000 a week, more than Jo-Jo the Dog-faced Boy or any other human curiosity at the time. In Philadelphia, they were examined by Dr Robert P. Harris, a leading paediatrician. He already knew about the Tocci brothers from the European literature and considered them 'the most interesting of all the double monsters in the world'. Since the Tocci brothers were decidedly top-heavy and their legs weak, Dr Harris predicted that they would never be able to walk. Like Rudolf Virchow, he deplored that the parents were always on guard at the exhibition, and that they did not admit any thorough medical examination of the twins, from a misguided belief that this would diminish their extraordinary children's attractiveness in show business. Actually, the medical press did its best to *advertise* the exhibition of the Tocci brothers. Apart from Dr Harris' article in the *American Journal of Obstetrics,* no less a periodical than the *Scientific American* called them 'probably the most remarkable human twins that have ever approached maturity'.

The anonymous writer in the *Scientific American* went on to describe the twins, who were now fourteen years old. He had probably been expecting some repulsive, idiotic freaks, and was amazed that Giovanni Baptista and Giacomo were actually good-looking young lads, with bright, intelligent faces. They lived on excellent terms with each other, and seemed 'unconscious of any misfortune in their condition.' They sometimes spoke to visitors through an interpreter, and signed their names as souvenirs. Photographs of the twins were for sale at the exhibition for $2; one is still kept at the New York Academy of Medicine, and several in private collections. The account in the *Scientific American* confirms the earlier observations of the twins' independent minds and actions. They could dress and undress themselves, and were able to stand, but could not walk a single step. Their locomotion consisted of crawling about on the floor, using all six extremities. Giovanni Baptista liked beer, and drank it in considerable quantities, but Giacomo preferred mineral water. Giovanni Baptista was also very fond of drawing, and maybe some American sideshow enthusiast has retained one of his sketches of visitors to the show. Giacomo was less bright than his brother, but the *Scientific American* writer instead found him the more talkative and voluble of the twins. When he found some fault in his brother's drawing, he kicked it off his knee, to the amusement of the spectators.

An old sideshow buff, Mr Charles E. Davis, saw the Tocci brothers exhibited in Hartford in 1891. He was one of the few people who actually spoke to the twins, through an interpreter, and they told him that far from delighting in travelling and earning lots of money, they were often sad and downhearted, and minded their abnormal condition very much. He described them as pathetic, and added that although they were able to stand up or sit down by themselves, they could not walk a single step. In March 1892, the twins went to New York. They were advertised as the marvellous two-headed boy who spoke French with one head and German with the other, and induced so much curiosity among the single-headed, simple-minded New Yorkers that their stay in town was extended to three full weeks before they were succeeded at the theatre by Jo-Jo, the Russian Dog-faced Boy. Under the management of Mr Frank Uffner, the Tocci brothers then went on to Boston, where a three-page exhibition pamphlet entitled *Tocci, The Wonderful Two-headed Boy (Giovanni and Giacomo). The Greatest Human Phenomenon ever seen alive* was published to advertise them; a copy is still kept in the Boston Public Library. An illustration depicts them standing up and waving their bowler hats. The pamphlet writer firmly regards them as *one* individual, whether out of ignorance or as an adver-tising gimmick is not known. An interesting observation is that

'Tocci usually eats with both mouths, although one can provide nourishment enough for the entire organism'. Signora Tocci by this time had no fewer than nine other children, all living and healthy. In October 1892, the *Million* newspaper reported that the Tocci brothers had arrived in Chicago.

The writer Samuel Langhorne Clemens, better known as Mark Twain, one day saw 'the picture of a youthful Italian freak' on exhibition in the sideshow, and decided to write a short story with a two-headed man for a hero. Mark Twain called the conjoined twins in his story Count Angelo and Count Luigi Capello, and put them through many ludicrous adventures, all described with his particular kind of heavy-handed humour. In the story, the twins insisted on being paid for two when they did any work, but travelled on the railway with just one ticket. A typical incident is that the twins have kicked a man and are brought on trial for assault. They are defended by a lawyer named Pudd'nhead Wilson, who manages to get them acquitted with the argument that it was impossible to say which twin had done the kicking, and that the guilty one could not be punished without wrongfully incarcerating also his innocent brother. This element of the story was probably originated by an incident in the lives of the original Siamese twins, Chang and Eng. Mark Twain had written a sketch about them in *Packard's Monthly* in 1869. He also paralleled their lives in making one of his twins a smoker and drinker, and the other one a teetotaller. At the end, Mark Twain decided to take the part about the conjoined twins out of his novel, *Pudd'nhead Wilson*, and make them ordinary identical twins; he also published the original farcical concept, under the title *Those Extraordinary Twins*. I personally find both these stories quite tedious, and the one about the twins somewhat repulsive, knowing the details of the true existence of the Tocci brothers. Both *Pudd'nhead Wilson* and *Those Extraordinary Twins* have been the subject of much admiration, however; they are hailed as great American classics, have Internet pages dedicated to them, and have been 'analysed' to bits by earnest sociologists and literary historians.

In November 1893, the arduous US tour of the Tocci broth-
ers took them back to New York, where they performed at the
Harlem Museum. Billed under them were Ad Carlisle's Dog
Circus and the Boxing Kangaroo. They were then at Huber's
Theatre for two weeks in mid-December, sharing the stage with
Tattooed Mac, The Turtle Boy, and Mlle Vallette and her Dancing
Goats. They remained active in US show business well into 1894,
and probably longer than that. According to the German circus
historian H.W. Otto, they had originally been contracted for a
one-year tour, but demand was so great that they toured the
country for five full years. In 1897, at the age of twenty, the Tocci
brothers decided to retire for good. They had had enough of the
degrading sideshow, and their mother and father, whose love of
money had got the better of whatever parental affection they
may still have nourished toward the family breadwinners, no
longer had any legal control of them or their earnings. Giovanni
Baptista and Giacomo returned to Italy and bought a pretty little
villa near Venice. This villa had a garden surrounded by very high
walls, to enable them to avoid the gaze of intrusive curiosity-
seekers. In 1900, H.W. Otto reported that the brothers were alive
and well, but living as recluses in their villa, determined never
to be exhibited for money again. In 1904, their names again
appeared in the French and Italian newspapers, after it had been
revealed that although they possessed only one set of genitals,
the Tocci brothers had married two separate women. There was
a light-hearted debate in both the newspapers and the medical journals about the legal implications of this extraordinary
marriage. Who of the twins was legally the father if one of the
wives begot a child, and how should the inheritance of the Tocci
brothers be divided if there were several children? The famous
French teratologist Marcel Baudoin speculated that each twin
was the legal owner of one of their testicles! A book, memo-
rably entitled *La vie sexuelle des monstres*, by a certain Dr A.P.
de Liptay, was inspired by this controversy. This bawdy-minded
author queries whether the Tocci brothers, when copulating,
would actually enjoy 'une *double* sensation voluptueuse'. He also

speculated what the result, physical and psychological, would be in an 'accouplement' between dicephali of different sexes, like the Tocci brothers and Ritta-Christina. Leaving no lewd avenue of thought unexplored, he even discusses the desperate situation that would ensue if one brother was 'all right' and the other one a homosexual! Some newspaper correspondents found the marriage of the Tocci brothers too disgusting to speculate upon further, and their wives were blasted as vulgar curiosity-seekers, particularly as most medical experts were of the opinion that the Tocci brothers were impotent. The simple explanation that the twins felt a need for human company in their lonely life, after their long and dismal career as sideshow 'monsters', does not seem to have entered anyone's mind.

It is not known how the Tocci brothers fared in their marriage, but if they had vowed to keep a veil of secrecy around the remainder of their lives, they certainly succeeded. From 1904 onwards, there is hardly any mention of them, in either the popular or the specialist press. In 1906, the French teratologists Lesbre and Forgeot actually announced that the Tocci brothers had died, but other writers insisted that they were still living. The German teratologist Hans Hübner affirmed that in 1911 they were still residing in their villa in Venice. The French teratologist Maurice Gille, writing in 1934, claimed that as far as he knew, the Tocci brothers had still been alive in 1912. They were still married, and 'had, it appears, children'! According to another version, in the French writer Martin Monestier's *Human Oddities*, they died childless in 1940, aged sixty-three.

The dicephalus variety of conjoined twins is by no means one of the rarest types: it encompasses 11% of all conjoined twins, with a slight female preponderance. The mechanism is that complete splitting of the fertilised ovum occurs only in the cephalic region. In the two- or three-armed subtypes, this fission occurs at a higher level than in the four-armed subtype. Of all three subtypes of dicephali, the vast majority are stillborn or less viable. This is most often due to heart and lung malformations in the right twin. The Tocci brothers demonstrated to the world that four-armed dicephalus twins could live for a prolonged period of time. In 1912, the German teratologist Hans Hübner postulated that while four-armed dicephali might well be viable, the two- and three-armed varieties were more poorly organised and had a higher incidence of malformations of the heart and lungs. In a series of papers published between 1929 and 1931, the German teratologist Professor Georg Gruber disagreed. From autopsy studies, he argued that three-armed dicephalus twins might well be sufficiently well organised to reach adult life. The level of conjunction was relatively random in between types, and twins who had four arms and two torsos did not exclude severe anomalies of the hearts; at the same time, a two-armed dicephalus might have two normal hearts and no obvious defects in the lungs and circulatory tract. It is interesting to note that conjoined twins who could not be surgically separated were legally considered as *one* person in Germany at that time. The parents of one pair of dicephalus twins objected to this reasoning, and Professor Gruber wrote a certificate to support them, with the argument that the children were two independent individuals; this was not enough to impress the rigid German bureaucrats, however, and the parents had to feed both mouths of their hungry infant with a single support from the *Kinderkasse*.

The majority of early twentieth-century instances of dicephalus twins were stillborn or less viable. In more than one medical thesis or article on dicephali, it is recommended that no attempt to treat or resuscitate the 'two-headed monster' should take place; this kind of 'mercy killing' of dicephali occurred as late as the 1960s, if not even later. Indeed, the English-language literature on the subject was more devoted to techniques of cutting one head off the 'monster' to facilitate labour than to the study of the anatomy and viability of dicephalus twins. According to a brief press report, a two-headed Russian girl was born in the 1930s. The two heads were baptised Ira and Galya, and she lived to be one year and twenty-two days old. Another, more lurid newspaper story told that some decades later, during the Cold War, a two-headed girl was kept in a Russian research institute, where she was subjected to various experiments. This may well be the same twins described in *Life* magazine in 1966 and on an Internet site. These Russian girls were called Masha and Dasha, and they were born in Moscow in 1950. Their anatomy was identical to that of the Tocci brothers, except that they had a short, vestigial third leg; thus, by definition, they are ischiopagus tripus twins just like the Florentine twins of 1313, but shared many characteristics with the four-armed dicephali. Interestingly, Masha and Dasha could walk quite well although each twin controlled one of the legs. According to Martin Monestier, they were the wards of the Soviet state, and permanently confined to a physiological research institute, circumstances not conducive to mental well-being in any person, whether a conjoined twin or not. When these twins were featured in a television documentary in 2001, they were still in reasonable health, but living in squalor in a dire Russian suburb.

In 1953, four-armed dicephalus twins were born near Petersburg, Indiana. Named Danny Kaye and Donald Ray Hartley, the twins very much resembled the Tocci brothers in structure, but they had apparent weaknesses in cardiac function, and the right twin was almost continually cyanotic. In spite of this, they developed well, and were discharged from hospital into the care of their parents. The parents were poor, but nevertheless refused all the intrusive attempts from the media to capitalise on the twins. They even turned down an offer of $1,000 a week – the same rate as for the Tocci brothers sixty years earlier – from a leading American showman. At the age of four months, the twins developed pneumonia, and died soon after, from acute cardiac dilatation. Interestingly, the description of these twins in a medical journal states that surgical separation of these twins was briefly considered: it was well-nigh impossible with the surgical techniques of the 1950s, and the moral and ethical problems involved were daunting.

The birth of another pair of viable dicephalus twins did not take place until 1977. These twins were of the three-armed variety (dicephalus tribrachius) and were referred to the Arkansas Children's Hospital a few hours after caesarean section delivery. It was soon clear to the doctors that the right twin had severe heart malformations, and that the extent of shared organs made it impossible to surgically separate the twins with the survival of both. The technical problems of surgically separating dicephali were daunting, and no such operation had been previously attempted. The parents wanted separation at all costs, however, even if this meant that one twin should die. The surgeons began to explore the possibility of amputating the right twin to save the left one. They first had to contact the County Prosecuting Attorney and the State Attorney General, to ensure that no criminal prosecution would result from the death of the right twin. When the dicephali were eighteen days old, the right twin had a prolonged episode of severe cyanosis, and it was noted that the heart rate of the left twin slowed down. It was decided to operate at once. The surgeons sawed through the right spinal column and spinal cord, and divided the junction between the right twin's small intestine and the common large bowel. The connection between the atria of the right and left hearts was divided. The chest wall was closed by wiring the ribs together. The outcome was that the left twin also died, seven weeks after the operation, without being weaned from the ventilator. Even if she had survived the ordeal, she would have been a one-armed, one-legged invalid, with multiple other defects including an imperforate anus, severe scoliosis, and considerable cosmetic problems secondary to the chest wall closure.

Katie and Eilish Holton, three-armed dicephalus conjoined twins born in Ireland in 1989, have been well described in two television documentaries. Their anatomy was quite different from that of the Tocci brothers, and their conjunction more extensive. The twins had one lower body, a shared thoracic cavity, and a short third arm between the two heads. In many respects, they were like the Arkansas twins born in 1977. In spite of their deformity, they seemed healthy and viable. The Irish paediatricians did not consider it possible to separate them surgically, nor did, at least initially, the parents desire separation. The twins grew and developed well, although it was known that Katie, the right twin, had some kind of heart malformation. In 1992, at the age of three, they were surgically separated at the Great Ormond Street Children's Hospital in London. Katie, the weaker twin, died three days after surgery. Eilish, who was still alive in 1995 at the age of six, had by that time learned to walk with a leg prosthesis.

The most remarkable modern instance of dicephalus conjoined twins is that of Abigail and Brittany Hensel, born in the American Midwest in 1990. Like Katie and Eilish, they were three-armed dicephali, but only had a short, deformed arm between the two heads. This rudimentary arm was amputated when the girls were three months old. In 1996, at the age of six, Abigail and Brittany were the subject of articles in *Time* and *Life* magazines, as well as a television documentary. The twins had developed remarkably well, both physically and emotionally. Since the operation to remove the third arm, they had required no further specialist medical attention. Although one twin controlled the arm and leg on each side, they were remarkably agile, and could not only walk, but ran, swam and rode a bicycle. Probably due to highly advanced tactile and propriosensitive capacities, developed during their six years together, they co-ordinated their movements perfectly. The excellent general health of the twins rules out any severe heart malformations, although their shared liver indicates a quite high level of conjunction of inner organs. It is interesting that one of the magazine articles mentions that Abigail has by far the greater appetite of the twins; this is likely to be caused by the fact that, like many other left-hand dicephalus twins, she has the larger stomach. The twins share the large bowel and probably parts of the small bowel as well, and the food eaten by Abigail also nourishes her sister. At their small local school, the twins became well adapted. Just like the Tocci brothers, they have differing characters and personalities, but although they sometimes tended to quarrel, their schoolteacher used them as a model to show the other children the advantages of teamwork in solving various problems. The parents of Abigail and Brittany never even considered the option of surgically separating the twins, but instead accepted them as they were and gave them a loving home. In one of the television documentaries about Katie and Eilish, the commentator criticised the Hensel family roundly for their 'eccentric' decision not to have their children separated, but the parents fortunately chose to ignore such ill-judged advice. The twins were alive and well, and still united, in 2002. They were lucky not only in that the random conjunction of their inner organs happened in a way that made them fit for prolonged life, but also in that they were born into a particu-larly harmonic family in a small rural town. Had they been the children of a 'dysfunctional' urban family, in which one or both parents had an entrepreneurial spirit and a thirst for money resembling that of Signor Tocci and his wife, their lives might well have paralleled that of their famous nineteenth-century counterparts, with the money-making media circus beginning when they were in the cot.

In view of the Hensel twins and their development, it is possible to re-evaluate some of the historical cases of dicephali. For example, the spectacle of the Turkish Archer no longer appears as incredible as before. The nineteenth-century teratolo-gists disbelieved the evidence from historical chronicles that the Scottish Brothers could walk, but the Hensel twins have shown that this is definitely possible. The failure of the Tocci brothers to walk has most often been blamed on Giacomo's clubfoot and the twins being decidedly 'top-heavy'. The main reason is likely to have been the boys' poor muscular development, however. This was, in turn, caused by too much bed rest and too little activity. The exhibition schedule was too demanding for the boys to get the exercise they needed, and their parents might actually have decided, at a later date, that it was advantageous to